D1096282

This picture of the Milky Way taken by the Cosmic Background Explorer (COBE) satellite shows the plane of our Galaxy in infrared light. All three COBE instruments produced major discoveries. COBE proved the Big Bang theory and the cosmic microwave background has its origin in the Big Bang. COBE also proved there were primordial temperature and density fluctuations that gave rise to the clusters of galaxies and the huge voids between them. COBE also found there is a far infrared cosmic background radiation that is brighter than all the known stars and galaxies combined, produced by a previously unknown population of objects, presumably dusty early galaxies.

To my Uncle Ned —
A gifted teacher who introduced me to the stars
And to my Mom and Dad —
Who made me believe I could reach them.

NASA SP-4312

DREAMS, HOPES, REALITIES

by Lane E. Wallace

NASA's Goddard Space Flight Center
The First Forty Years

The NASA History Series

National Aeronautics and Space Administration

NASA History Office
Office of Policy and Plans
Washington, D.C. 1999

Library of Congress Cataloging-in-Publication Data

Wallace, Lane E., 1961-
 Dreams, hopes, realities: NASA's Goddard Space Flight Center/The first forty
 years/by Lane E. Wallace.
   p. cm. — (The NASA history series)
 Includes bibliographical references and index.
 Supt. of Docs. no.: NAS 1.21: SP-4312
 1. Goddard Space Flight Center—History.
I. Title. II. Series.
TL862.G6W35 1999
629.4'0973—dc21   98-55745
                                                                   CIP

For sale by the U.S. Government Printing Office
Superintendent of Documents, Mail Stop: SSOP, Washington, DC 20402-9328
ISBN 0-16-049948-8

Table of Contents

Foreword

*T*hroughout history, the great achievements of civilizations and cultures have been recorded in lists of dates and events. But to look only at the machinery, discoveries, or milestones is to miss the value of these achievements. Each goal achieved or discovery made represents a supreme effort on the part of individual people who came and worked together for a purpose greater than themselves. Driven by an innate curiosity of the spirit, we have built civilizations and discovered new worlds, always reaching out beyond what we knew or thought was possible. These efforts may have used ships or machinery, but the achievement was that of the humans who made those machines possible— remarkable people willing to endure discomfort, frustration, fatigue, and the risk of failure in the hope of finding out something new.

An image of our "Big Blue Marble" taken from the GOES 8 weather satellite.

This is the case with the history of the Goddard Space Flight Center. This publication traces the legacy of successes, risks, disappointments, and internationally recognized triumphs of the Center's first 40 years. It is a story of technological achievement and scientific discovery; of reaching back to the dawn of time and opening up a new set of eyes on our own planet Earth. In the end, it is not a story about machinery or discoveries, but a story about ourselves. If we were able to step off our planet, and if we continue to discover new mysteries and better technology, it is because the people who work at Goddard always had a passion for exploration and the dedication to make it happen.

The text that follows is a testimony to the challenges people at the Goddard Space Flight Center have faced and overcome over almost half a century. Today, we stand on the threshold of a new and equally challenging era. It will once again test our ingenuity, skills, and flexibility as we find new ways of working with our colleagues in industry, government, and academia. Doing more with less is every bit as ambitious as designing the first science instrument to study the heavens. But if we are to continue exploring our world and our universe, it is every bit as important.

Robert H. Goddard once said, "The dream of yesterday is the hope of today and the reality of tomorrow." This is our heritage. Our challenge is to keep our spirit of dedication, vision, and innovative thinking alive, so we can turn today's dreams into a new century of possibility and progress.

Our journeys into space are the greatest ongoing adventure the human race has ever undertaken, and everyone here has played an important role in that endeavor. I encourage you to read this work with a sense of pride in our history and a cheerful anticipation of our future. This book is about everyone who has worked at the Goddard Space Flight Center.

A.V. Diaz
Center Director
May 1999

The Goddard Space Flight Center was the first NASA Center dedicated to the exploration of space. Since its inception in 1959, the Center has been involved in the design, building, and operation of over 200 Earth-orbiting satellites.

Preface

The Goddard Space Flight Center is a truly remarkable place. From its humble beginnings in borrowed offices, Goddard has developed into an impressive, sprawling campus that supports the work of over 11,000 people. In only 40 years, the Center successfully launched over 200 scientific satellites that investigated everything from the Earth's ozone layer to gamma ray bursts from distant reaches of the universe. Its work also covered every aspect of space science experiments, from developing theory to building the spacecraft, instruments, and launch vehicles; to operating and tracking the satellite in space; and finally, collecting, analyzing, and disseminating the data to the international scientific community.

At the same time, Goddard played an important role in developing communications, weather, and Earth resources satellites. Its Wallops Island facility has been central to the sounding rocket, balloon, and aircraft research NASA has conducted over the years. Goddard's tracking and data networks involved up to 24 countries, and it successfully managed numerous international projects in Earth and Space Science.

An illustrated book of this length could not possibly do justice to the history of this remarkable place. The rich history of Goddard is far too complex and far too rich to be covered adequately in a book even twice this length. This book simply attempts to convey the basic story and character that made Goddard the special place it is today. The hope is that readers will come away from this book with an appreciation of how Goddard evolved, what its strengths and challenges were, what it has accomplished, why that is important, and where it is headed.

Every person who worked at Goddard deserves to have his or her name mentioned in this book, because every single person played a critical role in making the Center's accomplishments possible. Likewise, every project deserves to have its full story told, because each project was its own adventure, and no two were alike. Unfortunately, there simply is not space. The projects and events included here serve to exemplify the unique talent, dedication, and spirit of innovation that was present in every project, directorate, and era of Goddard and made the Center what it is today.

CHAPTER 1:

Goddard's First Forty: The Quest to Learn

On the night of October 4, 1957, a large rocket lifted off from its pad at a remote, secret installation in the Kazakhstan region of the U.S.S.R. In its nose cone was a 22-inch diameter sphere weighing 175 pounds.[1] A few minutes later, the rocket disappeared from sight. But the reverberations from that launch were felt more than half a world away. Almost 200 years after the Battle of Lexington and Concord, another shot had been heard around the world. And it, too, would change the course of history.

The Russians' launch put Sputnik I, the world's first successful satellite, into orbit. In a single stroke, it also launched the space age and a race between two superpowers that would lead to the creation of a civilian U.S. space agency, a landing on the Moon, and

The ISEE-C satellite undergoing evaluation in a dynamic test chamber at Goddard.

Aerial view of the test and evaluation facilities at the Goddard Space Flight Center. (NASA Photo G93-010-030)

an unprecedented level of support for an entirely new field of science—one that would explore what lay beyond the atmosphere and give us a new perspective of Earth itself.

The sudden boom of the space age brought with it an acute need for new infrastructure to organize and manage projects that would involve thousands of people and millions of dollars. In 1958, the National Advisory Committee for

Aeronautics (NACA) had several aeronautical research centers around the country, but the size and scope of their projects were much smaller than the large-scale "big science" efforts a space program would require. As plans for the new National Aeronautics and Space Administration (NASA)[2] progressed throughout 1958, decision makers realized the need for new research centers devoted expressly to space projects.

This realization led to the creation of the Goddard Space Flight Center—NASA's first research center created specifically to support the space program. Over the past 40 years, the Center has grown from a small collection of scientists and engineers trying to solve the basic problems of space flight into a remarkably diverse organization supporting and pursuing an ever-widening range of scientific research that rockets and satellites have made possible.

In many ways, the history of Goddard reflects the history of the space program itself. The Center was formed at the same time as the new space agency, and its evolution has paralleled that of NASA. If Goddard has always been a complex Center, incorporating many diverse disciplines and groups, it is because the exploration of space is a complex challenge, requiring many different people and resources. A single scientist might conduct a wide range of experiments in a lab, but getting a satellite into space required support from government, industry, and universities; scientists, technicians, and engineers; and a tremendous amount of money. Balancing these different, and sometimes conflicting, resources has remained one of the major challenges for Goddard and for others in the space program.

At the same time, what has allowed Goddard to succeed, to overcome the many obstacles that stood in its way, especially in the early days of space flight, was the same unbridled enthusiasm that took us to the Moon in less than a decade.

Engineers and scientists did not go to work for Goddard or NASA for the money. They went to work there because they were fired up with excitement over the prospect of exploring a frontier no human had entered before. The challenge of space was bigger, tougher, and more awe-inspiring than any endeavor humankind had ever undertaken, and to work at NASA was to be on the cutting edge of the action.

When Goddard was founded, the field of space science—the term used to describe scientific research made possible or significantly aided by rockets and spacecraft[3]— was so new that a researcher could read all the related literature in 2 or 3 months. The newness of the field also meant that it had very few established experts. Most of the emerging space scientists were young men and women who were not already invested in some other research field, infusing

Technicians prepare a multimission modular component for the Space Shuttle cargo bay.

Goddard with a kind of youthful energy that resisted authority but excelled in innovation. The scientists and engineers who came to Goddard were young, energetic, fired up with a passion about space, and willing to overcome any obstacles to explore it.

This passion was important, because space was not a place for the fainthearted. A scientist might devote 3, 5, or 10 years to an experiment only to have the launch vehicle carrying it drop into the ocean. To stay with such an uncertain and sometimes discouraging field required an enormous amount of enthusiasm and dedication for the work. This enthusiasm became one of the defining characteristics of Goddard, especially in the early days. Employees both worked and played together, staying after work for volleyball games, recreation, and Center-sponsored drama club productions. They practically lived at the Center. Long hours and 7-day workweeks were taken in stride. This dedication allowed great progress to occur, but it probably caused the sacrifice of more than a few marriages in the first decade of the space program.

Mission planning at the Goddard Space Flight Center.

Goddard's place as the first space center also gave it a unique legacy in terms of the sheer scope of the work that it does. Goddard was formed when the space program was in its infancy and, as with many entrepreneurial organizations, it had to wear many hats. The number of projects involved in the early space effort was still small enough to be managed by one center, and even NASA managers did not quite realize yet how huge the space program would become. At the time Goddard was formed, there was no other space center to share its responsibilities. The Jet Propulsion Lab (JPL) in Pasadena, California, had been incorporated into NASA at the same time Goddard was founded, but JPL was given the task of managing planetary missions, not Earth-orbiting satellites.

As a result, Goddard initially was responsible not only for theoretical physics research to support space science, but also for all aspects of satellite development and operation, from project planning and development of instruments to fabrication and testing of the satellite itself, launch vehicle development, tracking, and data analysis. The Center initially even had responsibility for the human space flight program.[4] While the astronaut program never actually resided at Goddard, the Center has retained some level of responsibility for the vast majority of NASA's unpiloted, Earth-orbiting satellites.

Over the years, Goddard also incorporated the management of several other facilities and projects, including the worldwide manned space flight tracking and communications network during the Mercury, Gemini, and Apollo eras. Today, the Center's responsibilities still include a separate Institute for Space Studies in New York, a satellite tracking and data facility at the White Sands Missile Range in New Mexico, and the Wallops Flight Facility in Virginia, which continues to serve as one of the primary locations for the launching of sounding rockets.

The scientific component of Goddard also gave it a different organizational personality than other NASA Centers. Because aeronautics always has been an engineer's field, most of NASA's aeronautics and space centers focused on applied engineering tasks or diverse research efforts. Indeed, the human space flight program was fundamentally an engineering challenge until the Space Shuttle began to carry more scientific payloads into orbit. Goddard, however, focused primarily on space science efforts. The development of technology and the engineering aspects of getting satellites into orbit—while important contributions and a significant portion of Goddard's work—were not the sole goal of the Center. Most of Goddard's spacecraft were a means to an end; the tools that allowed scientists to get instruments up into space.

This mix of engineering and science has been one of the unique characteristics and strengths of the Goddard Space Flight Center. But it also presented a challenge for managers who had to incorporate scientists into an organization accustomed to

A Delta rocket stands ready to launch an ITOS weather satellite. Development of both the launch vehicle and satellite was managed by Goddard. (NASA Photo 71-HC-1182)

working with engineers. The academically oriented scientists who came to work at Goddard tended to have a very different working style than their engineering counterparts. The scientists were used to working independently, with more flexible deadlines and schedules. Engineers, on the other hand, were more accustomed to team efforts and a more structured work schedule and environment with milestones, deliverables, and fixed budgets. Goddard's managers had to find a way to accommodate both physicists who did their best work at 2:00 a.m., as well as the more structured needs of a space research program that had firm launch dates, test points, schedules, and budgets.

The scientific focus and culture at Goddard also complicated its relations with NASA Headquarters and the outside community. The individual research or "field" centers, even within the NACA, were known for their independence and resistance to central authority. In some ways, this tension between NASA's field centers and Headquarters was no different than that experienced by any similarly structured organization. Headquarters personnel, by definition, have different agendas and responsibilities than staff working out in the field, whether they are managing a corporation, a government agency, or a diverse university system. These different perspectives and job demands sometimes caused friction between Headquarters and field personnel.

This tension was probably heightened at Goddard because of the less structured, academic approach of the Center's scientists. "As professional scientists, these persons were by training and experience accustomed to deciding for themselves what ought to be done," explained one of NASA's early managers. "They questioned everything, including orders from above." Or, as another early Goddard employee expressed it, "What you had was a bunch of people who weren't quite sure you had to have a Headquarters. They were pretty sure they didn't need to talk to it."[5]

The scientists wanted to be left alone to do their research. But space science was an expensive endeavor, and taxpayers were footing the bill. So managers at NASA Headquarters were under constant pressure to provide information to Congress on the status and progress of different programs. The result was continual conflict between Headquarters' desire for first-hand, up-to-date information and researchers' desire to be left alone.

While this conflict existed in some form at every NASA Center, the fact that Goddard was located a mere 13.4 miles away from NASA Headquarters (a specific distance almost every Goddard employee can quote by heart) intensified the friction. In fact, some believe, Goddard's first director, Dr. Harry J. Goett, was replaced by Administrator James E. Webb in 1965 as a result of this conflict of wills between the Center and Headquarters.[6]

The science capability within Goddard complicated its relations with the scientific community outside of NASA as well. The NACA field centers (which evolved into the NASA aeronautical research centers)

This monstrous machine is Goddard's Launch Phase Simulator. It was designed to simulate the vibration, G-forces, and changing pressures a spacecraft would have to endure during its launch into orbit. It was this kind of thorough testing that gave Goddard satellites their remarkable success record.
(NASA Photo 6906313)

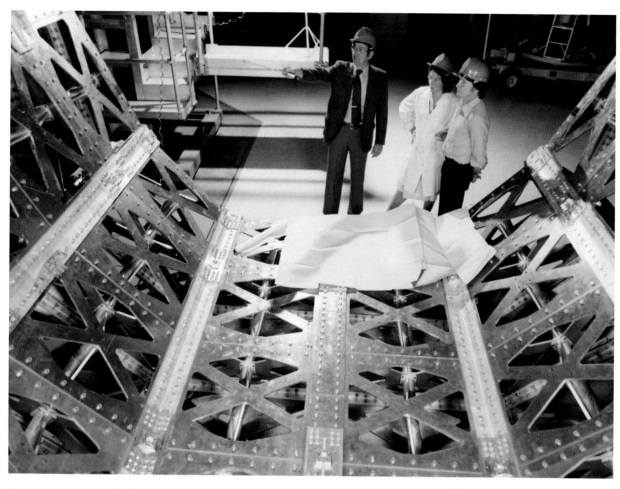

Goddard personnel oversee construction of a pallet for the Space Shuttle cargo bay. These pallets are used to hold satellites and other scientific research equipment. (NASA Photo G-79-07542)

focused on applied engineering research, and their primary customer was the commercial aviation industry. NACA/NASA researchers published the results of their work in technical reports that industry engineers used as reference guides when designing new aircraft or engines. The relationship was fairly smooth, because NASA researchers were providing a service that industry appreciated. By the same token, NASA's human space flight program was essentially its own customer.

Scientific satellites presented a different situation. The primary customer in space science was not a commercial industry, but an international scientific community; and the product was not a practical piece of technology, but a more esoteric piece of knowledge to fit into an evolving picture of the universe. Another complication was the fact that scientific and astronomical research, as opposed to human space exploration, was not exclusively NASA's domain. As a result, Goddard always had to maintain a delicate balance between supporting research conducted by its own scientists and supporting the needs and desires of the external scientific community.

Adding to the complexity of Goddard's projects was the international character of the space program. The National Aeronautics and Space Act of 1958 that established NASA specifically mandated that the new agency "cooperate with other nations and international

Explorer XIV, launched in October 1962, was designed to investigate solar wind and radiation phenomena.

groups in the peaceful application of space."[7] While these partnerships were extremely fruitful over the years and are more prevalent than ever in today's global environment, international projects were more complex to manage.

Goddard also relied on international cooperation to build and manage its series of ground tracking and communication networks, which involved up to 24 different countries. The colorful history of these ground station networks includes some unique situations, such as problems with labor unrest in Australia and political unrest in South America. At one point, troops had to surround the Guaymas tracking station in Mexico to protect it from "unruly mobs."[8]

While Goddard's diverse responsibilities and communities certainly created some unique management challenges, its diversity created some important strengths and capabilities as well. Goddard was one of the few places in the United States where the entire cycle of a space science experiment could be conducted. The Center had sufficient in-house resources to develop the theory behind an experiment, carry out the experimental design and engineering necessary to determine if it was feasible, fabricate and test the instruments and spacecraft, provide a launch vehicle, launch and track the satellite, and collect and analyze the data sent back from space. These data would then feed additional theoretical studies, sparking yet another cycle of experimentation. This unique ability to take an experiment "from

womb to tomb" has been one of the hallmarks of the Goddard Space Flight Center since it began.

Because Goddard was responsible for building instruments and spacecraft as well as conducting scientific research, the Center also developed a remarkable in-house ability to envision and build new kinds of instruments, satellites, and technology. Goddard's Explorer series of satellites was a product and a primary example of this in-house, innovative spirit. These satellites conducted experiments in almost every facet of space science and became one of the most successful series of spacecraft in NASA's history.

Goddard's engineers were looking constantly at ways to improve basic spacecraft design. Very soon after the first satellites reached orbit, Goddard engineers began work on standardized, modular spacecraft that would be more cost-effective and easy to upgrade. The first of these, the Orbiting Geophysical Observatory (OGO), was launched in 1964. Goddard expanded this concept in the early 1970s with its Multimission Modular Spacecraft (MMS), which was designed to be repaired in space by Shuttle astronauts. The concept was tested in 1984 when the Solar Max satellite was successfully repaired on station.

Because of Goddard's previous success in modular, serviceable spacecraft, the Hubble Space Telescope also was designed to be serviced in orbit. This design characteristic took on critical importance when a flaw was discovered in the telescope's primary mirror. The award-winning effort that serviced the Hubble telescope was the culmination of 30 years of innovative, pragmatic engineering efforts at Goddard. With the approach of the millennium, Goddard's engineers are continuing this innovative and pragmatic tradition as they develop new spacecraft technology and a new class of smaller, more capable satellites. At the same time, Goddard's roots as an "all-purpose" space center created a broad base of scientific capability that allowed the Center to expand its research efforts as technology improved. Space science efforts moved from simple particle and field research into visible, ultraviolet, and high-energy astronomy, tackling more and more complex problems in these areas. Weather and atmospheric satellite research expanded into the new field of Earth Science and remote sensing research. And Goddard's early work in communications satellites gave the Center the expertise to manage the development and operation of the space-based Tracking and Data Relay Satellite System (TDRSS), which now provides communication and tracking services for almost all Earth-orbiting satellites as well as the Space Shuttle.

These diverse technical and scientific strengths have allowed Goddard to make tremendously significant contributions to our knowledge of science and space technology. In addition, while its range of projects and responsibilities has meant that it was never the single or top priority of any one manager at NASA Headquarters, Goddard's diversity made it less vulnerable

to cutbacks or cancellation of any given role, mission, or program.

———

Goddard has experienced many changes over the past 40 years. The Center has grown from humble beginnings in borrowed offices and a Naval Research Laboratory warehouse to a sprawling campus with a workforce of 11,800 people and more than 30 buildings. The basic challenge of getting into space at all has long since given way to the ongoing challenge of going further and doing it more cheaply, quickly, and efficiently.

From a time when receiving a faint tone from a satellite passing overhead was

One of the most ambitious projects undertaken by Goddard was the 1993 first servicing mission of the Hubble Space Telescope, which had a flaw in its primary mirror. (NASA Photo 94-HC-26)

An image from the Hubble Space Telescope captures the stellar fireworks of two galaxies colliding. (NASA Photo PRC97-34A)

a major accomplishment, spacecraft now routinely provide breathtaking images of the Sun and distant galaxies, in wavelengths and detail that Earth's atmosphere had always hidden from view. In the early days, Goddard's scientists were simply trying to find out what existed in the space near Earth. Today, they are reaching back to the dawn of time to answer some of the biggest questions about the formation of the universe.

At the same time, Goddard's efforts in the field of space applications, which included not only weather and communication satellites, but also Earth resource imaging satellites, have helped create several thriving industries and a growing field of Earth Science research. If phrases like "El Niño" and "ozone layer depletion" are now household terms, it is largely because of research conducted at or with the Goddard Space Flight Center.

Without question, Goddard has had to change, adapt, and reinvent itself and its mission to meet the changing times and priorities of the country. But the changes have been more evolutionary than revolutionary. As the NASA research center primarily responsible for Earth-orbiting satellites, the Goddard Space Flight Center's mission has remained one of exploring the heavens and the Earth to improve the lives of Americans and our basic understanding of the universe. The satellites have become more capable and complex, the players have changed, and the goalposts have moved outward. But the mission, and the challenges inherent in that mission, have remained essentially the same.

Ever since it opened its doors, Goddard's biggest challenge has been to balance its complex array of activities, groups, external communities, and concerns while reaching beyond the limits of Earth. What has allowed it to succeed at that challenge is an enthusiastic spirit and entrepreneurial personality that has characterized the Center since its beginning. It was started by young scientists, engineers, and technicians inspired by the possibilities of space and willing to overcome whatever obstacles stood in the way of exploring it. Goddard is a place where people have a passion to find out more about how our world and universe work; to reach outside the boundaries of our planet to gain a better perspective on Earth and a clearer view of the galaxies and the cosmos beyond.

The story of the Goddard Space Flight Center is the story of an amazing expedition into a strange new realm. From our first stumbling steps, we have journeyed far. We have learned an amazing amount about our planet and our universe—and discovered how much vaster and more complex the picture is; how much we still have to learn. The journey has not been an easy one, but no exploration ever is. "One cannot discover new lands," the French author Andre Gide once wrote, "without consenting to lose sight of the shore for a very long time."[9]

Because the people at Goddard were willing to persevere through the rigorous demands, problems, and frustrations of space exploration, we have discovered many new lands. The journey continues because the ocean of space still stretches before us. For every question we have answered, every new land we have discovered, there are a thousand left to explore. This is still the mission, the passion, and the driving life force behind the Goddard Space Flight Center. Forty years after its founding, Goddard's researchers are still probing the mysteries of a territory that has proven to be the most complex and challenging frontier we have ever endeavored to explore.

A graphic image of ocean wind currents compiled from satellite data.

CHAPTER 2:
A Place for Science

Although the Goddard Space Flight Center received its official designation on the first of May 1959, Goddard's roots actually date back far earlier. In a sense, they extend almost as far back as civilization itself—for people have been gazing into the night sky and wondering about its secrets for thousands of years. In the fourth century B.C., Aristotle created a model of the universe that astronomers relied on for more than a millennium. His assumption that the universe revolved around the Earth proved to be incorrect, but his questioning was little different than that of modern scientists trying to solve the riddles of black holes or dark matter.[1]

The roots of Goddard's work in rocket development and atmospheric research also date back several centuries. The first

A new and much larger clean room facility was built at Goddard to accommodate servicing components for the Hubble Space Telescope. (NASA Photo 93C-5065)

*Robert H. Goddard
with vacuum tube
apparatus he built in
1916 to research rocket
efficiency.
(NASA Photo 74-H-1052)*

*The Goddard Space
Flight Center was
named in honor of
Dr. Robert H. Goddard,
a pioneer in developing
multi-stage rockets and
liquid rocket propellants.*

reported use of rocket technology was in the year 1232, when the Chin Tarters developed a "fire arrow" to fend off a Mongol assault on the city of Kai-feng-fu. In 1749, Scotsman Alexander Wilson was sending thermometers aloft on kites to measure upper-air temperatures. One hundred and fifty years later, meteorologists were beginning to accurately map the properties of the atmosphere using kites and balloons.[2]

Robert H. Goddard, for whom the Goddard Space Flight Center is named, received his first patents for a multi-stage rocket and liquid rocket propellants in 1914, and his famous paper on "A Method of Reaching Extreme Altitudes" was published in 1919. But it was not until the close of World War II (WWII) that all these long-standing interests and efforts came together to create the foundation for modern space science and, eventually, the Goddard Space Flight Center.[3]

Americans were conducting limited rocket research even during the war. But the Germans had made far greater advancements in rocket technology. German scientists had developed a large, operational

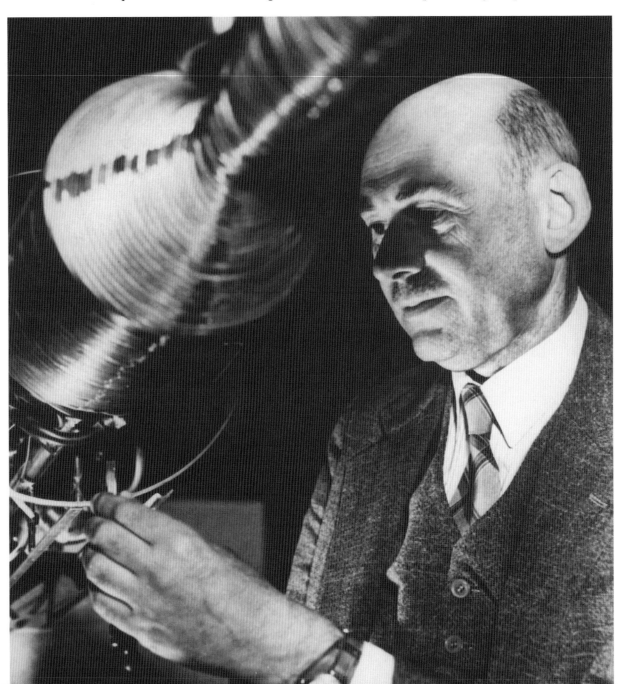

ballistic rocket weapon known as the "V-2." When the war came to a close, the U.S. military brought some of these rockets back to the United States to learn more about their handling and operation.

The Army planned to fire the V-2s at the White Sands Proving Ground in New Mexico. While the Army's interest was in furthering the design of ballistic missiles, the military also recognized the research opportunity the rocket firings presented and offered to let interested groups place instruments on them for high-altitude scientific research.[4]

The V-2 program helped spark the development of other rockets, and research with "sounding rockets" (as these small upper atmosphere rockets were called) expanded greatly over the next few years. The results from these rocket firings also began to gain the attention of the international scientific community.

In 1951, the International Council of Scientific Unions suggested organizing a third "International Polar Year" in 1957. The first two such events, held in 1882 and 1932, focused on accurately locating meridians (longitudinal lines) of the Earth. A third event was proposed after an interval of only 25 years because so many advances had been made in technology and instrumentation since the beginning of WWII. Scientists in the 1950s could look at many more aspects of the Earth and its atmosphere than their predecessors just a decade earlier. In 1952, the proposed event was approved by the Council and renamed the "International Geophysical

A V-2 rocket just after launch at the White Sands Proving Ground in New Mexico.

Year" (IGY) to reflect this expanded focus on studying the whole Earth and its immediate surroundings.[5]

The U.S. scientists quickly agreed to incorporate rocket soundings as part of their contribution to the IGY. But a loftier goal soon emerged.

In October 1954, the International Council's IGY committee issued a formal challenge to participating countries to attempt to launch a satellite as part of the IGY activities. In July 1955, President Dwight D. Eisenhower picked up the gauntlet. The United States, he announced, would launch "small, unmanned Earth-circling satellites as part of the U.S. participation in the IGY."[6] In September 1956, the Soviet Union announced that it, too, would launch a satellite the following year. The race was on.

Sputnik, Vanguard, and the Birth of NASA

The U.S. satellite project was a joint effort of the National Academy of Sciences (NAS), the National Science Foundation (NSF), and the Department of Defense (DOD). NAS was in charge of selecting the experiments for the satellite, NSF would provide funding, and DOD would provide the launch vehicle.

Sparked by the V-2 launch program, the Naval Research Laboratory (NRL) already had begun work on a rocket called the Viking, and the NRL proposed to mate the Viking with a smaller "Aerobee" rocket. The Aerobee had evolved from a rocket Jet Propulsion Laboratory (JPL) had first tested in 1945 and was used extensively for sounding rocket research. The Viking would be the first stage, the Aerobee would be the second stage, and another small rocket would serve as the third stage. The proposal was approved and dubbed "Project Vanguard."[7]

Yet, despite these efforts, the Americans would not be the first into space. On 4 October 1957, the Russians launched Sputnik I—and changed the world forever.

The launch of Sputnik was disappointing to U.S. scientists, who had hoped to reach space first. But they swallowed their pride and recognized the Soviets for their impressive accomplishment. The rest of the United States, however, had a very different reaction. Coming as it did at the height of the Cold War, the launch of Sputnik sent an astounding wave of shock and fear across the country. The Russians appeared

V-2 rockets, such as this one, carried some of the first scientific payloads into the upper atmosphere.

to have proven themselves technologically advanced. Aside from a loss of prestige and possible economic considerations from falling behind the Russians in technological ability, the launch raised questions of national security as well. If the Soviets could conquer space, what new threats could they pose?

The situation was not helped by a second successful Sputnik launch a month later, or the embarrassing, catastrophic failure of a Vanguard rocket 2 seconds after launch in early December 1957. Space suddenly became a national priority. Congress began accelerating efforts to deal with the "crisis." President Eisenhower created a post of Science Adviser to the President and asked his Science Advisory Committee to develop a national policy on space. That policy led to passage of the National Aeronautics and Space Act of 1958, which created the National Aeronautics and Space Administration.[8]

The months following the launch of Sputnik spawned numerous proposals about how to organize the development of a space capability. Ultimately, President Eisenhower decided that the fastest, most efficient way to pursue a civilian space program was to place it under the leadership of a strengthened and redesignated National Advisory Committee for Aeronautics (NACA). Proposed legislation for the creation of this new agency was sent to Congress on 2 April 1958 and signed into law on 29 July 1958.[9]

The Space Act outlined a tremendously ambitious list of objectives for the new agency.

The U.S. space program was to be of benefit to the security and general welfare of the United States and to all mankind. Peaceful objectives were to be pursued, human scientific knowledge in aeronautical and space-related matters be expanded, international cooperation in space be promoted, public and private efforts in space coordinated, U.S. leadership in space preserved, and the long-range efforts of a space program studied.[10]

Amid the administrative and political debate over a new space agency, work continued on the IGY satellite project. The Vanguard rocket project had been approved not because the Viking and Aerobee were the only rocket programs underway, but because the military did not want to divert any of its intercontinental ballistic missile (ICBM) efforts to the civilian IGY project. But the launch of Sputnik and the subsequent Vanguard failure changed that situation. Getting a satellite into orbit was now a top national priority.

In November 1957, the Army Ballistics Missile Agency was given permission to attempt the launch of a satellite using a proven Jupiter C missile from the Redstone Arsenal in Huntsville, Alabama. The United States finally achieved successful space flight on 31 January 1958 when a Jupiter rocket successfully launched a small cylinder named Explorer I into orbit.[11] In retrospect, it is interesting to speculate how history might have been different had the Army's Jupiter missile been chosen as the satellite launch vehicle from the outset, rather than the Vanguard. The United States might well have beaten the Soviets into space. But without the public fear and outcry at losing our technological edge, there might also not have been the public support for the creation of NASA and its extensive space program.[12]

Meanwhile, the struggling Vanguard program continued. A third rocket broke apart in flight just 5 days after the successful Explorer I launch. Finally, on 17 March 1958, a Vanguard rocket successfully launched Vanguard I—a 6-inch sphere weighing only 4 pounds—into orbit.

The Explorer I and Vanguard I satellites proved the United States could reach space. The next task was to create an organization that could manage the effort to explore it—an effort that would become one of the most daunting endeavors of the 20th century.[13]

Explorer I, America's first successful satellite, lifts off the launch pad at Cape Canaveral, Florida on 31 December 1958 on a Jupiter rocket. (NASA Photo KSC-68P-17)

ORIGINS OF THE GODDARD SPACE FLIGHT CENTER

As planning began for the new space agency in the summer of 1958, it quickly became clear that a research center devoted to the space effort would have to be added to the existing National Advisory Committee for Aeronautics (NACA) aeronautical research centers that made up the core of NASA. The space program was going to involve large contracts and complicated projects, and the founding fathers of NASA wanted to make sure there was enough in-house expertise to manage the projects and contracts effectively.

Even before the Space Act was signed into law, Hugh L. Dryden, who became the Deputy Administrator of NASA, began looking for a location for the new space center. Dryden approached a friend in the Department of Agriculture about obtaining a tract of government land near the Beltsville Agricultural Research Center in

Construction in progress on Building 2 at GSFC.

Maryland. Dr. John W. Townsend, Jr., who became the first head of the Space Science Division at Goddard and, later, one of the Center's directors, was involved in the negotiations for the property. The process, as he recalls, was rather short.

He (the Department of Agriculture representative) said, "Are you all good guys?" I said, "Yes." He said, "Will you keep down the development?" I said, "Yes." He spread out a map and said, "How much do you want?" And that was that. We had our place.[14]

On 1 August 1958, Maryland's Senator J. Glenn Beall announced that the new "Outer Space Agency" would establish its laboratory and plant in Greenbelt, Maryland. But Senator Beall's press release showed how naive decision makers were then about the size the space effort would become. Beall confidently asserted that the research center would employ 650 people and that "all research work in connection with outer space programs will be conducted at the Greenbelt installation."[15]

The initial cadre of personnel for the new space center—and NASA itself—was assembled through a blanket transfer authority granted to NASA to ensure the agency had the resources needed to do its job. One of the first steps was the transfer of the entire Project Vanguard mission and staff from the NRL to the new space agency, a move that was actually included in the Executive Order that officially opened the doors of NASA on 1 October 1958.[16]

The 157 people in the Vanguard project became one of the first groups incorporated into what was then called the

"Beltsville Space Center." In December 1958, 47 additional scientists from NRL's sounding rocket branch also transferred to NASA, including branch head John Townsend. Fifteen additional scientists, including Dr. Robert Jastrow, also transferred to the new space center from the NRL's Theoretical Division.

The Space Task Group at the Langley Research Center, responsible for the human space flight effort that would become Project Mercury, was initially put under administrative control of the Beltsville center as well, although the group's 250 employees remained at Langley. A propulsion-oriented space task group from the Lewis Research Center also was put under the control of the new space center. The space center's initial cadre was completed in April 1959 with the transfer of a group working on the Television Infrared Observation Satellite (TIROS) meteorological satellite for the Army Signal Corps Research and Development Laboratory in Ft. Monmouth, New Jersey.[17]

The Beltsville Space Center was officially designated as a NASA research center on 15 January 1959, following completion of the initial personnel transfers. On 1 May 1959, the Beltsville facility was renamed the Goddard Space Flight Center, in honor of Dr. Robert H. Goddard.[18]

GETTING STARTED

Although Goddard existed administratively by May 1959, the physical plant was established much later. Construction began on the first building at the Beltsville Space

Early aerial photo of GSFC showing a few complete buildings.

Center in April 1959,[19] but the Center's employees were scattered around the country until the facilities were complete. The Lewis and Langley task groups were still on site at those research centers. The NRL scientists worked out of temporary quarters in two abandoned warehouses next to the NRL facilities. Additional administrative personnel were housed in buildings at the Naval Receiving Station and at NASA's temporary headquarters in the old Cosmos Club Building, also known as the Dolly Madison House, on H Street in Washington, D.C. Robert Jastrow's Theoretical Division was located above the Mazor Furniture Store in Silver Spring, Maryland.[20]

These different groups may have been one organization on paper, but in reality operations were fairly segmented. The Center did not even have an official director until September 1959. Until then, working relationships and facilities were both somewhat improvised.

Not surprisingly, the working conditions in those early days were also less than ideal. Offices were cramped cubicles and desks were sometimes made of packing crates. Laboratory facilities were equally rough. One of the early engineers remembers using chunks of dry ice in makeshift "cold boxes" to cool circuitry panels and components. The boxes were effective, but researchers had to make sure they did not breathe too deeply or keep their heads in the boxes too long, because the process also formed toxic carbonic acid fumes.

But the employees had a kind of raw enthusiasm for the work—a pioneering challenge with few rules and seemingly limitless potential—that more than made up for the rudimentary facilities. It helped that many of the scientists also came from a background in sounding rockets. Sounding rocket research at that time was a field that demanded a lot of flexibility and ingenuity. Because their work had begun long before the post-Sputnik flood of funding, these scientists were accustomed to very basic, low-budget operations. Comfort may not have been at a premium in Goddard's early days, but scientists who had braved the frigid North Atlantic to fire rockoons (rockets carried to high altitude by helium balloons before being fired) had certainly seen a lot worse.[21]

As 1959 progressed, Goddard continued to grow. The new research center had 391 employees in the Washington area by June, and 579 by the end of the year.[22] As the staff grew, so did the physical facilities at the Greenbelt site. By September 1959, the first building was ready to be occupied.

The plan for Goddard's physical facilities was to create a campus-like atmosphere that would accommodate the many different jobs the Center was to perform. The buildings were numbered in order of construction, and the general plan was to put laboratories and computer facilities on one side, utility buildings in the center of the campus, and offices on the other side. Most of the buildings were one-, two-, or three-story structures that blended inconspicuously into the landscape. The one exception was Building 8, which was built to house the human space flight program personnel. Robert Gilruth, the program head, wanted a tall structure, so the building was designed with six stories. The original plan to locate the human space flight program at Goddard also resulted in the construction of a special bay tall enough to house Mercury capsules as part of the test and evaluation facility in Building 5. By 1961, however, this aspect of NASA's program had been moved to the new space center in Houston, Texas, and Building 8 was used to house administration offices instead.[23]

Even as the formal facilities developed, working at Goddard during the early days still required a pioneer's spirit. The Center was built in a swampy, wooded area, and wood planks often had to be stretched across large sections of mud between parking areas and offices. And on more than one occasion, displaced local snakes found their way into employees' cars, leading to distinctive screams coming from the parking lot at the end of the day.[24]

Workers install the main entrance sign to the Goddard Space Flight Center before its March 1961 dedication ceremony.

Improvisation and flexibility were also critical skills to have in the scientific and engineering work that was done. Space was a new endeavor, with few established guidelines—either in terms of what goals to set or how to accomplish them. Not only was there no established procedure to decide which experiments should be pursued, but also a shortage of space scientists who were interested or prepared to work with satellites. As a result, the first scientists at Goddard had a lot of freedom to decide what ought to be done. In 1959, NASA Headquarters announced that it would select the satellite experiments, but a shortage of qualified scientists at that level resulted in Goddard scientists initially taking part in the evaluation process. Experiments from outside scientists were incorporated into virtually all the satellite projects, but scientists and proposals soon outnumbered flight opportunities. The outside scientific community began to complain that Goddard scientists had an unfair advantage.

It took a while to sort out, but by 1961 NASA had developed a very deliberate procedure that is still the foundation of how experiments are selected today. Headquarters issues Announcements of flight Opportunities (AOs), and scientists from around the country can submit proposals for experiments for the upcoming project. NASA Headquarters organizes subcommittees to evaluate the proposals. Scientists from both NASA and the outside scientific community comprise the committees, but members do not evaluate proposals that might compete with their own work.

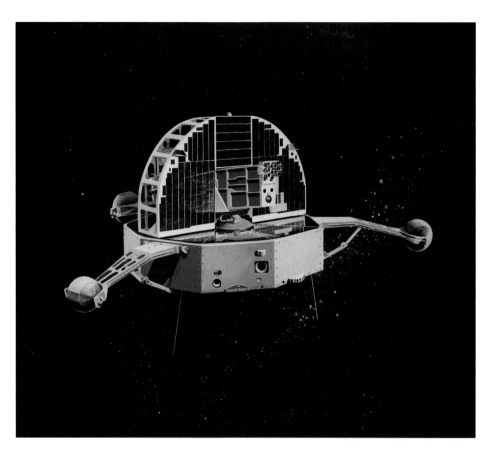

These groups also conduct long-range mission planning, along with the National Academy of Sciences' Space Science Board.[25] The final selection of experiments for satellite missions is made by a steering committee of NASA scientists.[26]

In the early days of Goddard, uncertainty about how to choose which experiments to pursue was only part of the challenge. The work itself required a flexible, pragmatic approach. No one had built satellites before, so there was no established support industry. Scientists drew upon their sounding rocket experience and learned as they progressed. Often, they learned lessons the hard way. Early summaries of satellite launches and results are peppered with notes such as, "Two experiment booms failed to deploy properly, however...," "Satellite's tracking beacon

Goddard's Orbiting Solar Observatory (OSO) satellites provided scientists with their first extended look at the Sun in the high-temperature ultraviolet, X-ray and Gamma ray portions of the electronic magnetic spectrum. The first OSO satellite, pictured here, was launched in March 1962. (NASA Photo G-63-3521)

failed...," and, all too often, "Liftoff appeared normal, but orbit was not achieved."[27] Launch vehicles were clearly the weakest link in the early days, causing major frustration for space scientists. In 1959, only 4 of NASA's 10 scientific satellite launches succeeded.[28]

In this environment of experimentation with regard to equipment as well as cosmic phenomena, Goddard scientists and engineers were constantly inventing new instruments, systems, and components. An actual flight test was often the only way to see if these creations would really work. This talent for innovation became one of the strengths of Goddard, leading to the development of everything from an artificial Sun to help test satellites to modular and serviceable spacecraft, to solid state recorder technology and microchip technology for space applications.

This entrepreneurial environment also spawned a distinct style and culture that would come to characterize Goddard's operations throughout its developmental years. It was a very pragmatic approach that stressed direct, solution-focused communication with the line personnel doing the work, and avoided formal paperwork unless absolutely necessary.

One early radio astronomy satellite, for example, required a complex system to keep it pointed in the right direction and an antenna array that was taller than the Empire State Building. After heated debate as to how the satellite should be built, the project manager approved one engineer's design and asked him to document it for

A researcher retrieves instruments from the remains of one of the early V-2 rockets after its flight. The rockets created large craters where they crash landed.

him. On the launch day, when asked for the still-missing documentation, the engineer ripped off a corner of a piece of notebook paper, scribbled his recommendation, and handed it to the project manager. As one of the early scientists said, the Center's philosophy was "Don't talk about it, don't write about it—do it!"[29]

DEDICATING THE NEW SPACE CENTER

This innovative and pragmatic approach to operations permeated the entire staff of the young space center, a trait that proved very useful in everything from spacecraft design to Goddard's formal dedication ceremonies. Construction of the facilities at Goddard progressed through 1959 and 1960. By the spring of 1961, NASA decided the work was far enough along to organize formal dedication ceremonies. But while several buildings were finished and occupied, the Center was still lacking a few elements necessary for a dedication.

A week before the ceremonies, the Secret Service came out to survey the site, because President Kennedy might attend. They told Goddard's Director of Administration, Mike Vaccaro, that he had to have a fence surrounding the Center. It rained for a solid week before the dedication, but Vaccaro managed to find a contractor who worked a crew 24 hours a day in the rain and mud to cut down trees and put in a chain link fence.

After all that effort, the President could not attend the ceremonies. But

Dedication ceremonies take place at Goddard Space Flight Center on 16 March 1961.

someone then decided that a dedication could not take place without a flagpole to mark the Center's entrance. Vaccaro had 3 days to find a flagpole—a seemingly impossible deadline to meet while still complying with government procurement regulations. One of his staff told him about a school being closed down that had a flagpole outside it, so Vaccaro spoke to the school board and then created a specification that described that flagpole so precisely that the school was the only bidder that fit the bill. He then sent some of his staff over to dig up the flagpole and move it over to the Center's entrance gate—where it still stands today.

There was also the problem of a bust statue. The dedication ceremony was supposed to include the unveiling of a bronze bust of Robert H. Goddard. But the sculptor commissioned to create the bust fell behind schedule and had completed only a clay

model by the dedication date. Vaccaro sent an employee to bring the clay sculpture to the Center for the ceremonies anyway. To make things worse, the taxi bringing the bust back to the Center stopped short at one point, causing the bust to fall to the floor of the cab. The bust survived pretty much intact, but its nose broke off. Undaunted, Vaccaro and his employees pieced the nose back together and simply spray painted the clay bronze, finishing with so little time to spare that the paint was still wet when the bust was finally unveiled.[30] But the ceremonies went beautifully, the Goddard Space Flight Center was given its formal send-off, and the Center settled back down to the work of getting satellites into orbit.

THE EARLY YEARS

In the view of those who were present at the time, the 1960s were a kind of golden

Esther C. Goddard with the bust of her husband, sculpted by Joseph Anthony Atchison.

age for Goddard. An entrepreneurial enthusiasm abounded, and NASA was too new and still too small to have much in the way of bureaucracy, paperwork, or red tape. The scientists were being given the opportunity to be the first in a new territory. Sounding rockets and satellites were not just making little refinements of already known phenomena and theories—they were exploring the space around Earth for the first time. Practically everything the scientists did was something that had never been done before, and they were discovering phenomena on almost every flight.

Because of the impetus behind the Mercury, Gemini, and Apollo space programs, space scientists also suddenly found themselves with a level of funding they had never had available before. In spite of the many frustrations associated with learning how to operate in space and develop reliable technology that could survive its rigors, support for that effort in the early 1960s appeared seemingly limitless to many Goddard managers. The Apollo program was "the rising tide that lifted all boats," as one Goddard manager put it. There was also a sense of mission, importance, and purpose that has been difficult to duplicate since. The nation was going to space and going to be first to the Moon, and our national security, prestige, and pride was seen as dependent on how well we did the job.[31]

THE GODDARD INSTITUTE FOR SPACE STUDIES

In this supportive environment, both the space program and Goddard grew

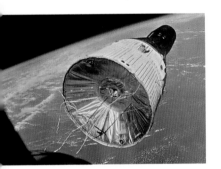

Gemini VI spacecraft as photographed by Gemini VII crew, 15 December 1965, 160 miles above the Earth.

quickly. Even before Goddard completed its formal dedication ceremonies, plans were laid for the establishment of a separate Goddard Institute for Space Studies in New York City. Two of the big concerns in the early days of the space program were attracting top scientists to work with the new agency and ensuring a supply of space-skilled researchers coming out of the universities. Early in NASA's development, the agency set aside money for both research and facilities grants to universities to help create strong space science departments.[32] But one of Goddard's early managers thought the link should be personal as well as financial.

Dr. Robert Jastrow had transferred to Goddard to head up the Theoretical Division in the fall of 1958. He argued that if Goddard wanted to attract the top theoretical physicists from academia to work with the space program, it had to have a location more convenient to leading universities. By late 1960, he had convinced managers at Goddard and Headquarters to allow him to set up a separate Goddard institute in New York. The Goddard Institute for Space Studies (GISS) provided a gathering point for theoretical physicists and space scientists in the area. But the institute offered them another dividend, as well—some of the most powerful computers in existence at the time. The computers were a tremendous asset in crunching the impossibly big numbers involved in problems of theoretical physics and orbital projections.

Over the years, the Goddard Institute organized conferences and symposia and offered research fellowships to graduate students in the area. It also kept its place at the forefront of computer technology. In 1975, the first fourth-generation computer to be used anywhere in the United States was installed at the Goddard Institute in New York.[33]

INTERNATIONAL PROJECTS

Goddard's international ties and projects were expanding quickly, as well. In part the growth was natural, because Goddard and the space program itself grew out of an international scientific effort—the International Geophysical Year. Scientists also tended to see their community as global rather than national, which made international projects much easier to organize. Furthermore, the need for a world-wide network of ground stations to track the IGY satellites forced the early space scientists and engineers to develop working relationships with international partners even before NASA existed. These efforts were enhanced both by the Space Act that created NASA, which specified international cooperation as a priority for the new agency, and by the simple fact that other countries also were interested in doing space research.

Early NASA managers quickly instituted a very simple policy about international space science projects that still guides those efforts NASA undertakes. There were only two main rules. The first was that there would be no exchange of funds between

Researcher checks out Explorer XVIII, the first Interplanetary Monitoring Platform spacecraft, prior to launch. The satellite measured cosmic radiation, magnetic fields, and solar wind beyond the Earth's magnetic field. (NASA Photo G-64-269)

NASA and international partners. Each side would contribute part of the project. The second was that the results would be made available to the whole international community. The result was a number of highly successful international satellites created by joint teams who worked together extremely well—sometimes so well that it seemed that they all came from a single country.[34]

In April 1962, NASA launched Ariel I —a joint effort between Goddard and the United Kingdom and the first international

Explorer X studied particles and fields in interplanetary space and near-Earth reaches. It was launched on 25 March 1961.

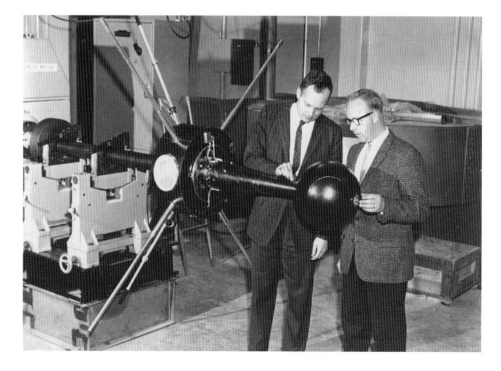

The Explorer XVII was designed to measure the density, composition, pressure, and temperature of the Earth's atmosphere. It was launched on 3 April 1963. (NASA Photo G-63-4001)

satellite. Researchers in the United Kingdom developed the instruments for the satellite and Goddard managed development of the satellite and the overall project. Ariel was followed 5 months later by Alouette I, a cooperative venture between NASA and Canada. Although Alouette was the second international satellite, it was the first satellite in NASA's international space research program that was developed entirely by another country.[35]

Over the years, Goddard's international ties grew stronger through additional cooperative scientific satellite projects and the development of ground station networks. Today, international cooperation is a critical component of both NASA's scientific satellite and human space flight programs.

THE WORK

The work Goddard conducted throughout the 1960s was focused on basics: conquering the technical challenges of getting into space, figuring out how to get satellites to work reliably once they got there, and starting to take basic measurements of what existed beyond the Earth's atmosphere.

The first few satellites focused on taking in situ measurements of forces and particles that existed in the immediate vicinity of Earth. This research quickly expanded to astronomy, weather satellites, and communication satellites. Indeed, one of the initial groups transferred to form Goddard was a group from the Army Signal Corps that was already working on development of a weather satellite called the Television Infrared Observation Satellite (TIROS). The first TIROS satellite was launched in April 1960.

Four months later, the first communications satellite was launched into a successful orbit. The original charter for NASA limited its research to passive communications satellites and left active communications technology to the Department of Defense. So the first communications satellite was an inflatable mylar sphere called "Echo," which simply bounced communications signals back to the ground. The limitation against active communications satellite research was soon lifted, however, and civilian prototypes of communications satellites with active transmitters were in orbit by early 1963.[36]

As the 1960s progressed, the size of satellites grew along with the funding for the space program. The early satellites were simple vehicles with one or two main experiments. Although small satellites continued to be built and launched, the mid-1960s saw the evolution of a new Observatory-class of satellites—spacecraft weighing as much as 1,000 pounds, with multiple instruments and experiments. In

The Television Infrared Observation Satellite (TIROS) spacecraft were the first meteorological satellites. The first one was launched in April 1960.
(NASA Photo G-65-5216)

part, the bigger satellites reflected advances in launch vehicles that allowed bigger payloads to get into orbit. But they also paralleled the rapidly expanding sights, funding, and goals of the space program.

The research conducted with satellites also expanded during the 1960s. Astronomy satellites were a little more complex to design, because they had to be able to remain pointed at one spot for a length of time. Also, astronomers were not as motivated as their space physics colleagues to undertake the challenge of space-based research, because many astronomy experiments could be conducted from ground observatories. Nonetheless, space offered the intriguing opportunity to look at objects in regions of the electromagnetic spectrum obscured by the Earth's atmosphere. The ability to launch larger satellites brought that opportunity within reach as it opened the door to space-based astronomy telescopes.

Goddard launched its first Orbiting Astronomical Observatory (OAO) in 1966. That satellite failed, but another OAO launched 2 years later was very successful. These OAO satellites laid the groundwork for Goddard's many astronomical satellites that followed, including the Hubble Space Telescope. Goddard scientists also were involved in instrumenting some of the planetary probes that already were being developed in the 1960s, such as the Pioneer probes into interplanetary space and the Ranger probes to the Moon.

The other main effort underway at Goddard in the 1960s involved the development of tracking and communication facilities and capabilities for both the scientific satellites and the human space flight program. Goddard became the hub of the massive, international tracking and communications wheel that involved aircraft, supertankers converted into mobile communications units, and a wide diversity of

Goddard was the hub of an international tracking and communications network organized to track and communicate with both scientific and crewed spacecraft.

ground stations. This system provided NASA with a kind of "Internet" that stretched not only around the world, but into space as well. Every communication to or from any spacecraft came through this network. A duplicate mission control center also was built at Goddard in case the computers at the main control room at the Manned Spacecraft Center in Houston, Texas, failed for any reason.

Whether it was in tracking, data, satellite engineering, or space science research, the 1960s were an exciting time to work for NASA. The nation was behind the effort, funding was flowing from Congress faster than scientists and engineers could spend it, and there was an exhilarating spirit of exploration. Almost everything Goddard was doing was totally new. Space was the new frontier, and the people at Goddard realized they were pioneers in the endeavor of the century.

EXTERNAL RELATIONS

This first decade at Goddard was not totally free of difficulties, frustrations, problems, and disappointments. Difficulties between the Center and NASA Headquarters increased as NASA projects got bigger. Goddard's first director, Harry J. Goett, came to Goddard from the former NACA Ames Research Center. He was a fierce defender of his people and believed vehemently in the independence of field centers. Unfortunately, Goddard was not only almost in Headquarters' backyard; it was also under a much more intense spotlight because of its focus on space.

This was a parabolic antenna at the Rosman, North Carolina tracking station, built in 1963. At one time, Goddard's tracking and data networks involved up to 24 countries.

Tension exists almost inherently between the headquarters and field installations of any institution or corporation. While both components are necessary to solve the spectrum of problems the organization faces, their different tasks and perspectives often put Headquarters and field personnel in conflict with each other. To run interference for field offices and conduct long-range planning, funding, or legislative battles, Headquarters personnel need specific information and a certain

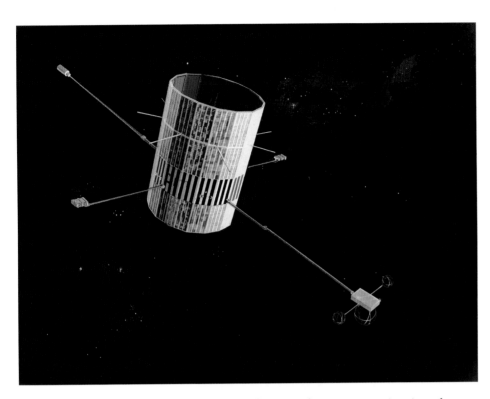

An artist's concept of an Interplanetary Monitoring Platform spacecraft. The IMP acronym for the satellite was chosen by its project scientist, Dr. Frank McDonald, "in honor of his children."

amount of control over organizational activities. Yet field personnel who are shielded from these upper-level threats and pressures may see this oversight and control as intrusion.

In the case of NASA, Headquarters had constant pressure from Congress to know what was going on, and it had a justifiable concern about managing budgets and projects that were truly astronomical. To allow senior management to keep tabs

Researchers prepare Explorer XX, the Topside Sounder IE-A, for launch. The satellite was put into orbit on 25 August 1964.

on different projects and to maintain a constant information flow between the Centers and Headquarters, NASA designated program managers at Headquarters to oversee the agency's long-term, continuing endeavors, such as astronomy. Those program managers also reviewed the shorter term individual projects, such as a single astronomy satellite, that were managed by Goddard or other NASA field centers.[37]

These program managers were something of a sore spot for Center Director Harry J. Goett and the Goddard managers. They felt they could adequately manage their own work and, like typical field office personnel, sometimes saw this oversight as unwelcome interference. Managers at other NASA Centers shared this opinion, but the tension was probably higher at Goddard because it was so close to Headquarters. Program managers wanted to sit in on meetings, and Goett wanted his project managers and scientists to be left alone. Anxieties over authority and management escalated between Goett and Headquarters until Goett's departure in 1965.[38]

The increasing attention paid to the space program had other consequences as well. While it created more support and funding for the work, it also put NASA projects in the eye of a public that did not necessarily understand that failure was an integral part of the scientific process. The public reaction to early launch failures, especially the embarrassing Vanguard explosion in December 1957, made it very clear to NASA engineers and scientists that failure, in any guise, was unacceptable.

This situation intensified after the Apollo 1 fire in 1967 that cost the lives of three astronauts. With each failure, oversight and review processes became more detailed and complex, and the pressure to succeed intensified.

As a result, Goddard's engineers quickly developed a policy of intricate oversight of contractors and detailed testing of components and satellites. Private industry has become more adept at building satellites, and NASA is now reviewing this policy with a view to eliminate costly duplication. In the future, satellites may be built more independently by private companies under performance-based contracts with NASA. But in the early days, close working relationships with contractors and detailed oversight of satellite building were two of the critical elements that led to Goddard's success.

THE POST-APOLLO ERA

The ending of the Apollo program brought a new era to NASA and to Goddard. The drive to the Moon had unified NASA and garnered tremendous support for space efforts from Congress and the country in general. But once that goal was achieved, NASA's role, mission, and funding became a little less clear. In some ways, Goddard's focus on scientific mis-

In its first decade of operation, the Goddard Space Flight Center was responsible for launching more than 100 different spacecraft carrying a wide variety of weather, communications, space physics, and astronomy experiments.

sions, along with its diversity of projects, helped protect it from some of the cutbacks that accompanied the end of the Apollo program in 1972. Nevertheless, there were two Reductions in Force (RIFs)[39] at Goddard after the final Apollo 17 mission that hurt the high morale and enthusiasm that had characterized the Center throughout its first decade. Despite the cutbacks, the work at Goddard was still expanding into new areas.

SPACECRAFT TECHNOLOGY

Even as the Apollo program wound down, NASA was developing a new launch vehicle that would become known as the Space Shuttle. The primary advantage of the Shuttle initially was its reusable nature.

NASA astronauts work to repair the Solar Maximum Mission spacecraft in the cargo bay of the Space Shuttle. The repair marked the first time a satellite was retrieved and serviced in space. (NASA Photo S13-37-1711)

But an engineer at Goddard named Frank Ceppolina saw another distinct opportunity with the Shuttle. With its large cargo bay and regular missions into low Earth orbit, he believed the Shuttle could be used as a floating workshop to retrieve and service satellites in orbit. Goddard had already pioneered the concept of modular space-craft design with its Orbiting Geophysical Observatory (OGO) satellites in the 1960s. But in 1974, Ceppolina took that concept one step further by proposing a Multi-mission Modular Spacecraft (MMS) with easily replaceable, standardized modules that would support a wide variety of different instruments. The modular approach would not only reduce manufacturing costs, but also make it possible to repair the satellite on station, because repairing it would be a fairly straightforward matter of removing and replacing various modules.

The first modular satellite was called the "Solar Max" spacecraft. It was designed to look at solar phenomena during a peak solar activity time and was launched in 1980. About a year after launch it developed problems and, in 1984, it became the first satellite to be repaired in space by Shuttle astronauts. The servicing allowed the satellite to gather additional valuable scientific data. But perhaps the biggest benefit of the Solar Max repair mission was the experience it gave NASA in servicing satellites. That experience would prove invaluable a few years later when flaws discovered in the Hubble Space Telescope forced NASA to undertake a massive and difficult recovery

effort to save the expensive and high-visibility Hubble mission.[40]

SPACE SCIENCE

Goddard made significant strides in space science in the years following Apollo, developing projects that would begin to explore new wavelengths and farther distances in the galaxy and the universe. The International Ultraviolet Explorer (IUE), launched in 1978, proved to be one of the most successful and productive satellites ever put into orbit. It continued operating for almost 19 years—14 years beyond its expected life span—and generated more data and scientific papers than any other satellite to date.

Goddard's astronomy work also expanded into the high-energy astronomy field in the 1970s. The first Small

The International Ultraviolet Explorer, shown here during assembly at Goddard, became one of the longest lasting and most productive satellites in the Center's history. When it was finally shut down, it had been returning useful data for nearly 19 years. (NASA Photo 77-HC-484)

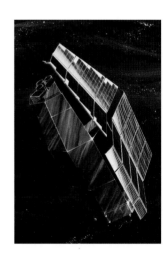

The High Energy Astro-nomical Observatories (HEAO) made tremendous strides in the extraordinary world of X-ray and gamma ray astronomy. Three HEAO spacecraft were built and launched successfully throughout the 1970s. (NASA Photo 74-H-524)

Astronomy Satellite, which mapped X-ray sources across the sky, was launched in 1970. A gamma-ray satellite followed in 1972. Goddard also had instruments on the High Energy Astronomical Observatory (HEAO) satellites, which were managed by the Marshall Space Flight Center.[41]

The HEAO satellites also marked the start of a competition between Marshall and Goddard that would intensify with the development of the Hubble Space Telescope. When the HEAO satellites were being planned in the late 1960s and early 1970s, Goddard had a myriad of projects underway. Senior managers at the Marshall Space Flight Center, however, were eagerly looking for new work projects to keep the center busy and alive. Marshall's main project had been the development of the Saturn rocket for the Apollo program and, with the close of the Apollo era, discussion arose about the need for this Center.

When the HEAO project came up, the response of Goddard's senior management was that the Center was too busy to take on the project unless it was allowed to hire more civil servants to do the work. Marshall, on the other hand, enthusiastically promised to make the project a high priority and assured Headquarters that it already had the staff on board to manage it.

In truth, Marshall had a modest amount of experience building structures for astronomy, having developed the Apollo Telescope Mount for Skylab, and the Center had shown an interest in doing high-energy research. When it got the HEAO project, however, Marshall still had extremely limited space science capability. From a strictly scientific standpoint, Goddard would have been the logical center to run the project. But the combination of the available workforce at Marshall and the enthusiasm and support shown for the project by Marshall led NASA Headquarters to choose the Alabama Center over Goddard to manage the HEAO satellites.

The loss of HEAO to Marshall was a bitter pill for some of Goddard's scientists to swallow. Goddard had all but owned the scientific satellite effort at NASA for more than a decade and felt a great deal of pride and ownership in the expertise it had developed in the field. It was quite an

The Small Astronomy Satellite-C, launched on 7 May 1975, studied X-ray sources within and beyond the Milky Way galaxy.
(NASA Photo G-71-2213)

adjustment to have to start sharing that pie. What made the HEAO loss particularly difficult to accept, however, was that it gave Marshall experience in telescope development—experience that factored heavily in Headquarters' decision to award the development of the Hubble Space Telescope to Marshall as well.

Other reasons for giving the Hubble telescope to Marshall included concern among some in the external scientific community that Goddard scientists still had too much of an inside edge on satellite research projects. Goddard was going to manage development of Hubble's scientific instruments and operation of the telescope once it was in orbit. If Goddard managed the development of the telescope as well, its scientists would know more about all aspects of this extremely powerful new tool than any of the external scientists. When Marshall received the assignment to develop the telescope project, that perceived edge was softened.

Indeed, Hubble was perceived to be such a tremendously powerful tool for research that the outside community did not even want to rely on NASA Headquarters to decide which astronomers should be given time on the telescope. At the insistence of the general astronomical community, an independent Space Telescope Science Institute was set up to evaluate and select proposals from astronomers wanting to conduct research with the Hubble. The important point, however, was that the telescope project was approved. It would become the largest

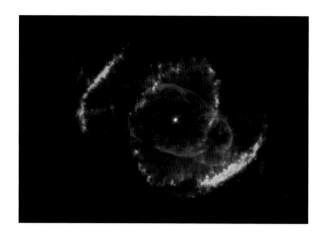

astronomical telescope ever put into space—a lens into mysteries and wonders of the universe no one on Earth had ever been able to see before.[42]

EARTH SCIENCE

The field of space-based Earth science, which in a sense had begun with the first TIROS launch in 1960, also continued to evolve in the post-Apollo era. The first of a second generation of weather satellites was launched in 1970 and, in 1972, the first Earth Resources Technology Satellite (ERTS) was put into orbit. By looking at the reflected radiation of the Earth's land masses with high resolution in different wavelengths, the ERTS instruments could provide information about the composition, use, and health of the land and vegetation in different areas. The ERTS satellite became the basis of the Landsat satellites that still provide remote images of Earth today.

Other satellites developed in the 1970s began to look more closely at the Earth's atmosphere and oceans. For example, the Nimbus 7 satellite carried new instruments that boasted the ability to measure the levels of ozone in the atmo-

This colorful image, taken by the Hubble Space Telescope, shows one of the most complex planetary nebulae ever seen. Planetary nebulae are actually not planets at all, but gas clouds formed by dying "red giant" stars. This particular one, called "Cat's Eye" nebula, is about 1,000 years old and was formed by a star that was once about the size of our own Sun. (NASA Photo PRC95-01a)

Artist's concept of a Landsat satellite. Using remote sensing technology, the Landsat spacecraft furnish data on a variety of Earth resources and environmental conditions. (NASA Photo G-75-07025)

sphere and phytoplankton in the ocean. As instruments and satellites that could explore the Earth's resources and processes evolved, however, Earth scientists found themselves caught in the middle of a politically charged tug-of-war between science and application.

Launching satellites to look at phenomena or gather astronomical or physics data in space typically has been viewed as a strictly scientific endeavor whose value lies in the more esoteric goal of expanding knowledge. Satellites that have looked back on Earth, however, have been more closely linked with practical applications of their data—a fact that has both advantages and disadvantages for the scientists involved.

When Goddard began, all of the scientific satellites were organized under the "Space Sciences and Applications" directorate. Although the Center was working on developing weather and communications satellites, the technology and high-resolution instruments needed for more specific resource management tasks did not yet exist. In addition, this period was the height of the space race, and science and space exploration for its own sake had a broad base of support in Congress and in society at large.

In the post-Apollo era, however, NASA found itself needing to justify its expenditures, which led to a greater emphasis on proving the practical benefits of space science. NASA Headquarters created a separate "applications" office to focus on satellite projects that had, or could develop, commercial applications. In an effort to focus efforts on more "applications" research (communications, meteorology, oceanography, and remote imaging of land masses) as well as scientific studies, Goddard's senior management decided to split out "applications" functions into a new directorate at the Center.

In many ways, the distinction between science and application is a fine one. Often, the data collected are the same—the difference lies only in how they are analyzed or used. A satellite that maps snow cover over time, for example, can be used to better determine whether snow cover is changing as a result of global climate system changes. But that same information also is extremely useful in predicting snow melt runoff, which is closely linked with water resource management. A satellite that looks at the upper atmosphere will collect data that can help scientists understand the dynamics of chemical processes in that region. That same information can be used to determine how much damage pollutants are causing or whether we are, in fact, depleting our ozone layer.

For this reason, Earth scientists can be more affected by shifting national priorities

than their space science counterparts.[43] The problem is the inseparable policy implications of information pertaining to our own planet. If we discover that the atmosphere of Mars is changing, no one feels an urgency to do something about it. However, if we discover that pollutants in the air are destroying our own atmosphere, this knowledge creates a pressure to take action to remedy the situation.

Scientists can argue that information is neutral—for example, that it can show less damage than environmentalists claim as well as more severe dangers than we anticipated. But the fact remains that, either way, the data from Earth science research can have political implications that affect the support those research efforts receive. The applicability of data on the ozone layer, atmospheric pollution, and environmental damage may have prompted additional funding support at times when environmental issues were a priority. But the political and social implications of these data also may have rendered Earth science programs more

A Landsat image of the Baltimore/Washington area.

susceptible to funding cuts when less sympathetic forces were in power.[44]

Despite the policy issues that complicate Earth science research, advances in technology throughout the 1970s certainly made it possible to learn more about the Earth and get a better perspective on the interactions between ocean, land mass, and atmospheric processes than we ever had before.

THE SPACE SHUTTLE ERA

As NASA moved into the 1980s, the focus that drove many of the agency's other efforts was the introduction of the Space Shuttle. In addition to the sheer dollars and personnel required to develop the new spacecraft, the Shuttle created new support

An artist's concept of the Tracking and Data Relay Satellite System spacecraft. Three satellites in this space-based system could do the same work as the worldwide tracking and data ground stations Goddard used until the late 1980s.

issues and significantly affected how scientific satellites were designed and built.

In the Apollo era, spacecraft traveled away from the Earth, so a ground network of tracking stations could keep the astronauts in sight and in touch with mission controllers at almost all times. The Shuttle, however, was designed to stay in near-Earth orbit, and therefore would be in range of any given ground station for only a short period of time. This was the case with most scientific satellites, but real-time communication was not as critical when no human lives were at stake. Satellites simply used tape recorders to record their data and transmitted it down in batches when they passed over various ground stations. Shuttle astronauts, on the other hand, needed to be in continual communication with mission control.

Goddard had gained a lot of experience in communication satellites in its early days and had done some research with geosynchronous communication satellite technology in the 1970s that offered a possible solution to the problem. A network of three geosynchronous satellites, parked in high orbits 22,300 miles above the Earth, could keep any lower Earth-orbiting satellite—including the Space Shuttle—in sight at all times. In addition to its benefits to the Shuttle program, the system could save NASA money over time by eliminating the need for the worldwide network of ground stations that tracked scientific satellites. The biggest problem with such a system was its development costs.

NASA's tight budgets in the late 1970s did not have room for a big-budget item like the proposed Tracking and Data Relay Satellite System (TDRSS). So the agency worked out an arrangement to lease time on the satellites from a contractor who agreed to build the spacecraft at its own cost. Unfortunately, the agreement offered NASA little control or leverage with the contractor, and the project ran into large cost and schedule overruns. It was a learning experience for NASA, and one that managers do not recall fondly.

Eventually, Goddard renegotiated the contract and took control of the TDRSS project. The first TDRSS satellite was launched from the Space Shuttle in April 1983. The second TDRSS was lost with the Shuttle "Challenger" in 1986, but the system finally became operational in 1989.

The TDRSS project also required building a new ground station to communicate with the satellites and process their data. The location best suited for maximum coverage of the satellites was the White Sands Missile Range in New Mexico. In 1978, Goddard began building the TDRSS White Sands Ground Terminal (WSGT). The first station became operational in 1983, and a complete back-up facility, called the Second TDRSS Ground Terminal (STGT), became operational in 1994. The second station was built because the White Sands complex was the sole ground link for the TDRSS, and the possibility of losing contact with the Shuttle was unacceptable. The second site ensured that there would always be a

working communications and data link for the TDRSS satellites.[45]

The decision that TDRSS also would become *the* system for all scientific satellite tracking and data transmission did not please everyone, because it meant every satellite had to be designed with the somewhat cumbersome antennae required to communicate with TDRSS. But the Shuttle's impact on space science missions went far beyond tracking systems or antennae design.

Part of the justification for the Shuttle was that it could replace the expendable launch vehicles (rockets) used by NASA and the military to get satellites into orbit. As a result, the stockpile of smaller launch rockets was not replenished, and satellites had to be designed to fit in the Shuttle bay instead.

There were some distinct advantages to using the Space Shuttle as a satellite launch vehicle. Limitations on size and weight—critical factors with the smaller

An aerial view of the White Sands Ground Terminal tracking station on the White Sands Missile Range in New Mexico. All the TDRSS data pass through this station before being networked throughout NASA. (NASA Photo 0691-1542)

launch vehicles—became much less stringent, paving the way for much bigger satellites. Goddard's Compton Gamma Ray Observatory, for example, weighed more than 17 tons. The Space Shuttle also opened up the possibility of having astronauts service satellites in space.[46]

On the other hand, using the Shuttle as the sole launch vehicle complicated the design of satellites. They now had to undergo significantly more stringent safety checks to make sure their systems posed no threat to the astronauts traveling into space with the cargo. But the biggest disadvantage of relying exclusively on the Shuttle hit home with the impact in January 1986 when the Shuttle "Challenger" exploded right after lift-off. The Shuttle fleet was grounded for almost 3 years and, because the Shuttle was supposed to eliminate the need for them, few expendable launch rockets remained. Even if a large number of rockets had been available, few of the satellites designed for the spacious cargo

A Black Brandt XII sounding rocket being launched at Wallops Island. Wallops launches approximately 35 sounding rockets to conduct scientific research each year. (NASA Photo WI-88-589-4)

bay of the Shuttle would fit the smaller weight and size limitations of other launch vehicles. Most satellites simply had to wait for the Shuttle fleet to start flying again.

WALLOPS ISLAND

The 1980s brought some administrative changes to Goddard as well. NASA's Wallops Island, Virginia, flight facility had been created as an "Auxiliary Flight Research Station" associated with the NACA's Langley Aeronautical Laboratory in 1945.[47] Its remote location on the Atlantic coast of Virginia made it a perfect site for testing aircraft models and launching small rockets. As the space program evolved, Wallops became one of the mainstays of NASA's sounding rocket program and also operated numerous aircraft for scientific research purposes. In addition, it launched some of the National Science Foundation's smaller research balloons and provided tracking and other launch support services for NASA and DOD.

Although its work expanded over the years, Wallops' small size, lower-budget projects, and remote location allowed it to retain the pragmatic, informal, entrepreneurial style that had characterized Goddard and much of NASA itself in the early days of the space program. People who worked at Wallops typically came from the local area, and a sense of family, loyalty, and independence characterized the facility. But as one of NASA's smaller research stations, Wallops was in a less protected political position than some of its larger, higher profile counterparts.

Launch row at the Wallops Island Flight Facility on the eastern shore of Virginia. Wallops became part of the Goddard Space Flight Center in 1982.

In the early 1980s a proposal emerged to close the Wallops Station as a way of reducing NASA's operating costs. In an effort to save the facility, NASA managers decided to incorporate Wallops into the Goddard Space Flight Center. Goddard was a logical choice because Wallops was already closely linked with Goddard on many projects. The aircraft at Wallops were sometimes used to help develop instruments that later went on Goddard satellites. Goddard also had a sounding rocket division that relied on Wallops for launch, range, tracking, and data support. As time went on, Wallops had begun to develop some of the smaller, simpler sounding rocket payloads as well. By the late 1970s, NASA Headquarters was even considering transferring Goddard's entire sounding rocket program to Wallops.

In 1982, Wallops Island Station became the Wallops Island Flight Facility, managed under the "Suborbital Projects and Operations" directorate at Goddard.[48] At the same time, the remaining sounding rocket projects at Goddard-Greenbelt were transferred to Wallops. The personnel at Goddard who had been working on sounding rockets had to refocus their talents. So they turned their entrepreneurial efforts to the next generation of small-budget, hands-on projects—special payloads for the Space Shuttle.[49] As the 1980s progressed, Goddard began putting together a variety of small payloads to take up spare room in the Shuttle cargo bay. They ranged from $10,000 "Get Away Special" (GAS) experiments that school children could develop to multimillion-dollar Spartan satellites that the Shuttle astronauts release overboard at the start of a mission and pick up again before returning to Earth.

THE POST-CHALLENGER ERA: A NEW DAWN

All of NASA was rocked on the morning of 28 January 1986 when the Shuttle "Challenger" exploded 73 seconds after launch. While many insiders at NASA were saddened by the tragic loss of life, they were not, as a whole, surprised. These were people who had witnessed numerous rockets with cherished experiments explode or fail during the launch process.

The Extreme Ultraviolet Explorer satellite, was launched on 7 June 1992 on top of a Delta launch rocket. The Delta rocket program, managed by Goddard, remains one of the most successful launch vehicle programs in NASA's history. (NASA Photo PL92C-11006)

They had lived through the Orbiting Solar Observatory accident, the Apollo 1 fire, and the Apollo 13 crisis. They knew how volatile rocket technology was and how much of a research effort the Shuttle was, aiming to become a routine transportation system for space. These were veteran explorers who knew that for all the excitement and wonder space offered, it was a dangerous and unforgiving realm. Even 25 years after first reaching orbit, we were still only beginners, getting into space by virtue of brute force. There was nothing routine about it.

The understanding of just how risky the Shuttle technology was drove a number of people within NASA to argue against eliminating the other, expendable launch vehicles. The Air Force also was concerned about relying on the Shuttle for all its launch needs. The Shuttle accident, however, settled the case. A new policy supporting a "mixed fleet" of launch vehicles was created, and expendable launch vehicles went back into production.[50]

Unfortunately, a dearth of launch vehicles was not the only impact the Challenger accident had on NASA or Goddard. The tragedy injured NASA's public image, leading to intense public scrutiny of its operations and a loss of confidence in its ability to conduct missions safely and successfully. Some within NASA wondered if the agency would survive. To make things worse, the Challenger accident was followed 4 months later by the loss of a Delta rocket carrying a new weather satellite into orbit, and the loss a year later by an Atlas-Centaur rocket carrying a DOD satellite. While these were not NASA projects, the agency received the criticism and the consequential public image of a Federal entity that could not execute its tasks.

Launches all but came to a halt for almost 2 years, and even the scientific satellite projects found themselves burdened with more safety checks and oversight processes. The Shuttle resumed flight in 1989, but NASA took another hit in 1990 when it launched the Hubble Space Telescope, only to discover that the telescope had a serious flaw in its main mirror. As the last decade of the century began, NASA needed some big successes to regain the nation's confidence in the agency's competence and value. Goddard would help provide those victories.

SPACECRAFT TECHNOLOGY

One of Goddard's biggest strengths was its expertise in spacecraft construction. Most of the incredibly successful Explorer class of satellites, for example, were built in-house at Goddard. But the size and complexity of space science projects at Goddard—and even the Center's Explorer satellites—had grown dramatically over the years. From the early Explorer spacecraft, which could be designed, built, and launched in 1 to 3 years, development and launch cycles had grown until they stretched 10 years or more. Aside from the cost of these large projects, they entailed much more risk for the scientists involved. If a satellite took 15 years from inception to launch, its scientists had to devote a major portion of their careers to the pro-

The Submillimeter Wave Astronomy Satellite, launched 1 December 1998, detects water vapor throughout the Milky Way.

ject. If it failed, the cost to their careers would be enormous.

In part, the growth in size and complexity of satellites was born of necessity. To get sharp images of distant stars, the Hubble Space Telescope had to be big enough to collect large amounts of light. In the more cost-conscious era following Apollo, where new satellite starts began to dwindle every year, the pressure also increased to maximize the use of every new satellite that was approved.

But in 1989, Tom Huber, Goddard's Director of Engineering, began advocating for Goddard to build a new line of smaller satellites. In a sense, these "Small Explorers," or SMEX satellites, would be a return to Goddard's roots in innovative, small, and quickly produced spacecraft. But because technology had progressed, they could incorporate options such as fiber optic technology, standard interfaces, solid-state recorders, more advanced computers that fit more power and memory into less

Hitchhiker payloads, developed at Goddard, offer researchers a low-cost opportunity to put small experiments in the Space Shuttle's cargo bay.

space, and miniature gyros and star trackers. Some of these innovations, such as the solid state recorders and advanced microchip technology for space applications, had been developed in-house at Goddard. As a result, these small satellites had more capability than some of the larger projects Goddard had built in the past. The goal of the SMEX satellites was to cost less than $30 million and take less than 3 years to develop. The program has proved highly successful, launching five satellites since 1992, and is continuing to develop advanced technology to enable the design of even more capable, inexpensive spacecraft.[51]

SPACE SCIENCE

In late 1989, Goddard launched the Cosmic Background Explorer (COBE) satellite aboard a Delta launch rocket. Originally scheduled for launch aboard the Space Shuttle, the COBE satellite, which was built in-house at Goddard, had been redesigned totally in less than 36 months after the Challenger accident to fit the nose cone of a Delta rocket. Using com-

plex instruments, COBE went in search of evidence to test the "Big Bang" theory of how the universe began—and found it. Famed cosmologist Stephen Hawking called the NASA-University COBE team's findings "the discovery of the century, if not of all time."[52] The COBE satellite had perhaps solved one of the most fascinating mysteries in existence—the origins of the universe in which we live. It had taken 15 years to develop, but the COBE satellite offered the public proof that NASA could take on a difficult mission, complete it successfully, and produce something of value in the process.

Goddard reached out into another difficult region of the universe when it launched the Compton Gamma Ray Observatory in 1990. The Compton was the second of NASA's planned "Four Great Observatories" that would explore the universe in various regions of the electromagnetic spectrum. The Hubble Space Telescope was to cover the visible and ultraviolet regions, the Compton was to explore the gamma ray region, and two additional observatories were to investigate phenomena in X-ray and infrared wavelengths. At over 17 tons, the Compton was the largest satellite ever launched into orbit, and its task was to explore some of the highest energy and perplexing phenomena in the cosmos.

Three years later, Goddard found itself facing an even more difficult challenge when the Center undertook the first Hubble servicing mission. The odds of successfully developing and implementing a fix for the

A sky map taken by the Differential Microwave Radiometer instrument on Goddard's Cosmic Background Explorer satellite. The map shows indications of anisotropy, or temperature fluctuations, in the background radiation of the universe. These irregularities reveal the original structures of the universe.

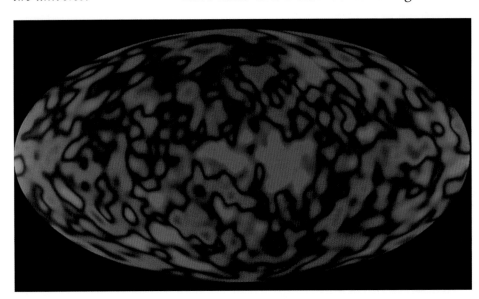

telescope, which had a flaw not in a single instrument but in its central mirror, were estimated at no better than 50 percent. But because of Goddard's earlier, successful pioneering efforts with serviceable satellites, the Hubble had been designed to be serviced in space. This capability, along with Goddard's previous experience repairing the Solar Max satellite, provided the critical components that made the Hubble repair possible. Fired with the same enthusiasm and sense of crisis that had fueled the Apollo program, the Goddard team assigned to manage the project, working with a hand-picked Shuttle crew from Houston's Johnson Space Center, succeeded beyond expectation. The success of such a difficult mission earned the team a Collier Trophy—the nation's highest award for the greatest aerospace achievement in any given year.[53]

EARTH SCIENCE

Even as Goddard launched the Compton Observatory and the Hubble Space Telescope to explore new regions of the universe, NASA announced the start of a massive new initiative to explore the planet we call home. Dubbed "Mission to Planet Earth" (MTPE) when it was introduced in 1990, the effort was expected to spend $30 billion over at least 15 years to take a long-term, systems-oriented look at the health of the planet. In some ways, the program was a natural outgrowth of increasing environmental concerns over the years and the improved ability of satellites to analyze Earth's atmosphere and oceans. But it received renewed attention with the

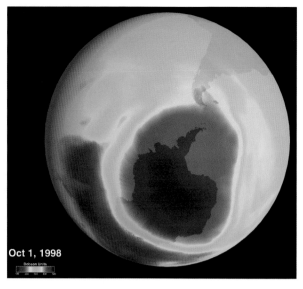

Oct 1, 1998

An image of the ozone "hole" over Antarctica. Blue/purple indicates areas of low ozone, while red areas indicate higher ozone levels.

discovery of a hole in the ozone layer in 1985. That discovery, as one researcher put it, "dramatized that the planet was at risk, and the potential relevance of NASA satellite technology to understanding that risk." In the wake of the Challenger disaster, MTPE was seen as one of the top "leadership initiatives" that could help NASA recover from the tragedy and regain the support of the American public.[54]

Although numerous NASA centers participated in the MTPE effort, the program office was located at Goddard. It was a natural choice, because Goddard was the main Earth science center in the agency. Earth science was broken out of the Space and Earth Sciences directorate, and its research began to take on new relevance in the public eye.

As with earlier Earth science efforts, the political and social implications of this data made the program more susceptible to shifting national priorities than its space science counterparts. In the past 8 years, the program has been scaled back. Its overall budget is now down to $7 billion for the life of the effort, and the program has been redesignated the Earth Science Enterprise.[55]

Numerous reasons exist for the cutback of the program. But it can be argued that Americans find money for items that are high national priorities. And one factor in the changing fortunes of the MTPE program is undeniably the shifting agendas that affect NASA funding. Nevertheless, the more moderate Earth Science Enterprise program will still give scientists their first real opportunity to study the planet's various oceanographic and atmospheric processes as an integrated system instead of individual components. This is a critical step toward understanding exactly how our planet operates and how our actions impact its health.

In short, Goddard's work in the early 1990s helped bring NASA out of the dark post-Challenger era and create a new energy, enthusiasm, and curiosity about both planet Earth and other bodies in the universe. We now had the technology to reach back to the very beginning of time and the outer reaches of the universe. The Hubble

servicing mission made possible the beautiful images of far-away galaxies, stars, nebulae, and planets that now appear in publications on a regular basis. These images have not only provided valuable clues to scientific questions about the cosmos, but also have fired the imaginations of both children and adults, generating a new enthusiasm for space exploration and investigation of the galaxy and universe we call home.

At the same time, we had the technology to begin to piece together answers about where El Niño weather patterns came from, how our oceans and atmosphere work together to create and control our climate, and how endangered our environment really is. These advances provided critical support for NASA at a time when many things about the agency and the Goddard Space Flight Center were changing.

BETTER, FASTER, CHEAPER

As the nation heads into the 21st century, the world is changing at a rapid pace. The electronic superhighways of computers and communications are making the world a smaller place, but the marketplace a more global one. Concerns about the United States' competitiveness are growing as international competition increases. The crisis-driven days of the space race also are over, and cost is now a serious concern when Congress looks at whether or not additional space projects should be funded.

This need to be more cost-efficient is driving changes both within Goddard and in its relationships with outside industry. Goddard recently underwent a major

This image combines data from several satellite sources, to show an anomoly in sea height and sea surface temperature in the year preceding the last strong El Niño climate condition.

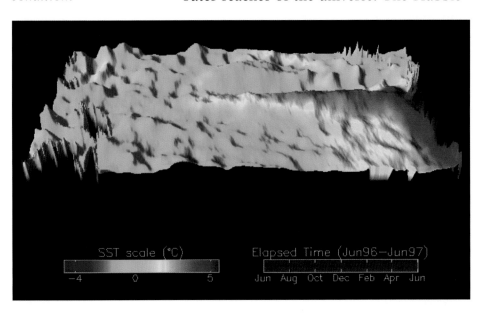

administrative reorganization in the hopes of making better use of its engineers' time. Instead of being scattered around the Center, its almost 2,000 engineers are being organized into either a new Applied Engineering and Technology (AET) directorate or a new Systems, Technology, and Advanced Concepts (STAAC) directorate. In essence, AET will provide the hands-on engineering support for whatever projects are underway at the Center, and STAAC will work on advanced concepts and systems engineering for future projects.

Again, this change in matrix structure within Goddard is not a new concept. The Center has fluctuated between putting engineers with scientists on project teams and trying to follow a stricter, discipline-oriented organization. The advantages of a project-based organization are that the engineers get to focus on one job at a time and build synergistic relationships with their scientist colleagues. These relationships often lead to innovative ideas or concepts that individual engineers or scientists might not have reached on their own. The disadvantage of this structure, which is a greater concern in times of tighter budgets, is that even if the engineers have lulls in the project, their excess time can not easily benefit anyone else in the Center. Their talent is tied up in one place, which can lead to territorial "fiefdoms" instead of a more ideal Center-wide cooperation.[56]

Currently, the changes are underway. How these changes affect the future remains to be seen. After all, the impact of any administrative change is determined more

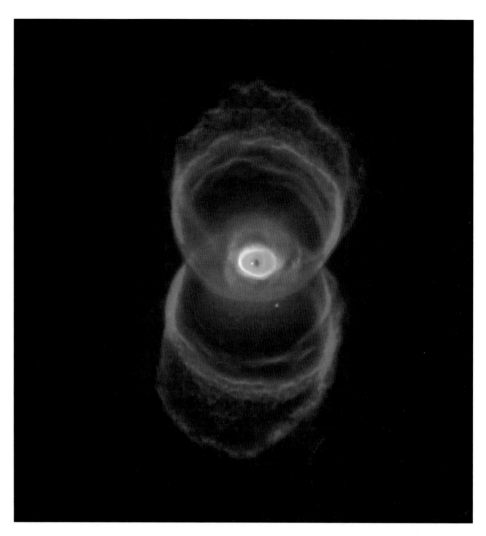

by how it is implemented than by how it looks on paper, and its success can only be determined once the change is in effect.[57]

Another issue facing Goddard is the recurring question of who should be building the spacecraft. One Goddard strength has been its in-house ability to design and build both spacecraft and instruments. The Center's founders created this in-house capability for two reasons. First, there was little in the way of a commercial spacecraft industry at the time Goddard was started. Second, although most of the satellites would be built by contractors, the founders of NASA believed that the agency had to have hands-on knowledge of building spacecraft in order to manage those contracts effectively.

An image of a planetary nebula, produced by a dying star, taken from the Hubble Space Telescope. (NASA Photo PRC96-07)

The Tropical Rainfall Measuring Mission satellite, shown here in one of Goddard's clean rooms, is part of the Earth Science Enterprise effort to study the Earth's climate as an integrated global system.

engineers' efforts on instrument building instead. The rationale was that industry was capable of building satellites and NASA should be working on developing advanced technology sensors and instruments. Yet, even aside from the argument that keeping in-house competence was necessary to manage contracts with industry effectively, this rationale had some flaws.

One issue was that building satellites in-house had a significant indirect effect on the employees at Goddard. The ability to design spacecraft helped attract bright young engineers to the Center, an important concern in a field where industry jobs generally pay better than NASA positions. Furthermore, knowing that some of the spacecraft sitting on top of launch vehicles had been built in-house gave Goddard employees a sense of pride and involvement in the space program that instrument building alone could not create. Taking away that element caused a huge drop in the Center's morale. Indeed, when A. Thomas Young became the Center's Director in 1980, one of his first actions was to restore the building of in-house satellites in the hopes of rebuilding morale.[58]

The commercial space industry has matured even further in the past 20 years, and the question has surfaced again about whether Goddard still should be building in-house satellites. In the end, the answer is probably "Yes." The question lies more in the type and number of satellite projects the Center should undertake. The goal is for Goddard to pursue one or two in-house projects that involve advanced

Over the years, the commercial spacecraft industry has grown and matured tremendously, leading to periodic discussions about whether NASA should leave the spacecraft building jobs entirely to the private sector. After all, there is general agreement that the government (in this case, NASA) should not perform work that industry is capable of doing. In truth, however, the issue is not quite that simple.

In the late 1970s, Goddard's senior management all but stopped in-house satellite building at the Center, focusing the

spacecraft technology and to contract out projects that involve more proven spacecraft concepts. At the same time, Goddard is taking advantage of the expertise now present in the commercial satellite industry by introducing a new "Rapid Spacecraft Procurement Initiative," with the goal of reducing the development time and cost of new spacecraft. By "pre-qualifying" certain standard spacecraft designs from various commercial satellite contractors, Goddard hopes to make it possible for some experiments to be integrated into a spacecraft and launched within only a year. Not every experiment can be fit into a standard spacecraft design, but there are certainly some that could benefit from this quick-turnaround system. The contracts developed by Goddard for this initiative are now being used by other NASA Centers as well as the Air Force.[59]

A more complex issue is how involved NASA should be in managing the spacecraft built by industry. Historically, Goddard has employed a very thorough and detailed oversight policy with the contracts it manages. One of the reasons the Center developed this careful, conservative policy was to avoid failure in the high-profile, high-dollar realm of NASA. As a result, NASA engineers are concerned with ensuring the job is done right, regardless of the cost. While industry engineers have the same interest in excellence and success, they sometimes are under greater pressure to watch the bottom line. Goddard managers quote numerous examples of instances contractors only agreed to

conduct additional prelaunch tests after Goddard engineers managing the contract insisted. They also recall various cases where Goddard finally sent its own engineers to a contractor's factory to personally supervise troubled projects.

Industry, on the other hand, can argue that Goddard's way of building satellites is not necessarily the only right way and this double-oversight slows down innovation and greatly increases the cost of building satellites. And in an era of decreasing federal budgets, deciding how much oversight is good or enough becomes an especially sticky issue. Currently, the trend seems to be a more hands-off, performance-based contract relationship with industry. Industry simply delivers a successful satellite or does not get paid. Some argue that a potential disadvantage to this approach is that it could rob industry engineers of the advice and experience Goddard might be

COBE under construction at the Goddard Space Flight Center. Originally designed to be launched aboard the Space Shuttle, the satellite had to be redesigned to fit on a Delta rocket after the Space Shuttle Challenger accident in 1986. (NASA Photo GSFC PAO#4)

able to offer. Goddard's scientists and engineers have a tremendous corporate memory and have learned many lessons the hard way. In the long run, sharing that expertise might prove more cost-effective than the bottom-line salary and labor allocation figures of a more hands-off system might suggest.

In the end, there is truth in all these perspectives. It is hard to say what the "right" answer is because, for all our progress in the world of space, we are still feeling our way and learning from our mistakes as we keep reaching out to expand our horizons.

The exact nature and scope of NASA's mission has been the subject of frequent debate since before the end of the Apollo program. But NASA certainly has an edict to do those things that for reasons of cost, risk, or lack of commercial market value, industry cannot or will not undertake. In the early 1960s, the unknowns and risk of

An image from the SeaWiFS satellite shows varying chlorophyll levels along the eastern seaboard of the United States.

failure were far too high and the potential profit far too uncertain for industry to fund the development of anything but communication satellites. Today, that situation is changing. In some cases, a commercial market for the data is developing. Some operations once considered too risky for anyone but NASA to perform are now considered routine enough to contract out to private companies, which are also much more capable than they once were.

To illustrate this point, some tracking and data functions that were a part of the Goddard Space Flight Center since its inception were recently moved down to the Marshall Space Flight Center, where they will be managed by a private company under contract to a supervising Space Operations Management Office at the Johnson Space Center.[60]

In addition, NASA is starting to relinquish its hold on the launching of rockets. In years past, all launches were conducted at government facilities for reasons related to safety and international politics. But that is beginning to change. The Commonwealth of Virginia is already in the process of building a commercial space port at the Wallops Island facility in partnership with private industry. The payloads and launch vehicles using the space port will be developed privately, and the consortium will contract with NASA to provide launch range, radar, telemetry, tracking, and safety analysis services.[61]

NASA also has used a privately developed, airplane-launched rocket called "Pegasus" to send a number of small satellites into space. It should be noted, however, that the Pegasus vehicle went through a series of developmental problems before it became a reliable system. The same is true of the SeaWiFS satellite, which is currently providing exceptionally useful data on ocean color, but was developed under a very different type of contract than most scientific satellites. The SeaWiFS spacecraft was developed independently by the Orbital Sciences Corporation, and NASA paid only for the data it uses. While the satellite is now generating superb data, it ran into many developmental difficulties and delays. Because NASA paid the majority of the money up front, that might have offered less incentive for the contractor to keep on schedule. On the other hand, the up-front, fixed-price lease meant that the contractor had to absorb the costs of the problems and delays when they occurred.[62]

Fixed-price contracts work well in many arenas. The complication with scientific satellites is that these spacecraft are not generally proven designs. It is difficult to foresee the problems that will arise in a research project that is breaking new ground.

Indeed, a lot of uncertainties exist in the tremendous atmosphere of change facing Goddard, NASA, and the world at large, and it remains to be seen how they will all resolve. Most likely, it will take a number of missteps before finding the right mix. The process also will undoubtedly entail the same pendulum swings between different approaches that has characterized Goddard throughout its history. And because external circumstances

and goals are constantly changing, there may never be one "correct" mix or answer.

In the end, our efforts in space are still an exploration into the unknown. On the cutting edge of technology and knowledge, change is the only constant—in theories of the universe as well as technology, priorities, and operating techniques. Once upon a time, Goddard's biggest challenge was overcoming the technical obstacles to operate in space. Today, Goddard's challenge is to find the flexibility to keep up with a rapidly changing world without losing the magic that made the Center so successful over its first 40 years.

The new frontier for Goddard is now much broader than just space itself. The challenge for the Center now is to be open to reinventing itself, infusing new methods and a renewed sense of entrepreneurial innovation and teamwork into its operations while continuing to push boundaries in technology development, space, and Earth exploration for the benefit of the human race. It has to be flexible enough to work as part of broader NASA, university, industry, and international teams in a more global and cost-constrained space industry and world. It has to find a way to reach forward into new areas of research, commercial operations, and more efficient procedures without losing the balance between cost and results, science and engineering, basic research and applications, internal and external efforts. And, most importantly, Goddard has to accomplish all of these things while preserving its most valuable strength—the people that make it all possible.

CHAPTER 3:

The Tools

*I*n its first 40 years, Goddard successfully launched more than

200 Earth-orbiting satellites. That is an amazing success record,

and yet that very fact makes it easy to take the magnitude of that

accomplishment for granted. Because the Center's satellites were so

successful, few people really give much thought to how difficult it

is to build, launch, stabilize, power, and operate a satellite or col-

lect and transmit its data back down to Earth.

Yet the truth is that conducting research in the harsh and

remote realm of space is a staggering and difficult task, and every

successful NASA mission is the result of the sweat and ingenuity of

thousands of engineers, scientists, and support personnel who

designed and built the tools to make it possible. Even today, the job

A Delta rocket lifts off carrying Goddard's 8th Orbiting Solar Observatory satellite.

is a demanding one as we stretch to design more capable spacecraft and take on more challenging missions. In the early days of the space program it was a truly Herculean task. Little was known about rocket and spacecraft technology or the environment in which these tools would have to operate. The engineers and scientists in the early space program did not know what materials would work best, how to assemble them to do the job, or under what conditions the tools would have to work. In addition, scientific satellites had another serious liability. Until the advent of the

Space Shuttle and modular, serviceable spacecraft, satellites could not be fixed by astronauts in space. All the potential problems of a mission had to be anticipated and fixes built in ahead of time. Once a satellite was in space, making changes was very difficult.

THE CHALLENGE OF SPACE FLIGHT

Scientific satellites, from the earliest Explorers to the most complex modern observatories, have two critical aspects to their design. First are the scientific instruments that collect the actual data from space. Second are the "housekeeping" systems that operate the spacecraft and get that data back to Earth. The housekeeping systems must provide power, temperature modulation, and control of the spacecraft, and allow for data reception and transmission. This sounds pretty straightforward, but providing these services in a lightweight package in space is an extremely difficult task.

Satellites are complicated vehicles to launch and control. The launch vehicles themselves have to be programmed to follow intricate computer-calculated trajectories that will place a satellite in a very precise and specific orbit. Some satellites are launched so that they will orbit north to south, over the poles of the Earth, while others follow a more equatorial orbit. Still others are launched into a geosynchronous orbit, which means that the spacecraft will stay "parked" over one spot on the Earth. In order to follow a geosynchronous orbit,

One of Goddard's Interplanetary Monitoring Platform satellites departs the launch pad in 1971.

however, a satellite has to be much further away from Earth. While the Space Shuttle and many Earth-orbiting satellites are positioned about 200 miles above the Earth, a geosynchronous satellite orbits almost 23,000 miles away.

Whether orbits are near or far, however, they have to be achieved with extreme precision. A polar-orbiting satellite, for example, might be designed to have an orbit with "an inclination of 101.56 degrees and a period of 115 minutes." An Interplanetary Monitoring Platform (IMP) satellite launched in 1964 failed because the final stage of its launch vehicle burned for *1 second* shorter than it should have. That 1-second loss resulted in an orbit only 50,000 miles high instead of the planned 160,000 miles.[1]

To reach and maintain orbits with this kind of accuracy is not easy. NASA launches its rockets on a coast so that failed or discarded rocket stages will fall harmlessly into the ocean. But the reason most of NASA's launches take place from Kennedy Space Center on the *east* coast is that the Earth rotates to the east, helping the satellites gain orbital speed. Polar-orbiting satellites are an exception to this rule. They typically are launched from NASA's Western Test Range at the Vandenberg Air Force Base in California because they can climb into a polar orbit over the ocean to the south of the range.

In either case, when the launch vehicle reaches the correct point and altitude for the orbit the researchers want, another rocket must fire correctly to kick the

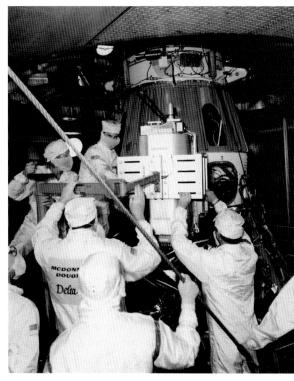

Technicians mounting a satellite package onto a Delta launch vehicle.

spacecraft into its orbital path. Most satellites also have an additional propulsion system on board in case their orbit needs to be adjusted or changed. And even in a stable orbit, many satellites use small, intermittent chemical rockets, high-pressure gas jets, or electric currents to maintain a particular attitude and orientation.

Although some of the very earliest satellites simply spun around as they made their orbit, researchers soon began looking at ways to stabilize satellites. Spin-stabilization was critical for providing good pictures of the Earth as well as for astronomical research, where the satellite needed to keep looking at a specific object for a length of time. One step further in complexity was not only to stop the spacecraft from spinning, but also to keep a particular side of it facing the Earth throughout its orbit. In many cases scientists had to know where the satellite was pointing to evaluate the significance of what it was seeing or the data it was receiving.

Over the years, satellites have been designed with various gyros, de-spin devices, and pointing mechanisms to accomplish these ends. One device to stop a satellite from spinning was called a "yo-yo," because it employed the same technique as the children's toy. String-like devices would deploy in the opposite direction from the way the satellite was spinning, slowing it down. To keep a satellite pointed in one direction, engineers often employed Earth-tracking or star-tracking systems. Star trackers fix on particular stars and send commands to the control units to adjust the spacecraft if the position of those stars drifts relative to the satellite. Earth-tracking systems work the same way, except they use the curve of the Earth instead of stars as their reference point.[2]

Of course, each of these systems had to be developed, and none worked perfectly the first time. Indeed, even today the stabilizing mechanisms in satellites can fail, causing them to "tumble" and go out of commission. A failure of a commercial communication satellite, for example, caused 90 percent of the hip-pocket "pagers" in the United States to stop working for more than 24 hours. While the satellite was not a NASA spacecraft, the incident underscores the challenges engineers still face in stabilizing and operating satellites in space.[3]

A satellite's instruments also have to be controlled. The individual instruments must be able to "talk" to each other and to the data and communication functions of the spacecraft. In some cases, individual instruments have to be turned on and off at various times. Other instruments have to be kept from ever pointing directly at the Sun. Instruments also have to be calibrated for accuracy, and that information has to be linked with the actual data collected when it is sent back to the ground.

All of these operations must be remotely controlled from Earth, which means the satellite has to be able to receive commands from ground stations. By the same token, the satellite has to have a way of recording the data it is collecting, putting it in a format and frequency that can be transmitted, and sending it back to stations on Earth. Because few of these transmitters or sensors existed on the market, the Goddard and industry engineers working on early satellites often had to develop the technology themselves. Goddard's achievements in the development of microchip technology for space applica-

Goddard's facilities include data and tracking control centers for its many scientific satellites. It also serves as the hub of NASA's internal communication, NASCOM, network.

tions, for example, stemmed from its need to make spacecraft components as lightweight as possible.

To run all these systems, a satellite needs a way of generating power for the months, even years, it is in orbit. Most Earth-orbiting spacecraft rely on solar cells to recharge on board batteries. But solar panels have their own complications, ranging from deployment of the arrays and the need to keep the collecting side of the panels pointed at the Sun to the basic problem of packing large panels into a tiny space aboard the satellite until it reaches orbit. The consequence of making the panels flexible and lightweight is that they also tend to be somewhat fragile, and several satellites have had to cope with damaged solar panels once in orbit.

In addition, all of the satellite's systems have to work in the extremely harsh environment of space, where temperatures away from the Sun are nearly absolute zero, and temperatures facing the Sun climb as high as 1200 degrees Kelvin. Thermal dynamics, therefore, is a critical issue in both spacecraft and instrument design. On one of the early Orbiting Geophysical Observatories (OGOs), for example, the spacecraft's attempts to compensate for the extreme temperature differences between the front and back sides of long booms extending from the main spacecraft caused serious problems with the control system. Engineers finally figured out that they needed to drill holes in the booms to allow some solar heat to reach the back side for the system to work.[4]

Spacecraft also need to operate in a micro-gravity vacuum, which creates its own set of difficulties. For one thing, a vacuum creates problems with dissipating heat, because the heat can not be carried away by passing air. In addition, some parts of a satellite are soldered together. It is not uncommon for some small remnants of soldering material to break off as a soldered object is moved around. In a television set, that is not a big deal. But in a

Since solar panels have to be packaged into small areas until a satellite gets into space, they can be a particularly troublesome part of satellites. Here, astronaut Kathy Thornton releases a damaged solar panel that was replaced during the first Hubble Space Telescope Servicing Mission in 1993.

Even small specks of dirt can cause satellites to malfunction in the vacuum of space. So components are assembled in "clean rooms" like this one at the Goddard Space Flight Center. In the foreground of this image, instruments are being fitted into a white pallet that will then go inside the Space Shuttle's cargo bay.

zero-gravity environment, those soldering balls can float all around the spacecraft, causing a variety of problems. Even worse, they can cause a problem like a short-circuit and then float away again, so that engineers trying to troubleshoot the system can not even find evidence of what caused the problem.

There are other difficulties, as well. High-voltage instrumentation has to be either turned off or protected during its passage through the electrically charged ionosphere and for the first few hours of its orbit while the satellite "out-gasses" the trapped molecules from the Earth's atmosphere so the high-voltage terminals do not arc and short-circuit. In astronomical satellites, a single fingerprint on a lens can render the instrument useless. The sensitivity of satellites to even the tiniest specks of dirt or grease is why they are built and tested in special "clean rooms." Goddard has several of these facilities, including one

large enough to house several spacecraft the size of the Hubble Space Telescope.

Another inherent problem in building any aspect of a satellite, especially in the early years, was the tremendous constraint designers faced on power and weight. The key to success was lightweight construction, which meant systems were not as robust as they could be for an Earth-bound machine. Tape recorders tended to be very temperamental because of their many moving parts, and more than one satellite had to transmit its data in real time because its data recorders failed. Power was also limited, even with solar panels and batteries on board, in part because satellites had to be so small and lightweight. But trying to force large amounts of data through the systems on little power created other problems, such as a tremendous amount of heat which then had to be dissipated. Indeed, engineers who worked at Goddard in the 1960s remember that the challenge of space came down to batteries and tape recorders, and reliability was achieved only through redundancy. Because systems were prone to difficulties or failure, engineers and scientists always tried to include back-up systems in a satellite's design.[5]

Experience has shown that designing and operating a spacecraft is an extremely difficult task, even when everything works well. So the fact that Goddard successfully has launched and operated over 200 satellites to date is an amazingly impressive feat.

The difficulties involved in building satellites also equate to a struggle in keeping a developmental satellite project within its initial budget. In the early days, a "good" project, according to former director John W. Townsend, Jr., only overran its budget by 30 percent or so. A "bad" satellite project could overrun by as much as 200-400 percent.[6]

In part, these overruns were a product of the conflicting pressures inherent in any space project. Managers have to balance the demands of schedule, budget, and reliability, and all three are difficult to attain. A project can be kept on schedule and budget, but reliability may suffer. If the goal is to make a spacecraft absolutely reliable, it may take additional money or more time than scheduled to test and complete. And if a project absolutely must launch on a particular date, its cost or risk of failure may go up or reliability may go down. In 40 years of space exploration, this triad of opposing pressures—cost, schedule, and risk—has never been completely resolved. Indeed, the acceptance of the fact that it cannot be resolved is a recognition of the nature of the enterprise. Each project simply falls in a slightly different place within the triangle.

Another difficulty in building scientific satellites within a predetermined budget is that in a research and development field, scientists and engineers could not predict what obstacles or difficulties they are going to encounter. And with the difficulties inherent in designing instruments and spacecraft, the opportunities for problems were almost unlimited. In addition, the scientists often changed their requirements or developed "better" ways to make an

instrument more effective or to get more instruments into a spacecraft.

There was, in fact, a constant but healthy tension between the scientists, who would have put every bell and whistle on a spacecraft to get as much data as possible, and the engineers, who were more interested in making sure the instruments and spacecraft worked correctly. This difference was recognized in Goddard's system of assigning both a project scientist and a project manager to each satellite project. The project scientist was responsible for the science requirements and the data the experiments would gather, and the project manager (usually an engineer) was responsible for making sure the overall system worked, as well as managing the logistics, manpower, budget, and schedule for the project.

Even then, the parties never quite reached a consensus on how to solve a project's problems. For example, there were two schools of thought regarding spacecraft schedules. Dr. Harry J. Goett, Goddard's first director, was a firm advocate for giving projects as much time as they needed to get the satellite right.

A geodetic laser satellite nestled inside the nose cone of a Delta rocket prior to its 1976 launch.

"We've waited 2000 years to get this data," he would argue to Headquarters. "We can wait another 6 months to get it right." On the other hand, some argued that the delays were caused by scientists wanting to constantly upgrade equipment instead of making do with what could be done in the time and money allotted. The end result was a constant pull between the constraints of budget and time and the risk of pushing research projects too quickly and having them fail in orbit. Space projects are inherently expensive, and the most expensive factor is the workforce attached to them. If a project is delayed 6 months because of a late component, the project team still has to be kept together, even though their time is not being well spent. Therefore, the cost skyrockets above the budget. Finding a successful balance is tricky, and not every project is able to do it.[7]

Indeed, if something goes wrong with a spacecraft, it is an extremely daunting challenge, because most satellites are unreachable except by remote command. Goddard engineers learned early to incorporate something called a "safe hold mode" into their spacecraft so that, in the event of a problem, the nonessential systems in the satellite could be "frozen" and its solar panels turned toward the Sun to maintain power to the spacecraft until the problem could be solved. This technique saved many satellites that otherwise would have lost power before corrective commands could be sent up to the spacecraft.[8]

Not every problem would cause the complete loss of a satellite, but the consequences of any failure or problem were severe, because it was difficult to fix anything in space. As a result, Goddard's managers put a tremendous emphasis on rigorous testing and evaluation of components and spacecraft before they were launched.

TEST AND EVALUATION

After spending several years on a single project, no scientist or engineer wanted to lose either a key instrument or an entire satellite because of a faulty battery, control system, or connection. As a result, developing thorough test and evaluation facilities and procedures was a high priority from the earliest days of Goddard.

The pressure to get satellites into space, and therefore to develop test facilities, was very intense in the early years of the space race. The first test buildings at Goddard were built in a mere 18 months,

A thermal vacuum test chamber at the Goddard Space Flight Center helped researchers test satellites in simulated space conditions prior to launch.

Goddard personnel maneuver carefully inside a dynamic test chamber in the Center's satellite test and evaluation facilities. (NASA Photo G64-5909)

and test engineers began working in the buildings before the structures were even completed. The engineers simply moved in section by section, right behind the construction crews.

The basic idea behind the test facilities at Goddard was to simulate the conditions of launch and space as closely as possible.

The satellite and its components would be put in a vibration machine to simulate the rough and tumble conditions of a launch and put in a vacuum chamber to test the operation of its systems and instruments in a space-like environment. Spin-stabilized satellites were spin-balanced, like an automobile tire. A "launch phase simulator,"

Technicians assembling Explorer XVII, launched in April 1963 to conduct atmospheric research. (NASA Photo G63-4002-C)

which was built around a large centrifuge machine, was sometimes used to simulate the vibration, acceleration, and decreasing air pressure a satellite would experience during its launch into space. Another test unit could vary the magnetic field around the component or spacecraft to test the operation of instruments designed to measure magnetic fields and their influences.

Goddard's test engineers even went so far as to create an artificial Sun to test satellites in a thermal vacuum chamber.

Based on solar measurements taken by a couple of early satellites, they assembled 2 megawatts of light (the equivalent of twenty thousand 100-watt light bulbs), focused through a series of reflectors into a concentrated beam. That "Sun" was then placed at the top of one of two 40-by-60 foot vacuum chambers housed in the test facilities at Goddard. These "space chambers" were so large that they were built first, and the rest of the building was constructed around them.

One of Goddard's Orbiting Astronomical Observatories prior to launch.

The possibility of a launch failure, especially in the early days, was great enough that Goddard developed a policy of building a prototype and two flight models of any given satellite. If the first one or the launch vehicle carrying it failed, the team could quickly launch the back-up model. In the case of the second Orbiting Astronomical Observatory (OAO II), the back-up satellite was actually a prototype that had been on display at the 1964 World's Fair in New York City. Engineers brought it back to NASA after the first OAO failed, refurbished it with new experiments and launched it successfully—which speaks to the amazing quality and reliability of even the satellite prototypes Goddard built. Indeed, Goddard personnel were so concerned about building spacecraft correctly that it had a separate division or directorate dedicated to "systems reliability." If Goddard's satellites had an impressive success rate, it was because reliability and quality assurance were always such a high priority at the Center. In fact, Goddard's satellites were so reliable that eventually not only the spares, but also the prototype models of a spacecraft, upgraded for flight, routinely began to be launched into space.[9]

In either case, all components and spacecraft were thoroughly and rigorously tested before launch. Scientists were not always comfortable with this approach, preferring that a non-flyable prototype model be tested and shook and the flight model left alone. But the test engineers at Goddard were insistent that any one satel-

lite could have flaws, and it was better to discover the problems on the ground than in space. To illustrate this point, the test engineers often would treat a satellite in a space chamber as if it were really in space. If a researcher said, "Oh, I know what the problem is. Take it out and let me fix it," the test personnel would shake their heads, replying, "It's in space. You can't touch it. Now what do you do?" It was their way of helping to develop the necessary mind-set for space science along with the hardware necessary to accomplish the job.[10]

The meticulous and rigorous testing paid off. Between 1959 and 1976, Goddard had a 100 percent success rate for the 31 contractor and Goddard-built satellites it tested in its own facilities.[11] The Explorer satellites, many of which were built in-house at Goddard, had a particularly impressive success rate. In the 1960s, every Explorer satellite that was properly placed in orbit by its launch vehicle

Goddard's Explorer XII satellite, launched in August 1961, was designed to investigate the solar wind and the magnetosphere. (NASA Photo G-62-344)

An early sounding rocket called the Javelin on its launch pad. Sounding rockets are used to launch non-orbiting scientific payloads into the upper atmosphere.

achieved its mission. As one of NASA's early managers summarized, "Explorer satellites were simply expected to succeed, and they did."[12]

Of course, there were problems and failures. Usually, the only things lost were weekends at home, sleep, pieces of hardware, and data. But in 1964, three men were killed and several others seriously injured in an accident involving an Orbiting Solar Observatory (OSO). The satellite was completing some final pre-launch testing in a hangar at Cape Canaveral in Florida when the accident occurred. The OSO had just been mated to the third stage of its launch rocket when spark of static electricity caused the rocket to fire. It was a sobering reminder that even if the spacecraft contained no people and was tested as thoroughly as possible, this was still a potentially dangerous business.[13]

LAUNCH VEHICLES

Of course, the spacecraft itself is only part of the equation. Something has to get the instruments into space (or, in some cases, the upper atmosphere). The research conducted at Goddard over the years has relied on a number of vehicles to do that, ranging from aircraft, balloons, and small sounding rockets to large intercontinental ballistic missile-sized launch vehicles and the Space Shuttle.

SOUNDING ROCKETS, BALLOONS, AND AIRCRAFT

Space science research began right after World War II with what became known as "sounding rockets." Sounding rockets were so named because as they passed up and back through the atmosphere, they could make measurements at various altitudes in the same way as sounding equipment tested various depths in the ocean. They could not achieve orbit, but they could reach high altitudes in the atmosphere or space for short periods of time.

Even after satellites became an option for scientists, they still continued to use sounding rockets for various types of research. Sounding rockets could make measurements in a regime difficult to access by either aircraft or orbiting spacecraft. Also, the smaller, less powerful sounding rockets were, and still are, a much cheaper way of performing some research. In a sense, sounding rockets were "better, faster, cheaper" 30 years before NASA adopted the saying as an organizational philosophy.

As a result, sounding rockets can provide a good testbed for new measurement approaches or instruments. An experiment is sometimes initially put on a sounding rocket. If the initial results are interesting, a satellite project is then planned to gather further data. Similarly, many instruments designed for satellites are first tested on less-expensive sounding rockets. Space for experiments on satellite projects is extremely limited, leading many scientists to use sounding rockets as a way to get at least some data in a timely manner. At the same time, sounding rockets serve as a wonderful training ground, giving new researchers an opportunity to conduct hands-on work and get familiar with the requirements and perspective necessary for working in space.

Another advantage of sounding rockets is that they can take *in situ* measurements in areas of the atmosphere that orbital satellites only passed on their way to orbit. Consequently, sounding rockets can pro-

Scientific balloons, like this one, are a cost-effective method to get lightweight research equipment into high altitudes.

vide good profiles of density, moisture, temperature, or other parameters throughout the different levels of the atmosphere. In some cases, the payload of sounding rocket flights can be recovered again, although this feat is tougher if they are launched over the ocean. In one instance, the military helicopter pilots who flew out to recover a Wallops Island payload from the Atlantic Ocean returned and reported that all they had found was a big cylinder with something attached to it floating in the water. Of course, the cylinder was the rocket payload, but it had sunk by the time the crew attempted a second recovery attempt.[14]

Sounding rockets can be launched from almost anywhere. When a supernova was sighted in 1987, for example, scientists wanted immediate gamma ray data from the high-energy explosion. But NASA's Shuttle launches had been halted because of the Challenger accident, and there were no suitable spacecraft ready to launch on any other vehicle. So a team from Goddard's Wallops Island facility traveled to Australia and launched two sounding rockets with gamma ray detectors to investigate the phenomenon.[15]

One of the reasons sounding rockets can be so flexible is that their range varies greatly. From the early Aerobees and Nike-Cajun rockets, the stable of solid-propellant rockets has grown and expanded. Researchers at Wallops would sometimes take different surplus rocket stages and put them together into new and different combinations, leading to rockets such as the Taurus-Nike-Tomahawk or the Nike-Orion.[16] Today, although some very small meteorological rockets stay below 100 miles, most sounding rocket launches can reach 180-240 miles in altitude. A lightly loaded Black Brant 12, however, can climb as high as 800 miles above the Earth.[17]

Small satellites can be placed in orbit with the Pegasus rocket which is drop-launched off a transport aircraft at over 35,000 feet.

Sometimes, however, scientists need endurance rather than altitude. In those cases, a scientific balloon or aircraft can provide a better testbed than a rocket. Scientific balloons are sandwich-bag-thin polyethylene balloons filled with inert helium. Although launching them can be tricky, as any wind can rip the balloon bag, they offer scientists the opportunity to take instruments up as high as 26 miles for as long as 24 hours. Of course, the trajectory is determined by the wind, but these balloons can be launched from almost anywhere. Goddard took over management of scientific balloon launches from the National Science Foundation in 1982 and now launches approximately 35 balloons a year.

Aircraft are much more limited in altitude than either rockets or balloons, but they offer extremely quick turnaround times and are an excellent testbed for many different types of instruments and sensors. At Goddard's Wallops Flight Facility, researchers use aircraft to test new lasers, computers, and other instruments for Earth and space science investigations. In addition, the aircraft can be used for conducting certain types of Earth science research, including the study of ice formations, plant life, and *in situ* measurements after natural events such as volcanic eruptions.[18]

VANGUARDS AND DELTAS

Balloons, aircraft, and small atmospheric rockets were all available before satellites came into existence. The obstacle to space flight was making a rocket powerful enough to get a payload high enough and fast enough to achieve orbit. Although NASA's Lewis Research Center focused on propulsion and the Marshall Space Flight Center would become known for building the large Saturn launch rocket, Goddard was given responsibility for developing and managing the rockets NASA planned to use to launch Goddard's scientific satellites.

When NASA opened its doors, six of the seven rockets available for its research came from the military. The seventh was the developmental Vanguard rocket, which was transferred from its original home at the Naval Research Laboratory to Goddard as soon as the new space agency was formed. The Vanguard itself did not prove to be a highly successful rocket. Indeed, the spectacular and humiliating explosion of an early Vanguard test vehicle in December 1957 only 2 seconds after launch was etched into the nation's memory for years to come. A Vanguard successfully launched the Vanguard I satellite into space in March 1958, but 8 of 11 subsequent Vanguard launch attempts failed.[19]

The biggest problem with the Vanguard was the first of its three stages. So researchers at Goddard and the McDonnell Aircraft Corporation, which built the Delta rocket, decided to substitute the first stage of a Douglas Aircraft Company Thor missile that was being used successfully by the Air Force. The hybrid rocket was designated the Thor-Delta, a name later shortened to simply "Delta."[20]

The first successful launch of a Delta rocket took place in August 1960. The

original Delta's payload was limited to a few hundred pounds for a low-Earth orbiting satellite and around 50 pounds for a geosynchronous satellite, but the Delta team kept trying to improve the rocket's capability. They added small solid rocket boosters around the base of the vehicle, lengthened the first and second stage, gave it bigger third stage rocket motors, and added space for more propellant. Fifteen years later, that capacity had increased to 2,400 pounds, and today a Delta can put about 4,000 pounds into orbit.[21]

The Delta has been an extremely successful launch vehicle, with very few failures in its 30-year history. But the Delta still almost became extinct in the 1980s

The Delta rockets have had one of the best success rates of any expendable launch vehicle.

when a new, reusable launch vehicle appeared with promises as the all-purpose space transportation system of the future—a vehicle more commonly known as the Space Shuttle.

THE SPACE SHUTTLE

The 1986 Challenger accident may have changed NASA's plans to revert to a single-vehicle launch fleet, but the Space Shuttle still carries a fair number of scientific spacecraft and instruments into space. In addition to large satellites like the Hubble Space Telescope that it releases into orbit, the Shuttle carries several other types of scientific payloads.

The "Spartan" class of satellite is designed to be released at the beginning of a Shuttle mission. Spartan satellites orbit freely for several days before being

retrieved and brought back to Earth at the end of the mission. Smaller "Hitchhiker" payloads, on the other hand, stay attached to the Shuttle bay, allowing them to use the Shuttle's systems for power, data, or communications functions.

Even smaller payloads called "Get Away Specials" (GAS) are packaged into small trash can-size containers in unused corners of the Shuttle's service bay. GAS payloads are self-contained experiments that are not connected to the Shuttle's electrical systems. The idea behind the GAS program was to offer an opportunity for extremely low-cost space experiments. Some of the GAS payloads cost as little as $3,000, making them a convenient way to test instruments in space and making space science experiments directly available to college, high school, and elementary school students. As of 1997, a total of 138 GAS payloads had been taken into space by the Shuttle.[22]

TRACKING, DATA, AND COMMUNICATIONS

The final component of an operational spacecraft system, beyond a launch vehicle and an operating satellite, is a way of getting commands up to the spacecraft and data back down to researchers on the ground. Researchers at the Naval Research Laboratory realized this even as they began planning for a possible satellite launch in conjunction with the 1957-58 International Geophysical Year (IGY).[23] They developed a "Proposal for a Minimum Trackable Satellite (Minitrack)" in April 1955 that suggested a series of ground stations to spot

The Spartan 201 satellite being released from the Space Shuttle using the shuttle's robotic arm.

the satellite in orbit. Because signal strength from the satellite would be weak and launch tracking data might not be entirely reliable, the "Minitrack" network, as it became known, consisted primarily of a "detection fence" of closely spaced stations along the 75th meridian. This would help ensure that at least one station would "spot" the satellite as it popped over the horizon.

The Minitrack network became operational in October 1957 with nine original stations and was put under the control of Goddard in 1959. The network eventually grew to about 11 stations and served as the main tracking network for orbital satellites until 1962.[24]

THE MERCURY SPACE FLIGHT NETWORK

The onset of the human space flight program, however, created much more complicated tracking and communication needs. The satellites were in range of the Minitrack stations for only a few minutes on each orbit. A piloted spacecraft had to be tracked continuously and had to have two-way communications available. In 1961, Goddard tracking and data engineers were given responsibility for designing and managing this more complex network, designated as the Mercury Space Flight Network (MSFN). Goddard's efforts to develop and maintain this worldwide system created another invaluable center of expertise in the Center and were critical to the success of not only the Mercury missions, but also all the NASA human space flight endeavors that have followed.

The Mercury network consisted of 17 ground stations in locations around the world, from Cape Canaveral, Florida, to Woomera, Australia. To cover gaps between the continents, two ships were outfitted with tracking and communications equipment and stationed in the Indian and Atlantic Oceans. Even then, there were still times during the Mercury flights that the astronauts were out of communication range, although for much shorter periods than any of the scientific satellites.[25]

A number of difficulties arose with getting the MSFN operational. One of the biggest challenges stemmed from the need to work with so many different countries to get the stations built and staffed. For example, to get permission to build the station in Guyamas, Mexico, President Eisenhower finally sent his brother to personally ask Mexico's President for assistance. Even

Goddard's satellite tracking and data network spanned the globe.

then, the Guyamas station sometimes had to be guarded with troops during missions to keep protesting mobs at a distance.[26] Most of the time, however, cooperation was easy to get. Many countries even donated services, time, and labor. This was the heyday of NASA and the dawn of an exciting new adventure. Simply put, people wanted to be a part of it.

All of the international stations were networked through a control center at Goddard, which then relayed the information to and from Mission Control at Cape Canaveral in Florida. Even this was a dicey operation at first, because the computers and communications systems in the early 1960s were less than reliable. So, as with the early satellites, reliability was achieved through redundancy. If there were six different voice channels going between Goddard and any given station, the system managers would try to use different cables or lines for each one so that if any one line failed, the others would still work. The system was still questionable enough that

One of two supertankers converted to floating communications facilities during the Apollo Program.

flight controllers were flown to each station around the world for every Mercury flight. That way, even if the network failed, controllers would be in contact with the flight at almost all times.

The human space flight program was pushing the limits of technology in every area, and the Goddard and NASA personnel working on the program were well aware of how marginal their systems were. During the Mercury launches, for example, phone communications were still unreliable between Goddard and the Bermuda tracking station, even though the Bermuda station provided critical information for mission abort decisions. Christopher Kraft, flight director of the human space flight missions during the 1960s, recalled that, "During the launch of an Atlas rocket, we had somewhere between 30 seconds and 2 minutes after main engine cutoff to decide whether to continue a mission or to abort. Initially, there were very few people who believed that this would be possible."[27] The tension of these Mercury launches was especially great because the Atlas rocket used for the orbital Mercury flights was not a highly reliable rocket at the time.

With the advent of the Gemini flights, several things changed. First, the Manned Spacecraft Center in Houston, Texas, was completed, and mission control was moved from Cape Canaveral to Building 30. Communications technology also had improved enough that controllers were no longer dispatched around the world. Instead, a secondary mission control center was set up at Goddard with systems completely redundant to those in Houston. The Goddard Center was the conduit for data and communications between Mission Control, the tracking stations, and the spacecraft. But if the Houston system failed, the control center facilities at Goddard would allow the Center to pick up coverage of the mission instantaneously.[28]

Even with improved technology, the manned missions were always stressful. Managers at Goddard's control center would keep one eye on the trajectory data of the rocket, another on the maintenance panels of the network's computer system, and another on the network connections themselves. Not surprisingly, tension in the control center at Goddard during these flights was every bit as high as at Mission Control in Houston.

Goddard's worldwide network proved its worth on every mission. But during the Gemini 8 flight it proved critical, when the spacecraft carrying astronauts Neil Armstrong and David Scott spun out of control during a practice docking maneuver. The rest of the mission was cancelled, and the network engineers had to find the spacecraft again, recalculate its orbit and re-entry trajectories, and then move a recovery ship to an alternate landing location to rescue the astronauts, all in a matter of hours.[29]

Yet the Gemini missions were still simpler than the next task facing the manned space flight network—keeping track of a spacecraft all the way to the Moon and back. In addition to the ground stations already in place, Goddard commissioned the modification of two huge supertankers

into floating behemoths capable of carrying 30-foot parabolic antennas, increasing NASA's tracking fleet to a total of five ships. In addition, nine KC-135 aircraft were modified with special radar noses and launched to fill in the gaps between the ships and the ground stations.

As one Goddard manager put it, "We had the whole world cranked up in these missions." It was true. And the effort was as much a matter of national pride for NASA's partners as it was for the space agency itself. Many times services and labor were donated to the cause, which was fortunate, because the costs of such a worldwide system would have been prohibitive. As it was, the "phone bill" for NASA's system totalled somewhere around $50 million a year.

The personnel at the international tracking stations were deeply committed to the success of the missions, sometimes going to great lengths to ensure they did not let

A mission controller tracks the progress of a satellite in one of Goddard's mission operations centers.

Goddard's NASCOM facility prior to a Space Shuttle launch.

the network down. On a test flight of the Saturn vehicle that would launch the Apollo spacecraft, for example, the communication lines to the remote Carnarvon Station in western Australia broke down. Using frontier resourcefulness, the Australians passed launch information to and from Carnarvon with the help of ranchers at "stations" over more than 1,000 miles across the Australian outback, using the top wire of the ranch fences as a makeshift telegraph line.[30]

That same level of dedication was present at Goddard's control center throughout its history. It is one of the reasons that, although there were glitches in the system, the Manned Space Flight Network[31] never had a serious problem that affected the outcome of any of the manned missions.

THE SATELLITE TRACKING AND DATA ACQUISITION NETWORK

At the same time as the human missions were being conducted, the robotic satellite program was growing by leaps and bounds, creating new tracking and data problems for researchers. The bigger satellites, including the "observatory-" class spacecraft like the Orbiting Solar Observatory (OSO), needed more capable ground equipment than the Minitrack network had.

As a result, Goddard developed a new worldwide web of stations known as the Satellite Tracking And Data Acquisition Network (STADAN), with as many as 21 different sites spread over every continent in the world except for mainland Eurasia. The STADAN stations had improved 40-foot and 85-foot parabolic antennae so they could handle the larger amounts of data the more advanced satellites were generating. The Orbiting Geophysical Observatory (OGO) launched in 1964, for example, was downloading several full-length books worth of data on every pass over a ground station.[32]

The STADAN network also had its share of interesting events because of the unique politics of various locations around the world. The South African station was eventually closed because of controversy over the apartheid practices of the country, and NASA personnel at the station in Tananarive, Madagascar, had to be evacuated in the middle of the night after a tense stand-off with the country's dictator.[33]

The stations also provided a unique opportunity for the nations involved, however, because NASA made an effort to train and employ local workers at all the network sites. These countries then had the expertise and equipment to provide services to commercial satellite companies and networks. They also could run their own communication networks instead of relying on foreign personnel.

SPACEFLIGHT TRACKING AND DATA NETWORK

As the Apollo program came to a close, the need for such an extensive, separate human space flight network decreased. So between 1969 and 1973, Goddard gradually consolidated the two separate networks—the MSFN and the STADAN—into a single network of ground stations known as the Spaceflight Tracking and Data Network, or STDN. By 1973, the STDN system incorporated 20 different stations around the world, including one ocean-going ship.

In 1971, the two Goddard directorates that had been managing the separate tracking networks also were reorganized to reflect the changing mission requirements. The new Mission and Data Operations Directorate managed the data processing activities and the computer-based tracking projections of the network, and the Networks Directorate oversaw the internal NASA Communications network (NASCOM) and coordinated the operations of the various STDN stations.[34] Yet even more dramatic changes were coming down the pike.

TRACKING AND DATA RELAY SATELLITE SYSTEM

The Apollo missions could be well serviced by ground stations because, aside from the beginning and end of each mission, the spacecraft was a fair distance away from Earth and, therefore, in sight of at least one or more of the widely-spaced ground sites. The Space Shuttle, on the other hand, was going to remain in low-Earth orbit. Keeping in touch with it would be a more difficult task.

The solution, however, was already being tested in space. Goddard managed the development of a series of Applications Technology Satellites (ATS) designed to test advanced meteorological and communications satellite technology. The geosynchronous ATS spacecraft were in a good position to track and communicate with anything in a near-Earth orbit because they were positioned 23,000 miles above the planet.

The ATS satellites were not part of Goddard's official tracking and data network. But the NASA networks never had firm lines of demarcation. For example, although the Deep Space Network (DSN) that tracked planetary probes and distant missions was a separate entity from the MSFN, its antennae were used in helping to track the Apollo spacecraft. And the ATS spacecraft, though not officially part of the MSFN or STDN systems, were still used to

help provide communications for the Earth-orbiting Skylab missions in 1973.[35]

Goddard's ATS research in the 1970s led NASA officials to look at using geosynchronous satellites as a means of tracking not only the Space Shuttle, but also Earth-orbiting satellites of the future. The result of this research was the Tracking and Data Relay Satellite System (TDRSS).

The TDRSS plans called for three geosynchronous satellites—one positioned over the western hemisphere, one over the eastern hemisphere, and a "spare" positioned between the first two. This would allow the system to provide 100 percent coverage for

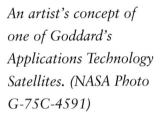

An artist's concept of one of Goddard's Applications Technology Satellites. (NASA Photo G-75C-4591)

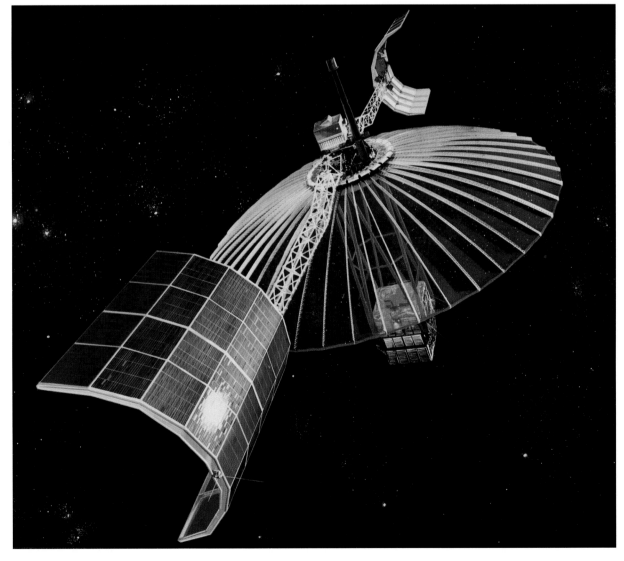

satellites orbiting in an altitude range between 745 and 3,100 miles and 80 percent coverage for satellites below that altitude. Satellites further away than that would be tracked by the DSN. As a result, Goddard's extensive STDN ground network would no longer be needed.

Getting the TDRSS network operational involved numerous challenges, most of which related to the financial contracting aspects of the project. But a rocket booster malfunctioned on the first satellite after it was launched from the Shuttle and, although NASA was able to use the satellite's small, onboard jets to nudge it into its correct orbit, it was never fully effective. The second TDRSS spacecraft was then destroyed in the Challenger accident.

There were numerous difficulties with the TDRSS ground system, as well, especially with a computerized automatic scheduler that was supposed to coordinate time on the TDRSS satellites for the 20-plus scientific satellites the TDRSS might be tracking at any given time.

In addition, the original goal for the Space Shuttle was to be able to launch a new mission every 2 weeks, and the TDRSS ground stations at Goddard and White Sands would have to support that kind of demanding launch schedule. That was a daunting goal at a time when it was sometimes difficult to keep the ground system up and running for 24 hours at a time. In the early days, Goddard had two crews working on the system simultaneously—one to operate the system and a second to troubleshoot its problems at the

One of the Tracking and Data Relay Satellites being released from the Space Shuttle's cargo bay. (NASA Photo JCS/S26-31-065)

same time. After 2 years of long hours, 7-day weeks, and much lost sleep, the staff was just getting the scheduler problems resolved and the system up to the two-mission-per-month goal when the Challenger exploded. It was a devastating blow to the staff, who realized the goal they had worked so hard for would never be relevant again. The Shuttle began flying again in 1988, but the program did not attain the frequency of flights its designers originally envisioned.[36]

A CLOSING CIRCLE

Interestingly enough, recent changes in technology have led NASA to return at least part of its satellite tracking and data tasks to a ground-based system. The failure-prone tape recorders on satellites were once one of the weakest links of the system, but the advent of solid-state recorders, a technology developed by engineers at Goddard, has changed that. With increased reliability of onboard data storage, the need to stay in constant touch with some satellites is decreasing. Ground station technology also has improved, making it much less expensive to operate ground system terminals.

In addition, using TDRSS for down-linking data can be expensive. A satellite does not need a very big TDRSS antenna to receive command and control orders from ground operators. But sending giga-bytes of data back down to Earth requires a much larger and more powerful and complex antenna system. Because NASA is trying to shrink the size and cost of satel-lites, researchers have begun looking at other options.

NASA's new Earth Science Enterprise program, for example, will incorporate sev-eral large Earth-oriented satellites generat-ing approximately a terabyte of data per day. A terabyte is a staggeringly large num-ber equivalent to 10^{12} bytes, or a million megabytes. In practical terms, this means that in 4 months, the program's Landsat 7 and EOS AM-1 satellites will have doubled the amount of information collected on the Earth from satellites since the beginning of the space program. The first of these satel-lites, called EOS AM-1, will use the TDRSS satellites for both commands and data transmission. But the rest of the satellites in the 15-year program will rely on TDRSS only to uplink commands to the spacecraft. The data will be downlinked to one of five possible ground stations.

Because the Earth Science Enterprise spacecraft will be primarily polar-orbiting satellites, the two main ground stations will be in Fairbanks, Alaska, and Svalbard, Norway. A ground station in McMurdo, Antarctica, will serve as a back-up facility. Two existing ground stations in the United States—the Earth Resources Observation System (EROS) data center in Sioux Falls, South Dakota, and a research center at Goddard's Wallops Island facility—are being upgraded so they can provide back-up support, as well.

The TDRSS satellites also will contin-ue to support the Shuttle missions and a number of large NASA satellites, including the Hubble Space Telescope and the Compton Gamma Ray Observatory. But the advances in technology that are enabling more satellites to rely on ground stations also have changed one of the fundamental issues of satellite research. Once upon a time, the problem was how to get enough data back to Earth. With the Earth Science Enterprise, the problem

A polar-orbiting satellite, such as the EOS-AM spacecraft depicted here, will scan the entire Earth as the Earth rotates.

is not getting enough data—it is finding a way not to drown in it.

DATA

Transmitting and translating the data received from satellites has always been a tricky procedure. In the earliest days, the "data" consisted of audio "tones" sent from the passing satellites. If a sensor found what it was designed to identify, it would emit a different tone than if the substance or force was not present. Satellite systems for transmitting data improved dramatically over the years, but scientific data always required some interpretation.

Goddard offered scientists three different levels of data from their satellite experiments. Level 0 was fundamentally raw data, with only some spacecraft attitude and orbit information added. Level 1 data included instrument calibration information, and Level 2 data was generally a customized product that processed the information in a specific way for a particular scientist.[37]

At first, the individuals who designed the experiments on the satellites got exclusive use of the data until they published their results. The system made a certain amount of sense, because space was a very risky research field. A scientist could devote years to developing an instrument only to have the launch vehicle carrying it explode on the launch pad, so it was agreed that they deserved first crack at the results of a successful satellite experiment. When the scientist was "done" with his or

her data, the results were catalogued in the National Space Science Data Center at Goddard and became available to anyone.

Yet in both the space and Earth science fields, individual investigators sometimes dragged their feet in making the data generally available. In addition, the principal investigators often did not remove their particular research modifications, or "signatures," from the results, so the data was virtually useless to anyone else.

As a result of concerns on both of these points, Goddard and NASA began looking at ways to improve the system. Space physics research results are difficult to distribute in a generic fashion, but several years ago, Goddard began to archive its astronomy data in wavelength-specific archive centers around the country. Goddard's Space Science Directorate is in charge of the High Energy Astrophysics Science Archival Research Center, which catalogues X-ray and gamma ray astronomy data for users in the general science com-

Scientists pore over results from the International Ultraviolet Explorer (IUE) Satellite. IUE operations were simple enough to allow outside researchers to conduct their own observations with the satellite.

munity. Results of research in other wavelengths are catalogued in archive centers at other NASA Centers and universities.

Topic-specific Distributed Active Archive Centers (DAAC) now are cataloguing Earth science data at Goddard and other research centers around the country. Goddard, for example, manages any data on climate, meteorology, or ocean biology.

The philosophy of allowing principal investigators to "own" data also has changed. In space science, the amount of time an investigator is given sole access to data has shortened considerably. With Earth science research, results are considered essentially public property almost as soon as the data can be verified and interpreted.

With the advent of the Earth Science Enterprise program in the late 1990s, Goddard is entering a new generation of

The Earth Observing System Data and Information System facility was created to handle large amounts of data that will be generated by the EOS satellites.

data processing and dissemination. To handle the large quantity of data coming in and make it accessible to the public as quickly as possible, NASA has developed the Earth Observing System Data and Information System (EOSDIS), managed and located at Goddard. EOSDIS processes the data from the spacecraft and distributes it in various levels of complexity to the different DAACs, which then make it available via traditional networks and the internet. The goal is to make the science data available and usable to everyone from high school students to sophisticated research scientists.[38]

CONCLUSION

Although few people give it much detailed thought, designing, building, testing, launching, and operating satellites, as well as processing and distributing the information they gather, are very complex and difficult tasks. There are a million ways something can go wrong and, unlike ground-based research or activities, most problems occur hundreds or thousands of miles away from the engineers who need to fix them.

Tracking and communicating with satellites always has required the cooperation of nations around the world. This fact has even greater relevance today, as more and more satellite projects are developed as cooperative efforts between two or more countries. Every satellite that passes overhead in the night sky is being "flown" and watched after somewhere in the world. Somewhere, someone is telling the satellite which direction to turn next or which

instrument to turn on, or perhaps trying to figure out why the power has dropped suddenly in its onboard electrical system.

The efforts of NASA's Mission Control personnel in Houston, Texas, are perhaps better known than the efforts of the technicians at the STDN station in Fairbanks, Alaska, the designers of the Cosmic Background Explorer's infrared instruments, or the test engineers who made sure the Explorer satellites worked. But the work of these other professionals is every bit as important. It takes an army to get a satellite into space—an army of scientists, engineers, technicians, and support personnel from industry, universities,

NASA, and foreign countries, working together for a common cause.

Space holds fascinating secrets, wonderful mysteries, and the opportunity to look back at ourselves and better understand the planet we call home. But it is a demanding task master, unforgiving of mistakes or neglect. If we have discovered useful, important, or amazing things in our journeys off the planet, it is because of people like those at Goddard who were willing to attend to the less-glorious but all-critical details—the spacecraft, the launch vehicles, the ground stations, and the information systems—to bring those discoveries within our reach.

The Tropical Rainfall Measuring Mission (TRMM) satellite, launched in November 1997, is helping scientists better understand the transfer of heat and water vapor between the ocean and the atmosphere.

CHAPTER 4:

Exploring the Heavens

Many of the 200-plus satellites the Goddard Space Flight Center has built, managed, or operated over the past 40 years have been dedicated to exploring the heavens—the almost limitless space that extends billions of light years beyond our planet. At the time Goddard was founded, this territory was truly a new frontier. We could look through telescopes at stars and distant galaxies, and we could theorize about the forces and dynamics at work in the universe. But a mere 50 years ago we had as little concrete knowledge of what surrounded our planet as Lewis and Clark had of what lay between them and the Pacific Ocean.

The first steps in charting the frontier beyond our planet came with the early V-2 and sounding rocket flights in the late 1940s

This spectacular Hubble Space Telescope image shows the majestic pillar structure and embryonic stars in the Eagle Nebula. (NASA Photo PRC-9544A)

An image of the Orion constellation created by the Hubble Space Telescope's near-infrared NICMOS instrument. (NASA Photo PRC97-13)

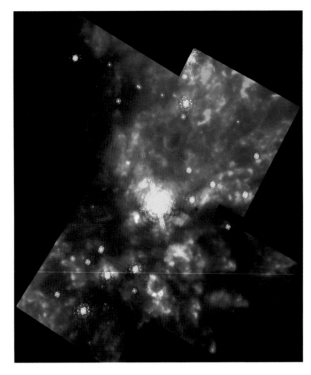

and early 1950s. But satellites were the first ships that could explore the heavens in real detail and depth. The satellites Goddard launched into space gave physicists and astronomers the opportunity to turn theory into science, opening the door to whole new areas of experimentation and revitalizing the field of science itself.

In the process, their research has challenged many of our beliefs and sparked our collective imagination. For the scientific exploration of space is really a search for answers about where we came from, how our planet and life forms evolved, and what other life, planets, and phenomena might exist beyond our own world. In the last 40 years, we have found some answers and stumbled on even more complex mysteries and questions. Theorists now contemplate the possibility of a 10-dimensional universe, while experimental researchers are finding evidence of black holes, energy bursts hundreds of times greater than a

supernova star explosion, and data to support many aspects of Albert Einstein's most mind-bending theories. Recently, for example, scientists discovered possible evidence for Einstein's theory that the space-time "fabric" can be dragged, or warped, by the gravitational fields around rotating stars and planets.[1]

From a time when most of us thought that Earth must be the only inhabited planet in the universe, we have learned enough about how elements and galaxies evolve that numerous scientists now believe there has to be life somewhere else. We have found evidence that indicates the universe really may have started with a single, explosive "bang" of energy and has been expanding ever since. We have learned a tremendous amount about the birth, evolution, and death of stars; the formation of planets; and other perplexing cosmic events; but we still are probing only the surface of these mysteries.

For centuries, we have been trying to put together the puzzle of how the universe works. Indeed, our curiosity to know more about our world and our universe, without any immediate practical application to our daily lives, is one of the unique characteristics of the human race. The puzzle is far from complete, but gaining the ability to explore space from space—a capability that the Goddard Space Flight Center has played a pivotal role in developing—has revealed many important pieces.

For the most part, the exploration of space has been pursued in two different fields of science, although the lines between the different types of research are not always clear or distinct. One of the lasting legacies of the space age, in fact, is that it has prompted the integration of previously independent fields of scientific research.

One of the main focuses and strengths of space science at Goddard has been what might be generally termed space physics. This is the realm of physicists who investigate gravitational, magnetic, and electrical fields in space and a variety of particle radiations, such as electrons, protons, and the nuclei of many elements that are emitted from the Sun, the galaxy, and the cosmos beyond. In addition to giving us a better understanding of the near-space environment and the substances, forces, and dynamics that affect our planet, this research can provide clues as to how other planets and galaxies are formed.

Complementing this research at Goddard is the work of astronomers, who use the electromagnetic spectrum (from radio waves to visible and ultraviolet light to gamma rays) to study the physical and chemical properties of more distant objects and phenomena in the universe. In contrast to space physicists who tend to use satellites to make *"in situ,"* or on site, measurements, astronomers have to rely on remote sensing techniques, because the objects they are investigating are still long distances away, even from a satellite in space. While a space physics satellite might measure the number of particles hitting a detector in a given period of time, an astronomy satellite looks at the radiated light or energy coming from objects at

At 17 tons, the Compton Gamma Ray Observatory was the largest scientific satellite ever launched from the Space Shuttle.

different wavelengths in the electromagnetic spectrum.

The early satellites were dominated by the space physicists for several reasons. Many of Goddard's satellite scientists came out of the sounding rocket community, which had focused more on space physics than astronomy. In addition, astronomy experiments generally required more sophisticated satellites that could point to particular objects for a length of time.

Space physicists also needed satellites more than their astronomy colleagues, because experiments in space physics could not be performed on the ground. They required *in situ* measurements, which made physicists more willing to undertake the risks and rigors of satellite research than astronomers, who could still conduct a fair amount of research from ground-based observatories.

Yet space still offered astronomers something valuable. Satellites gave them not only the opportunity to observe objects

The Pleiades constellation as seen by the Roentgen X-ray satellite.

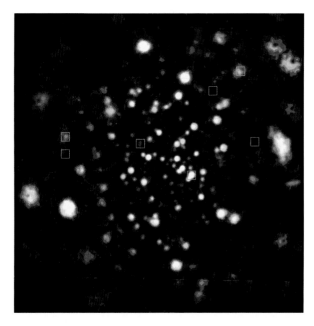

in greater clarity, but also the chance to look at objects in portions of the spectrum that were blocked by the Earth's atmosphere. The results of these efforts have surpassed expectation. Over the past 40 years, Goddard's scientific satellites have discovered possible answers to some of our oldest questions and opened doors to worlds we did not know even existed.

SPACE PHYSICS

Goddard's early work in space science focused on simply figuring out what existed in the upper reaches of the atmosphere and beyond. Scientists already had determined that the atmosphere consisted of several different regions. Closest to the Earth was an area called the troposphere, where our weather occurs. Above that was the more stable stratosphere. Directly above the stratosphere was a highly charged region called the ionosphere. The ionosphere is what allows radio signals to travel beyond the horizon, because its elec-

trically conductive properties reflect radio waves back down to Earth. In the mid-1950s, however, there was little information about what lay above that region.

Dr. James A. Van Allen, a researcher at the University of Iowa, made one of the first fundamental discoveries in this unexplored space above the atmosphere when his instruments on sounding rockets and the Explorer I and Explorer III satellites detected a mysterious "belt" of radiation above the ionosphere. Scientists had deduced that there must be energetic particles from the Sun that flowed toward the Earth. The polarized magnetic field of the Earth would split and deflect those particles at the equator, sending the positive particles traveling toward one pole and the negative particles toward the other. Among other things, these particles were thought to be the cause of the polar auroras, commonly known as the Northern and Southern lights.

What Van Allen discovered was that the dynamics of the Earth's magnetic field were more complex than scientists had thought. In an area near the equator, the Earth's magnetic field not only deflected particles, but also trapped some of the lower energy particles, creating high-altitude "belts" of radiation around the Earth at lower latitudes.

The existence of the "Van Allen Radiation Belts," as they were called, forced scientists to revise their theories of how the Sun's particle radiations affected the Earth's atmosphere.[2] In the process, they made another fundamental discovery that occu-

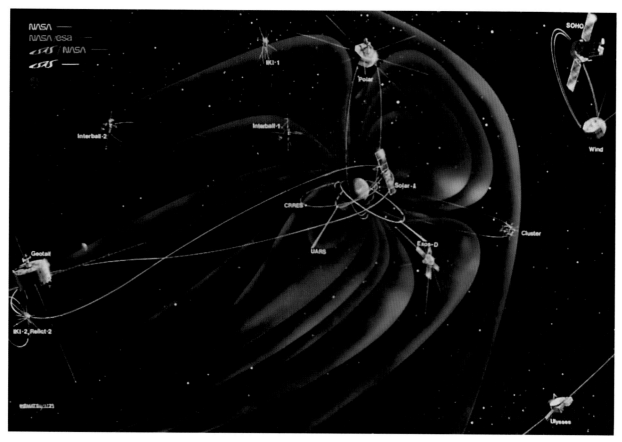

An artist's concept of the planned orbits of the various International Solar-Terrestrial Program satellites in relation to the Earth's magnetosphere.

pied much of space physicists' satellite research in the 1960s—the existence of a previously unpredicted region above the ionosphere called the magnetosphere.

The discovery of the Van Allen Belts focused attention on the interaction between the Sun and the Earth's magnetic field. Many of Goddard's early satellites focused on this area and, as more data was collected, a new picture began to emerge. The Sun, it appeared, radiated particles in a steady stream into space. Dubbed the *solar wind*, these particles were deflected around the globe by the Earth's magnetic field in much the same way as water is deflected around the bow of a boat. In 1963, a Goddard satellite called Interplanetary Monitoring Platform (IMP) 1 detected a distinct, turbulent "bow shock" area where the solar wind hit the magnetic

field of the Earth. Additional Goddard satellites determined that this flow also created a magnetospheric "tail" behind the Earth, similar to the wake created by a boat. Inside that wake, confined by the solar wind, was the region known as the magnetosphere.

Understanding the dynamics of the magnetosphere—why particles were trapped at certain latitudes and not at others, how it was affected by events on the Sun such as solar flares, and how it affected other processes in the atmosphere and in interplanetary space—was the subject of many of Goddard's satellite research projects in the 1960s. In fact, understanding the larger scale dynamics of the interactions between the Sun and the Earth remains a goal of numerous satellite research projects.

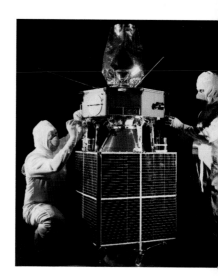

Technicians work on one of Goddard's Interplanetary Monitoring Platform satellites prior to launch. (NASA Photo G-66-7252)

EXPLORERS

In many ways, the Explorer class of spacecraft epitomized the Goddard Space Flight Center. The first Explorer was developed and launched before Goddard was formed, but Goddard's scientists, engineers, technicians, and support staff were responsible for making the Explorer series the amazing success story that it is. To date, there have been more than 75 successful Explorer missions, and the new Small Explorer series promises to carry that tradition into the 21st century. The Explorer satellites were innovative, most of them were relatively small and simple, and many were built in-house at Goddard. They conducted research in almost all the space science disciplines, from particle and field research to high-energy astronomy. In the early days, however, the Explorers perhaps were best known for their particle and field research in the magnetosphere and interplanetary space.

One of the early concerns of NASA's managers, for example, was micrometeorites and the threat they might pose to both robotic and human space missions. Several early Explorers[3] included micrometeorite detectors, which discovered that the threat of damage from these particles was much lower than some scientists had feared.

Another concern was the possible radiation hazard solar cosmic ray events might pose for astronauts, especially on the Apollo Moon missions. Cosmic rays are actually energetic particles that travel through space. Scientists now have identified three distinct types of cosmic rays, each of which brings us information on a different aspect of the universe. One type, known as "anomalous cosmic rays," offers a sample of the interstellar gas in the nearby region of our galaxy. So-called "galactic cosmic rays" travel at much higher speeds, reaching us from distant regions of the galaxy and perhaps from beyond. "Solar cosmic rays" emanate from solar flares and other events on the Sun.[4]

During the Apollo program, NASA was concerned primarily with solar cosmic rays. When events such as solar flares occur on the Sun, a greater number of solar cosmic rays are released into space. One of the goals of Goddard's Interplanetary Monitoring Platform[5] (IMP) series of satellites was to determine how great a hazard these events might create for humans traveling in space.

The IMP series of Explorers, which project scientist Frank McDonald named in honor of his children, consisted of 10 separate satellites that investigated galactic and solar cosmic rays, the interplanetary medium, and the distant magnetosphere. They also provided real-time monitoring for possibly hazardous cosmic radiation events during the Apollo missions.

Another Explorer spacecraft played an important role in measuring the results of the Starfish high-altitude nuclear bomb test in 1962. The test had been an effort to analyze the effects of an explosion in the upper atmosphere, but the blast cloud had traveled much higher than the test designers had intended, and both the military and NASA were noticing difficulties with a couple of their satellites. At the request of President John F. Kennedy, Goddard initiated an intense effort to modify a satellite from another mission to go up and measure the actual test results. Designated Explorer 15, the satellite discovered that the explosion had created an artificial radiation belt around the Earth. Goddard also discovered that the radiation from the blast was responsible for damaging several satellites in orbit at the time, including the Alouette spacecraft and a Telstar communication satellite.[6]

Other early Explorers made important discoveries about the composition and boundaries of the Earth's magnetosphere, ionosphere, and upper atmosphere and how these regions were affected by solar "weather" and other cosmic events.[7] By the end of the 1960s, these and other satellites had given scientists a good general description of the magnetosphere, the features of the Sun-Earth relationship, and the interplanetary medium. The task since then has been to refine and expand that knowledge with more detail and depth.[8]

THE ORBITING GEOPHYSICAL OBSERVATORY PROJECTS

The Explorers were not the only spacecraft geared toward helping scientists understand the near-Earth environment and how it is affected by the Sun. The Orbiting Geophysical Observatory (OGO) projects that Goddard managed were an attempt to get a more integrated picture of the dynamics at work by co-locating many

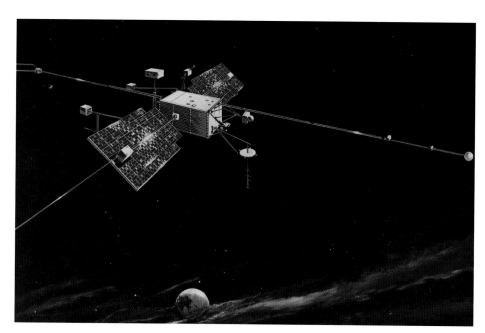

An artist's concept of Goddard's Orbiting Geophysical Observatory, which incorporated 20 different research experiments. (NASA Photo G-62-2835)

different experiments on a single satellite. The OGO I satellite launched in September 1964, for instance, included 20 different instruments.

The OGO series actually incorporated two unique concepts. One was the inclusion of so many different experiments on a single spacecraft, which was a radical change from the smaller, more focused Explorers. The second was that the OGO spacecraft and interfaces with experiments were designed to be standardized. In addition to cost savings, this "streetcar" design would allow experiments that were not ready by the deadline for one launch to "catch" the next spacecraft in the series, like catching the next streetcar on a commuter schedule.

The OGO concept was a learning experience for the scientists and engineers involved, and it never worked as well as its designers would have liked. Having so many experiments on one satellite created numerous interference problems, and the success of the instruments varied widely.

The performance improved over time, and eventually six different OGO satellites were launched, the final one in 1969. Although the OGO concept was abandoned, the OGO satellites laid the groundwork for future standardized spacecraft designs. This standardized spacecraft approach has remained a recurring theme at NASA, first with the Multi-mission Modular Spacecraft (MMS) of the late 1970s, and even more recently with the Rapid Spacecraft Procurement Initiative.[9]

INTERNATIONAL SUN-EARTH EXPLORER

Another approach to getting a more integrated picture of Sun-Earth dynamics was the International Sun-Earth Explorer

Originally launched to investigate solar-Earth phenomena, the orbit of this spacecraft, renamed the International Cometary Explorer, was modified to intercept the Giacobini-Zinner comet in 1985.

(ISEE) satellite series, a joint project between Goddard and the European Space Agency (ESA). The ISEE A satellite, built at Goddard, and ISEE B satellite, built by ESA, were launched together on a single Delta rocket in October 1977. By placing the satellites in similar orbits at a variable distance from each other, scientists could pinpoint fluctuations in the boundaries of the Earth's magnetosphere. Ten months later, a third ISEE satellite built by Goddard was launched into a complementary orbit and gathered additional data on the same phenomena being measured by the first two satellites.[10]

In 1982, a Goddard project engineer named Robert Farquhar realized that a near pass of the Giacobini-Zinner comet predicted for 1985 created a golden opportunity for scientists to learn more about the composition and evolution of a comet nucleus. So the orbit of ISEE 3 was altered to fly by the comet. In a complex 3-year maneuver, the ISEE 3 satellite was moved into an orbit that swung through the Earth's magnetospheric tail, sling-shotted around the Moon to put the satellite into an orbit around the Sun, and came in close enough range to gather data from the comet in 1985. Renamed the International Cometary Explorer (ICE), the satellite was also able to observe the solar wind upstream of Halley's comet on its visit in 1986.

INTERNATIONAL SOLAR-TERRESTRIAL PHYSICS

As satellite technology improved, it allowed scientists to add more detail to our understanding of the dynamics between the Sun and Earth. For example, we know that there are particles from the Sun that flow continuously toward and around the Earth, creating the boundaries of our magnetosphere.

The number of particles flowing toward Earth is not constant, however. Active solar events such as flares and Coronal Mass Ejections (CMEs) release high quantities of energetic particles that shoot toward Earth at speeds up to 2 million miles an hour. Influxes of these particles result in geomagnetic storms around the Earth that cause a number of strange effects. These storms are believed to be the cause of the spectacular Northern and Southern lights, but they can also cause numerous problems. They can interfere with telephone, television, and radio signals; damage the electronics in spacecraft; disturb compasses and marine navigation instruments; and create power outages. As a result, we have more than just a scientific interest in learning more about these events, especially as our society has become more reliant on electronic technology. If we can figure out the dynamics that lead to these storms, we can take measures to mitigate their effect.[11]

In 1988, Goddard was given responsibility for a comprehensive international effort to explore these "solar-terrestrial" dynamics with much more precision and depth. The collaborative program was called the International Solar-Terrestrial Physics (ISTP) program, and its goal was to observe the impact and behavior of the

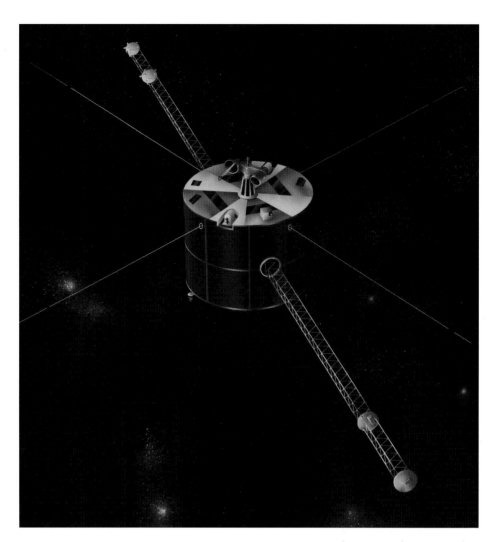

solar wind and its interaction with the Earth simultaneously from different perspectives. The program's initial goal was to look at these interactions simultaneously from three different spacecraft, called Wind, Polar, and Geotail, for at least 6 months in space. In 1992, the program was expanded to include plans for two additional spacecraft, called SOHO and Cluster.

The first of the ISTP spacecraft was "Geotail," a joint project between the Japanese Institute of Space and Astronautical Science (ISAS) and NASA. Launched in 1992, it looked at the dynamics and effect of the solar wind in the magnetospheric "tail" on the night side of the Earth.

The Geotail spacecraft was designed to conduct research on the effect of the solar wind on the magnetospheric "tail" on the side of the Earth away from the Sun.

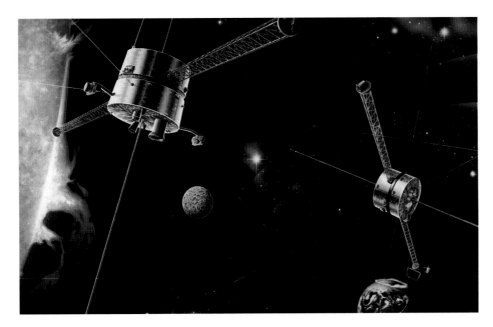

The Wind satellite (left) and the Polar satellite (right) were part of the International Solar-Terrestrial Physics (ISTP) program. The goal of the international ISTP effort was to use several different satellites, in different orbits, to study the various effects of the Sun on Earth.

NASA's Wind spacecraft was launched initially into an unusual orbit around the Earth, with the furthest point in the orbit almost a million miles away. Researchers then moved the satellite's orbit to a spot known as the Earth-Sun Libration point, or Lagrangian point L1. L1 is a point approximately 1/100th of the distance from the Earth to the Sun, where the centrifugal and gravitational forces of the two balance each other. The goal of the Wind satellite was to gather data on the solar wind before it reaches the Earth's magnetosphere—first at the point where it encounters the "bow shock" of the Earth's magnetosphere, and then at point L1, before the solar wind reaches the influence of the Earth at all. In 1998, the satellite's orbit was changed once again to a "petal" orbit of successive elliptical loops around the Earth to explore the solar wind in additional locations.

The third spacecraft in the ISTP series was the NASA-ESA Solar and Heliospheric Observatory (SOHO). In 1995 it was launched into an orbit around the L1 point to study the physical processes in the Sun that affect the release of solar cosmic rays and the solar wind itself.

A fourth project, developed by ESA, was named "Cluster" because it was actually a set of four spacecraft designed to gather three-dimensional information on the shape and dynamics of magnetic structures. Unfortunately, the Ariane-5 booster rocket carrying the Cluster spacecraft exploded during its launch in 1996. But in 1997, the ESA announced that it would launch a replacement, Cluster II, on two Soyuz rockets in mid-2000.

The last ISTP spacecraft, called "Polar," was launched in 1996. It was placed into a polar orbit of the Earth to observe the activity of solar particles once they entered the Earth's magnetosphere, ionosphere, and atmosphere.

The ISTP program was an ambitious one, and coordinating the efforts of numerous research institutions and countries on several different satellites was challenging from both management and technical perspectives. For example, Goddard had development responsibility for both the Polar and Wind satellites. The idea was to get all five satellites into orbit at the same time, but both Polar and Wind encountered numerous technical difficulties and fell behind schedule. Goddard's management decided to solve the problem by finishing the Wind satellite first and then tackling the Polar spacecraft. This caused some difficulties with Goddard's partners, because most of the instruments built by Goddard scientists just happened to be on the Wind spacecraft. But eventually, both Wind and Polar were successfully launched and are still returning useful data.

Despite the challenges of a multi-spacecraft, international effort, the ISTP program has achieved major breakthroughs in scientific observations of the Sun and its effect on the Earth, including the processes by which solar plasmas and particles are transported to the Earth. These findings are adding valuable pieces to the puzzle of the Sun's relationship with our home planet.[12]

ACE/SAMPEX/FAST

Although they are not part of the official ISTP program, Goddard also has developed and launched three additional spacecraft to enhance our understanding of cosmic rays. The first of these missions was a satellite called the Solar, Anomalous, and Magnetospheric Particle Explorer (SAMPEX).

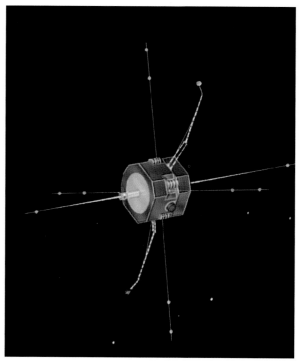

An artist's concept of the Fast Auroral Snapshot Explorer satellite, launched in 1996 to explore the polar aurora of the Earth.

It was put into orbit with an air-launched Pegasus rocket in 1992 to study the composition of particles arriving from the solar atmosphere and interstellar space and how they are transported into our atmosphere. A second satellite, called the Fast Auroral Snapshot Explorer (FAST), is taking a closer look at the plasma physics of the polar auroras. The auroras are created by accelerated electrons from particles in the magnetosphere hitting the upper atmosphere, just as a television picture is created by a beam of electrons hitting the inside of the front screen. The goal of the FAST satellite, launched in 1996, is to understand better exactly how those particles are accelerated.[13]

A third satellite, the Advanced Composition Explorer (ACE), was launched in 1997 and is in orbit around L1, almost a million miles away from Earth. Its nine instruments are measuring the type, charge, mass, energy, direction of travel, and time of arrival of anomalous,

Launch of the Advanced Composition Explorer satellite in August 1997.

A series of SOHO images reveals the ejection of matter from the solar corona.

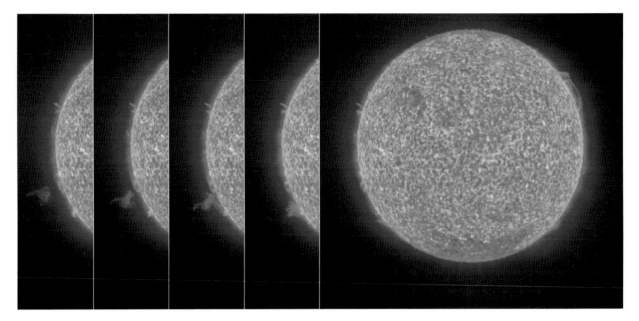

galactic, and solar cosmic rays in an attempt to find clues as to their source and the processes that brought them here.

Because the different kinds of cosmic rays contain matter from vastly different times and places, researchers hope the satellite can help us better understand the formation and evolution of the solar system, among other things. The effort is not that different from the earlier satellites such as the Interplanetary Monitoring Platforms (IMPs); the difference is that technological advances have given the ACE instruments collecting power 10 to 1,000 times greater than previous satellite instruments.

The goal of space physics satellites has not changed dramatically over the past 40 years. Scientists are still looking to spacecraft to gather data on the particles, magnetic fields, and dynamics in both the near-Earth environment and interstellar space. And their goal is still to understand what exists beyond our atmosphere, how those particles and fields affect us here on Earth, and what all of this can tell us about the

formation of our own solar system and other planetary systems that lie beyond our reach. What has changed is the technology. The early Explorer satellites drew the rough outlines of the picture. As we have developed better and more capable spacecraft, we have continued to fill in the colors, the details, and the depth of what is turning out to be a very complex picture, indeed.

UNDERSTANDING THE SUN

One of the critical steps in filling in the details of the Sun's relationship with the Earth has been to learn more about the Sun itself, and several Goddard satellites have been devoted to this goal. Actually, the Sun offers a unique opportunity for several fields of study. In addition to its direct impact on Earth, the Sun is also a star. In the universal scheme of things it may be only a very average-sized star, but it is a star nevertheless, and the only one close enough for us to observe in any great detail. In learning more about our Sun's internal processes and its impact on our own planet and solar system, we can infer a great deal about the dynamics of stars in remote parts of our galaxy and beyond. And because the Sun is relatively close to Earth, scientists can obtain *in situ* measurements of the particles it releases as well as remote images of its processes in various wavelengths of the electromagnetic spectrum.

The Sun consists of a complex nuclear furnace surrounded by several different layers of gaseous plasma. Most of the elements in the universe are created within stars when nuclei of "lighter" elements fuse together to make heavier and more complex elements. Hydrogen, for example, is the simplest element known, with only a single proton in its nucleus. Helium is next, with two protons. Hydrogen can be turned into helium in high-speed collisions between nuclei that then release tremendous amounts of energy, but those collisions require temperatures of at least 5 million degrees. The formation of more complex elements require even higher temperatures, which is why scientists think most elements heavier than iron are formed in supernova explosions of dying stars.

The energy of our own Sun is a result of hydrogen nuclei fusing into helium at its core. That energy travels outward through the Sun, slowly degrading from gamma rays to X-rays, and then ultraviolet, and finally to visible light as it nears the visible surface, or photosphere, of the Sun. The process is a slow one. Light travels from the photosphere to Earth in approximately 8 minutes, but that energy was created by fusion reactions that took place thousands of years ago in the Sun's core.

Near the surface of the Sun, energy begins to be transported by convection as well as radiation. Scientists have long surmised that dark "Sun spots" on the surface of the Sun are masses of cooler gas where strong magnetic fields limit the typical convective currents that would otherwise keep bringing heat up from lower regions.

At times, eruptions called solar flares explode outward from the photosphere, sometimes associated with huge ejections of up to 100 million tons of mass from the Sun. The particles released in those eruptions and Coronal Mass Ejections travel outward into space at speeds up to 2 million miles an hour, contributing significantly to the solar wind and sometimes causing numerous problems on Earth.

The region above the photosphere is called the chromosphere, an area of decreasing density analogous to the Earth's upper atmosphere. Above that is the Sun's corona, a region whose density is so low that we generally cannot see it from Earth except when a solar eclipse blocks out the

A finely resolved image of Sun spots returned by SOHO.

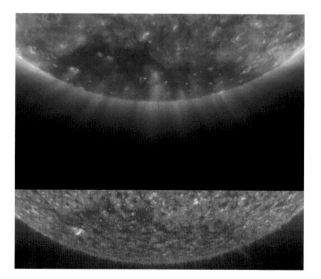

So-called polar plumes extend into space from the polar regions of the Sun, seen in SOHO image.

scattered sunlight in the Earth's atmosphere. During an eclipse, the corona appears as a white halo around the edges of the Sun. High-speed, feathery jets of plasma, called polar plumes, can be observed shooting out from the Sun's corona at its poles, where its magnetic field lines are more open.

Scientists have been observing the processes of the Sun since at least the days of Galileo. But many of the Sun's internal processes can be studied only by looking at the radiation they create, and ground observatories are limited in the type of electromagnetic wavelengths they can see. Rocket and satellite solar astronomy allowed scientists to view the Sun's processes in ultraviolet, X-ray, and gamma ray wavelengths that would have been blocked by the Earth's atmosphere. This opened up an invaluable window to understand the Sun, because many critical solar processes involve these short wavelengths in essential ways.[14]

ORBITING SOLAR OBSERVATORIES

The first Goddard satellites designed specifically to look at the Sun were the Orbiting Solar Observatories (OSOs). The

The Solar Maximum Mission satellite as photographed by an astronaut during the 1984 Space Shuttle mission to repair the ailing satellite. (NASA Photo G84-1158)

first OSO spacecraft was launched in 1962 and successfully measured electromagnetic radiation from the Sun over time in ultraviolet, X-ray, and gamma ray regions of the spectrum. The next two OSO satellites, however, ran into trouble. The second OSO was destroyed in a prelaunch accident, and the third stage of the Delta launch vehicle carrying the next OSO satellite fired prematurely. The result, according to Goddard's matter-of-fact mission notes, was that "the satellite thus entered the Atlantic Ocean rather than planned 350-mile circular orbit at 33-degree inclination."[15]

Eventually, eight OSO satellites were launched into orbit, all with the same basic goal of observing the Sun's processes in wavelengths not visible on Earth. OSOs V, VI, and VII had an additional focus on studying solar flares because of the potential threat these events might pose to astronauts in space. These OSO satellites provided the first close, extended look at the Sun in important regions of the spectrum that could not be observed by any ground-based methods. They also provided the first steps toward understanding the complex processes of the star that has a critical impact on life here on Earth.

SOLAR MAX

Activity on the Sun increases and decreases over the course of a cycle that typically lasts about 11 years, although there are exceptions to that time frame. In 1980, Goddard launched a spacecraft to try to get a more comprehensive understanding of solar events, particularly solar flares. The satellite was called the Solar Maximum Mission (SMM) because its 1980 launch was timed to coincide with the peak activity of the Sun's 11-year cycle. The Solar Max satellite incorporated gamma ray, X-ray, and ultraviolet spectrometers to look at solar flares across all the higher energy portions of the spectrum. These results were coordinated with ground observations in the visible and radio wavelengths in an effort to compile a comprehensive picture of the dynamics involved in these powerful solar events across the entire electromagnetic spectrum. The picture was filled out even further by the ISEE 3 satellite, which took *in situ* measurements of the particles released by the solar flares that the SMM satellite and ground stations were observing.

The SMM marked the first time a satellite was designed and launched specifically to look at solar flares. It also demonstrated one of the advantages satellites offered scientists. In addition to allowing observations of particles and radiations that cannot be seen or measured from the ground, satellites make it possible for scientists from different disciplines to work together to get a much bigger and more comprehensive picture of cosmic phenomena.

The Solar Max satellite also marked the first time a satellite was repaired successfully in space. The SMM was the first of Goddard's Multi-mission Modular Spacecraft (MMS) designed to be serviceable in orbit by Space Shuttle astronauts.[16] The concept had the opportunity to be

tested 8 months after SMM's launch, when three fuses in the satellite's attitude control system failed. These failures made it impossible for the spacecraft to point precisely at observation targets on the Sun, severely compromising the potential success of the mission.

So in 1984, astronauts aboard the Shuttle Challenger retrieved the satellite into the Shuttle's cargo bay, replaced the damaged components, and released the spacecraft back into orbit. Although the repair mission was ultimately successful, it underscored the difficulties of such an endeavor. The SMM spacecraft had been designed with a special attach point that could be mated with a docking device carried by an astronaut to retrieve the satellite and bring it back into the Shuttle cargo bay. But a screw head near the satellite's attach point was apparently sticking up out of place, and the astronaut was unable to get a lock on the spacecraft. To make matters worse, the astronaut grabbed onto one of the satellite's solar arrays in an attempt to get a better hold on the satellite, sending the spacecraft tumbling out of control.

Down at the control center at Goddard, engineers began a frantic effort to restabilize the spacecraft. Engineers estimated that the batteries on the tumbling satellite would be dead within 8 hours, after which it would have to be brought back to Earth for repair or abandoned in space. To conserve power, the engineers decided to turn off even the satellite's transmitters. This meant that they would have no information on the health of the crippled satellite, but they were desperate to buy more time to gain control of the spacecraft. After 19 tense hours, controllers managed to use the Earth's magnetic field and the magnetic torquers on the satellite to stop the spacecraft's tumbling, point it toward the Sun to re-power its batteries, and restabilize its movement. The Shuttle astronauts were then able to use the orbiter's robotic arm to capture the satellite the next day. The Solar Max repair mission underscored the difficulty of conducting science in the unforgiving realm of outer space. But the resourcefulness of the ground controllers at Goddard and the Shuttle astronauts made the mission a success. The effort also gave Goddard's engineers valuable experience in space repair missions—experience that would prove critical to the success of the first Hubble servicing mission a decade later.[17]

SOHO/TRACE/ULYSSES/SPARTAN 201

The next maximum activity time in the Sun's 11-year cycle is expected around 2001. So in the last years of the 20th century, several new spacecraft have been launched to look at the Sun in even more detail as it transitions from a low-activity time to the height of its active cycle. The biggest of these is the Solar and Heliospheric Observatory (SOHO) satellite, a joint ESA-NASA project that was launched in 1995 as part of NASA's International Solar-Terrestrial Physics (ISTP) program. The SOHO satellite is orbiting the L1 Lagrangian point, which gives it a view of the Sun unobstructed by the Earth. The 12 SOHO instruments each gather a particular type of information to help give scientists a better picture of the inner workings and dynamics of the Sun and its complex magnetic field, as well as what causes its plumes, flares, and coronal mass ejections.

Complementing the SOHO satellite is the Transition Region And Coronal Explorer (TRACE). TRACE is a Small Explorer satellite built by Goddard and launched in April 1998. The TRACE instruments do not have as wide a range as SOHO's instruments, but they can take images of the photosphere, transition region, and corona of the Sun in much finer detail. Between the two satellites, scientists hope to obtain simultaneous measurements of all the temperature ranges of the solar atmosphere as it moves toward the height of its activity cycle.

Complementing this research is a NASA-ESA satellite called "Ulysses," which is in a unique polar orbit around the Sun. Most satellites have orbits that are still

This image from the TRACE satellite shows the fine structure in loops of plasma that are contained by large-scale magnetic fields on the surface of the Sun. (NASA Photo PAOT98_03.TIF)

within what is called "the plane of the ecliptic," which means on the same horizontal plane as the rest of our solar system. Our solar system, looked at from a distance, would appear as a flat disk. All the planets rotate around the Sun in pretty much the same horizontal plane, and most satellites stay within that same horizontal path as they orbit the Earth. But to orbit the poles of the Sun, the Ulysses satellite had to be flung out of that plane, into an orbit that operated perpendicular to the rest of the solar system. It was a difficult maneuver that required sling-shotting the satellite around Jupiter before turning it back to the Sun in order to give it the energy to break away from the flat disk of the solar system. But its orbit has allowed the Ulysses satellite to obtain valuable information about the dynamics of the Sun at its poles, which appear to play a major role in the creation of the solar wind.

Goddard also developed the Spartan 201 satellite, which is a short-duration spacecraft released overboard by Shuttle astronauts at the beginning of a mission and then retrieved and brought back to Earth when they return. The Spartan 201 satellites have carried various instruments to look at specific aspects of the Sun's perplexing corona.

The combined efforts of these spacecraft have revealed some amazing data about how our Sun works. One of the mysteries of the Sun, for example, is the temperature difference between its outermost layer, the corona, and the chromosphere layer beneath it. Because the majority of the

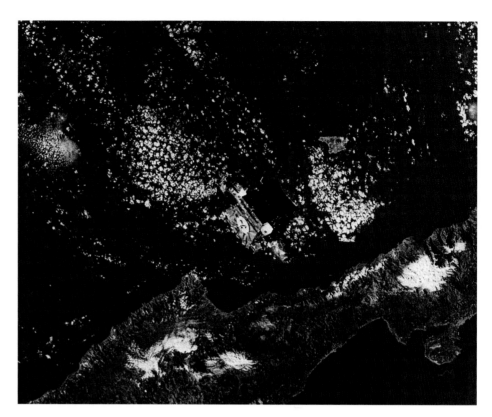

Sun's energy is generated at the core, one might assume that its layers should be progressively cooler as its energy travels outward and dissipates. But that is not what happens. Earlier satellites discovered that while the Sun's photosphere and chromosphere are about 6,000 and 10,000 degrees Kelvin, the corona beyond them is a blistering 2 million degrees Kelvin. How the corona can be so much hotter than the regions below it has mystified solar physicists.

Based on observations from these latest satellites, scientists have concluded that at least one source of the corona's high temperature is a process called "magnetic reconnection." In essence, the surface of the Sun has a very complex magnetic field structure that is changing constantly. As these magnetic structures continually "snap" and break down, they appear to release energy up into the corona, in the form of heat.

The Spartan 201 satellite after release from the Space Shuttle cargo bay. The Spartan satellites are retrieved by the Shuttle before the end of the mission.

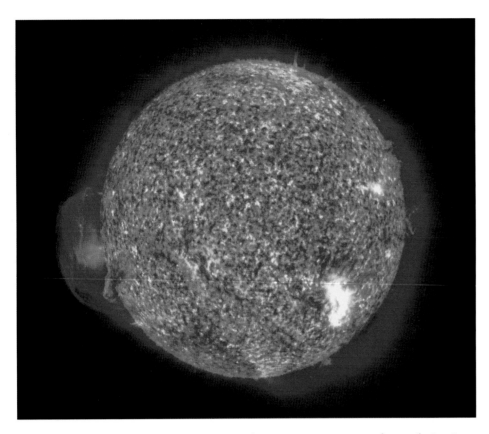

This image from the SOHO satellite shows the active and granular surface of the Sun. A large eruptive disturbance is visible on the left side of the image.

But the picture spacecraft are bringing back to us is even more complicated than that. Indeed, one of the main discoveries these solar satellites have made is just how amazingly complex the Sun's processes are. Recent observations from the SOHO spacecraft, for example, have detected streams of plasma that move across the Sun's surface and dive deep into its interior, almost as the jet stream, trade winds, and ocean currents circulate around the Earth. Those streams do not all move at the same speed or direction, however, and the Sun itself appears to rotate at different speeds in different places. In its interior, the Sun rotates as a unified object, but on its visible surface the Sun rotates slower at its poles than it does at its equator. Scientists now think this churning interaction between different rotation patterns and charged plasma currents may be what

creates the Sun's complex magnetic field and causes the turbulent eruptions of solar flares and coronal mass ejections.

Instruments on SOHO and Ulysses have also looked at the polar plumes and coronal holes near the Sun's poles, which scientists now believe play a significant role in the creation of the solar wind. Once, scientists assumed that the solar wind streamed out from the Sun in all directions. Satellite data now has shown that the picture is much more complex. The Sun's surface, chromosphere, and corona are highly structured with very complex magnetic fields. At places, the fields cause plasma to "loop" out and back, trapping it on the Sun. In other places, "holes" in the fields allow plasma to escape at high speeds, becoming the solar wind. And the turbulent interactions of the various parts of these magnetic fields may be the cause of more explosive ejections of material, such as solar flares or coronal mass ejections, which release tremendous amounts of plasma in a short period of time. One such solar storm in January 1997, for example, released a magnetized cloud that stretched 30 million miles across, pounding the Earth's magnetosphere with particles for 30 hours, interrupting communications, and causing spectacular polar auroras. With the new generation of solar satellites, scientists are beginning to put together enough pieces to start to make sense of this complex solar puzzle. Before long, we may actually learn enough not only to understand these storms, but also to predict them.[18]

EXPLORING THE UNIVERSE

The Sun offers a unique opportunity to study the processes of a star at close range, allowing scientists to examine both the particles and the electromagnetic radiation it emits. Goddard scientists also designed instruments for space probes and planetary missions to examine the magnetic fields and particles of other planets and regions within our solar system. To figure out the composition and behavior of material, planets, or stars beyond our immediate surroundings, however, scientists rely on analyzing the light and energy that reaches us in various wavelengths of the electromagnetic spectrum. Another main focus of Goddard's scientific endeavors over the years has been building spacecraft to explore the universe in different regions of this spectrum.

The electromagnetic spectrum progresses from radio waves, with the lowest energy and lowest temperatures, to microwave radiation, to infrared light, to visible light, to ultraviolet light, to X-rays, and finally to gamma rays, which have the highest energy and occur at the highest temperature of any waves in the spectrum. The upper end of the scale contains very short wavelengths with a higher frequency, while the lower end consists of much longer wavelengths with a lower frequency. In a sense, the spectrum behaves much like a rope held between two people. To get the rope to undulate in big motions does not require much energy. But to get it to move up and down in frequent oscillations requires quite a lot of energy.

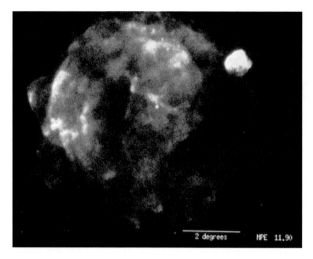

Energy is also linked to temperature. High energy events have high temperatures, while lower energy events are much cooler. So each particular point on the spectrum correlates to a very particular temperature as well as energy or light level. Scientists spend a lot of effort looking at the Sun in X-rays and gamma ray regions, for example, because some of the processes they want to study take place at very high temperatures. This means they can be observed only at the high frequency end of the electromagnetic spectrum.

Each element of the periodic table also has a particular "fingerprint" in the electromagnetic spectrum. If nitrogen is present somewhere, for example, emissions from that location will show a particular spike at a very precise wavelength in the spectrum. Other elements will spike at different unique wavelengths. This is how scientists can determine the chemical composition of gas clouds, comets, or other matter in the galaxy.

In exploring the universe, yet another factor comes into play. When we look at a distant star, galaxy, or nebula, the light or energy we are receiving has traveled up to

This ROSAT satellite image shows the round shape of the Vela supernova explosion, which occurred about 11,000 years ago, about 1500 light-years away from Earth. The remnant shape of the event can be detected in ROSAT's X-ray image because a supernova explosion heats the interstellar gas enough to generate a glow in the X-ray region of the spectrum.

An X-ray image from the ROSAT satellite against a visible light image of a small galaxy group, showing the presence of a hot gas that would not be visible to the eye.

that infrared light is coming from an object in a distant galaxy, it may have begun as visible or even ultraviolet light. Scientists call this phenomenon "red shift" because the starlight from distant galaxies "shifts" down toward the redder, longer wavelength end of the spectrum as the galaxies move away from us. The more distant they are, the faster they are moving, and the greater the red shift.

So when scientists look for light from the very early days of the universe, for example, they are looking for light that is very old and has come from very far away. It may have been extremely bright at one time, but now we are more likely to detect it as a dim light and in the lower, infrared and microwave portions of the spectrum. Radiation from closer, more highly energetic events in the universe, by contrast, will be detected in the higher ends of the spectrum. Unfortunately for scientists, the Earth's atmosphere blocks many of these portions of the spectrum. So it has been only since the advent of satellite technology that we have been able to explore fully many of the universe's greatest mysteries.

Individual objects or phenomena may be especially bright in one particular region of the spectrum, and observations in new regions, such as X-ray wavelengths, may tell us things about objects we never knew before. But one of the biggest advantages of conducting satellite astronomy across the entire electromagnetic spectrum is that it gives scientists the ability to look at the same objects and phenomena in many different wavelengths.

13 billion light-years to reach us. So when we look at any of these objects or phenomena, we are really looking back in time. What we see is the light that star generated many years ago, and the further away the source is, the dimmer it will appear. The universe is also expanding. So the stars in distant galaxies are not only old; they are actually moving away from us. And the more distant they are, the faster they are receding. This movement affects the light we see.

Light waves, like sound waves, change as they travel toward or away from us. Just as a train whistle appears to get higher in pitch as it approaches and lower in pitch as it recedes into the distance, the light from objects in the universe will get longer in wavelength if those objects are moving away from us. If astronomers detect an infrared source in our own galaxy, it probably began as an infrared source. But if

Many so-called X-ray stars, for example, are also visible to the eye. What X-ray satellites told scientists was that these stars were *also* emitting peculiar, high-temperature energy, which meant there was something different about these stars than visible stars that did not show up in X-ray wavelengths. Radio astronomers detected pulsars several years before X-ray satellites discovered that these phenomena also had high-energy emissions. The Crab Nebula, the remnant of a star that exploded almost 1,000 years ago, can be observed in almost every wavelength. Yet each different wavelength provides a slightly different piece of information that helps us put together a more accurate and complete picture of any particular object or phenomenon in the universe.

So while some findings may be touted as "X-ray," "gamma ray," or "ultraviolet" discoveries, all of these depend heavily on observations in other wavelengths. One of the greatest difficulties in figuring out the source of the exotic "gamma ray bursts" that satellites have detected for three

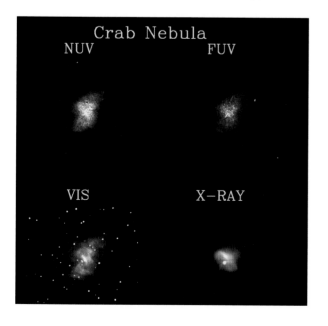

decades, for example, was that scientists were unable to link these high-energy bursts with any visual objects or phenomena until 1997. And even then, only three or four out of thousands of gamma ray bursts have been identified.

Clearly, there is much left to learn. But Goddard's achievements in space-based astronomy, along with ground-based astronomy efforts over the last 40 years, already has shown a universe that is more dazzling, complex, mysterious, and powerful than we ever even imagined.

RADIO ASTRONOMY

The lowest energy portion of the electromagnetic spectrum consists of radio waves. It is one of the few regions of the spectrum other than visible light where the waves can penetrate the dust clouds in our galaxy and the water vapor, dust, ozone, and other elements of our atmosphere. As a result, radio astronomy has played an important role in the exploration of the universe, uncovering signs of many phenomena and objects that are invisible to the eye. Astronomers were studying intergalactic radio wave signals before there were satellites. But from the ground, radio signals may be affected by the ionosphere and extraneous radio noise. Radio astronomy satellites offered a chance to monitor signals from the solar system, galaxy, and the cosmos without any of those interferences.

Goddard's first radio astronomy satellite, Explorer 38, was launched in July 1968 to look at radio signals from the Earth's magnetosphere, Jupiter, and other

The Crab Nebula as it appears in four different wavelengths of the electromagnetic spectrum: visible light, near ultraviolet, far ultraviolet, and X-ray.

cosmic sources. In order to receive the weak radio wave signals, the satellite had twin antenna booms that were extended from the main body of the spacecraft once it was in orbit. Tip to tip, the antenna were taller than the Empire State Building. Seven years later, Goddard launched another radio astronomy satellite, Explorer 49, to look for radio signals at slightly different wavelengths.

Among other things, radio astronomy can identify certain elements whose "fingerprints" fall in the radio wave portion of the spectrum. Goddard's Submillimeter Wave Astronomy Satellite (SWAS), for example, is designed to examine the chemical composition of interstellar galactic clouds to help determine the process of star formation. The SWAS satellite is the third mission in Goddard's Small Explorer (SMEX) program and was launched in December 1998.[19]

MICROWAVE/INFRARED ASTRONOMY

COSMIC BACKGROUND EXPLORER

Some of Goddard's most significant astronomical research has been conducted in the microwave/infrared region of the spectrum, right above radio signal wavelengths. It is a very difficult region to explore, because it involves such low temperatures. The phenomena scientists are trying to detect have temperatures as low as 3 degrees Kelvin, or almost absolute zero. The heat most instruments and detectors generate is higher than that and would obscure

The Cosmic Background Explorer satellite under construction in a clean room.

any signals at these wavelengths. So an infrared or microwave satellite has to have cryogenically cooled instruments, which is very cumbersome and difficult to accomplish. Yet this portion of the spectrum offers our best window back to the dawn of time, prompting scientists to try to solve the difficulties inherent in exploring it.

Over a 15-year period, a Goddard team succeeded in designing, building, and launching a spacecraft capable of exploring portions of the universe in this challenging region of the spectrum. The Goddard-built satellite, called the Cosmic Background Explorer (COBE), went in search of data to test the "Big Bang" theory of the origin of the universe—and found it.

The origins of the COBE satellite actually date back to at least 1965, when two researchers at Bell Telephone Labs in Holmberg, New Jersey, detected a background microwave "noise" coming in equally from all directions of the universe, not related to any particular object or event.

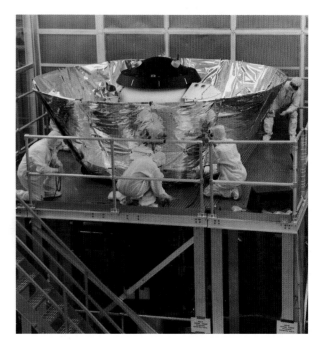

Scientists realized that this low-energy background noise might hold the secret to how our universe was formed.

Several different theories had been put forth as to how the universe began and how it was evolving. One of the most popular was the "Big Bang" theory, which held that all the matter and energy in the universe was created in one initial explosion and had been expanding ever since. According to the theory, matter and energy had been changing and evolving in various combinations since then, but no additional major inputs of energy or matter had occurred in the 14 billion years since that initial explosion.

If the Big Bang theory was correct, the very beginning moments of the universe would have consisted of a cosmic oven of tiny particles of matter and anti-matter colliding into each other at tremendous rates. Each collision would have annihilated the matter, creating energy, but the temperature of this primordial soup would have been so hot that that energy, in turn, would be constantly creating new matter and anti-matter. As the energy decreased and dissipated from the initial explosion, a point would have been reached when new matter would no longer be created. At that point, there was evidently a little more matter than anti-matter. The matter clumped together to form galaxies, and the remaining energy became the cosmic background radiation.

If no additional energy inputs had occurred in the billions of years since then, that background radiation should behave

After the Challenger accident, the COBE satellite had to be redesigned into a much smaller, lighter package so it could be launched on a Delta rocket.

like a "blackbody," which emits heat in a uniform and specific manner at all points. If there had been some other source of heat or energy during the evolution of the universe, that smooth blackbody curve of radiation would have distinctive bumps in it where the energy increased.

To find out the behavior of this cosmic background radiation, scientists had to develop instruments that could detect wavelengths typical of a body with a temperature of 3 degrees Kelvin—the wavelength at which that very old cosmic background radiation would be at its brightest. A young Goddard scientist named John Mather had completed his doctoral thesis on cosmic background radiation, and in 1974 he proposed a follow-on experiment that might work on such a satellite. The result was COBE—a project that eventually

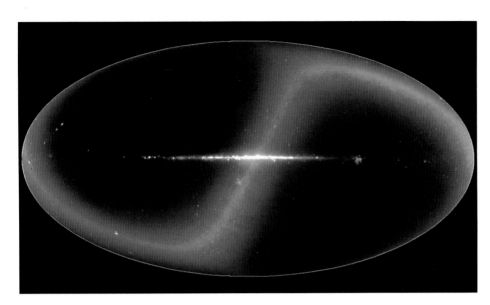

The thin bright horizontal line represents the disc of our galaxy as recorded by COBE in far infrared light.

involved the efforts of almost 1500 people, cost between $300-400 million, and took 15 years to complete—but which unlocked the door to the dawn of time.

The COBE satellite consisted of three main instruments, all of which had to be cryogenically cooled to almost absolute zero. The Far Infrared Absolute Spectrophotometer (FIRAS) would examine the cosmic background radiation to see if it behaved like a blackbody in the 3-degree Kelvin temperature range. If it did, the radiation should increase in a smooth curve approaching the wavelength equivalent to 3 degrees Kelvin, peak at the 2.78 degrees Kelvin wavelength, and then decrease in a similarly smooth manner as the wavelength and frequency increased beyond that.

A second instrument, called the Differential Microwave Radiometer (DMR), was designed to make an all-sky map of the brightness of the background radiation to look for evidence of how galaxies developed from the homogeneous soup of the universe's earliest stages.

Miniscule temperature fluctuations in the cosmic background radiation would reveal places where matter was denser than others, pointing out where and how galaxies began to form.

The third instrument, called the Diffuse Infrared Background Experiment (DIRBE), was designed to search for residual light from the earliest galaxies. If there had been galaxies in the early universe, it was so long ago that we probably could not detect individual light sources. But there might be a distinct residual "afterglow" from those galaxies at very long wavelengths. Scientists hoped the DIRBE instrument could detect this faint evidence of celestial bodies in the primordial universe.[20]

As with numerous other Goddard satellite projects, COBE was a tremendous challenge, requiring great technological leaps and innovation. Engineers and scientists could not write a specification for the instruments or spacecraft to operate them because nobody knew how to build them. It had never been done before. So the COBE team simply set out to design its own systems and instruments. It was not an easy process. Instruments would work on the bench and then fail when they were put into the cryogenic containers. Problems in weight, power, and cryogenic systems plagued the effort. If they did not know it already, researchers soon found out that there was a good reason no one had done this before. As John Mather later put it, "The team's naivete was a blessing and a strength. We didn't know how hard it was going to be, so we went ahead and did it."

The satellite was originally designed to be launched into its 560-mile high orbit from the Space Shuttle. But the loss of the Space Shuttle Challenger, just as the COBE team was nearing launch readiness, changed that. The Shuttle fleet was grounded and would probably never launch from the west coast site COBE needed. Scrambling to save the project, the COBE team decided to redesign the satellite to fit onboard a smaller Delta rocket that could be launched from the west coast. Among other things, that meant the satellite had to be much lighter and smaller.

In an intense 2$^{1}/_{2}$-year effort, COBE was redesigned successfully to fit the alternate launch vehicle. Ironically, the emergency situation and limitations actually made the effort easier in some ways. There was no question of expanding weight or size, and there was no time to discuss multiple options at length. Choices had to be made quickly and decisively. The team was helped by the fact that, in the wake of Challenger, NASA saw COBE as an opportunity for a much-needed agency success story. Consequently, the effort suddenly became a high-priority project. Team members who previously had to split their time with other projects were put on COBE full time, and the team was relocated so the engineers and scientists could all work together in the same place.

In January 1989, COBE was successfully launched into orbit. The effort to get it there had been tremendous, and some Goddard employees jokingly referred to COBE as "the project that ate the Center,"

because so many people were involved in it by the time the satellite was finally launched. But when the results started coming in, everyone realized the effort had been well worth it.

As the data from the FIRAS instrument began to come in, the project scientists were rendered almost speechless. The data points and the predicted curve were not just close—they were identical. The results were so astounding that when they were presented to the American Astronomical Society in January 1990, they drew a standing ovation from the nor-

The redesigned COBE satellite launched on 18 November 1989.

mally reserved society scientists. There could be no doubt about it. COBE's data pointed clearly to a universe whose energy had been generated in one initial explosion and had been radiated out in a uniform manner at all points ever since.

It took a little longer to get firm results from the DMR instrument, but eventually it indicated that there might be enough of a temperature differential in the cosmic background radiation to account for the clumping of matter into galaxies. The DIRBE results took even longer to analyze but, in early January 1998, the team scientists finally announced that they had, in fact, found evidence of an infrared background glow from the earliest stars and galaxies.

Do these results mean that we have conclusively settled the question of the universe's origins? No. If anything, the lesson of the past 40 years has been that the more we learn about space, the more we realize how much we have left to learn. Every step we take into the cosmos seems to reveal an even more complex universe than the one we previously thought we inhabited. The task of COBE was a staggeringly difficult one. Its scientists were like archaeologists trying to peer back more than 13 billion years in time and detect the faint whisper of clues that still lingered, ghost-like, in a world at the dawn of time. And the project uncovered an astounding piece of evidence no one had ever been able to see before. But there are still unanswered questions and anomalies in the Big Bang theory.

Goddard's Orbiting Astronomical Observatory was one of the first significant attempts to pursue visual and ultraviolet astronomy from a satellite platform. (NASA Photo G-71-2148)

Because we know there is much left to learn, Goddard is already planning a follow-on mission to the COBE satellite. Scheduled for a launch date around the year 2000, the Microwave Anisotropy Probe (MAP) satellite will explore the tiny temperature differences discovered by COBE in even greater detail. Among other things, scientists hope that by learning more about the density and arrangement of matter in the early years of the universe, we can begin to predict whether or not the universe will keep expanding.[21]

VISUAL/ULTRAVIOLET SATELLITES

ORBITING ASTRONOMICAL OBSERVATORIES

The very first astronomy satellites concentrated on the visual and ultraviolet regions of the spectrum. In part, this was because scientists had yet to realize the potential of some of the other wavelengths, but it was also because the very high and low frequency wavelengths required more complex technology to explore.

But even these first astronomy satellites came after the initial round of simple particle and field-detecting spacecraft,

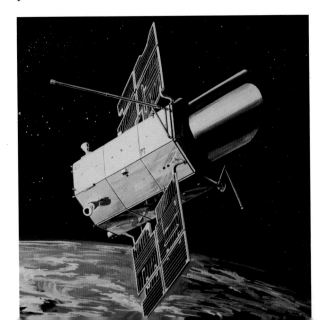

because astronomy satellites in general were harder to develop. Goddard had inherited some very good optical technicians from the Naval Gun Factory that had been located next to the Naval Research Laboratory, but developing a spacecraft for a telescope was harder. An astronomy satellite had to be stabilized and have the ability to point at one object for a relatively long period of time.

Goddard's first astronomy satellite also was its first attempt at a larger, observatory-class spacecraft. Called the Orbiting Astronomical Observatory (OAO), it was designed to explore the sky in both the visual and ultraviolet regions of the spectrum. Ultraviolet light is one of the wavelengths blocked by the Earth's atmosphere, and it was one of the regions astronomers were most interested in pursuing in the early 1960s. The astounding high-energy world of neutron stars and black holes had yet to be discovered. The OAO satellite, however, was a tremendous technological leap that incorporated new sensor technology, new experiment technology, and complicated ground system software that required constant updating. Experimenters on the ground who were commanding the OAOs were often only a couple of orbits ahead of the spacecraft, which made it a high-stress project.

The first OAO was launched in April 1965 but developed problems soon after reaching orbit. The high-voltage system on the star trackers that it needed to stabilize itself began arcing, and its battery overheated. After 20 orbits, the satellite failed.

It was not until December 1968 that the first successful astronomical satellite, OAO-2, reached orbit. OAO-2 allowed the Smithsonian Astrophysical Observatory to compile the first complete ultraviolet map of the sky, creating a catalog for use by astronomers. The satellite also provided new information on the composition of interstellar dust and hot stars.

Four years later Goddard launched OAO-3, also known as the "Copernicus" Observatory, which lasted 8 years and was an extremely successful astronomy satellite. Copernicus reached much farther into the ultraviolet region of the spectrum than the earlier OAOs and gave scientists much more detailed information about the chemical composition of certain stars and interstellar gases.

The OAO satellites were complex to operate and somewhat limited in their abilities, because they were pioneers in the space astronomy effort. But they provided valuable information and laid the groundwork for further discoveries by the Hubble Space Telescope and Goddard's International Ultraviolet Explorer.[22]

THE HUBBLE SPACE TELESCOPE

The origins of the Hubble Space Telescope date back to the late 1960s, when NASA managers began thinking about follow-on projects to the OAO satellites. Originally called the "Large Space Telescope," the facility was renamed before launch in honor of Edwin P. Hubble, an astronomer who determined in 1929 that the speeds with which galaxies are moving

The Hubble Space Telescope was launched from the Space Shuttle in 1990.

away from us are proportional to their distance. This "Hubble's Law" is a crucial tool still used by astronomers in trying to determine not only the location of distant galaxies, but also the size and shape of the universe itself.

NASA Headquarters decided to award management of the Hubble project to the Marshall Space Flight Center, although the scientific instruments and ground system would be Goddard's responsibility. Goddard would also be responsible for operating the telescope once it was commissioned in orbit. To reassure the external scientific community, which feared NASA scientists might have too much of an inside edge on this powerful astronomical tool, selection and processing of individual experiments using the telescope were delegated to an independent Space Telescope Science Institute set up specifically for that purpose in Baltimore, Maryland.[23]

Goddard scientists and engineers had fought hard to get full responsibility for developing the telescope, and hard feelings over the decision lingered between the two NASA Centers for years. As one scientist described it, the fight over Hubble was not just a disagreement, "It was a war." But with the decision made, Goddard's team shrugged their collective shoulders and, as usual, got down to the work at hand. However, the decision to split the responsibility between the two centers would come back to haunt the agency.

The Space Shuttle Challenger explosion delayed the launch of the Hubble, which was designed to be launched from a Shuttle. In April 1990, the telescope was finally put into orbit, amidst great hope and expectation. This was the largest telescope ever put into space, and it was expected to return images clearer and more detailed than anyone had ever witnessed before. But as operation of the telescope was turned over to Goddard and the first images began to appear, it became obvious that something was wrong. The images were blurry.

The flaw in the Hubble telescope was a blow to NASA's credibility in the scientific community and the public at large. Goddard engineers knew what was at stake. But they were at a severe disadvantage in terms of troubleshooting the problem, because they had been involved only nominally in building the actual telescope.

Goddard quickly put together a team to start working on a fix. In addition to Goddard personnel, the team included representatives from the Marshall Space Flight Center and the Space Telescope Science Institute. Lockheed, which had built the spacecraft, and the Perkin–Elmer[24] company, which had an excellent reputation in optics and had built the telescope's primary mirror, also sent experts to Goddard to join the troubleshooting team.

The team members agreed they had three top priorities. First, they had to figure out what was wrong with the telescope. Second, they had to figure out what it would take to fix it. And third, they had to figure out how scientists could use the telescope until they could get it fixed.

The team soon discovered that the error was caused by a tiny flaw in the telescope's primary mirror. A piece of tooling used to test the mirror's accuracy had been installed backwards, causing the $2^1/_2$-meter diameter mirror to be 2.34 microns flatter at its edges than it should have been. The discrepancy was microscopic, equivalent to 1/50th the width of a human hair. But it was enough.

The good news was that the Hubble telescope had been designed to be serviced in space, so it had modular instruments and components that could be pulled out and replaced. The bad news was that because the error was in the telescope's primary mirror, it affected the operation of all five of the telescope's instruments.

One of the instruments, the Wide Field/Planetary Camera, was scheduled to be replaced in a servicing mission, anyway, so a corrective optical lens could be built into the upgraded replacement camera. But

replacing all the instruments would be far too costly.

A group headed by researchers at the Space Telescope Science Institute that also included engineers from Goddard, Marshall, and the European Space Agency (ESA) began studying other possible solutions. In the meantime, scientists and engineers began looking at what *could* be done with the telescope until it was repaired.

Even the blurry images were better than anything that had been available before, which was encouraging. And scientists soon found that the telescope's performance was acceptable for bright objects. Faint objects caused the biggest problem. Some of the images also were degraded because the telescope's flexible solar arrays, which had been designed and built by the Europeans, had developed a "jitter"

Images of Supernova 1987A and its circumstellar rings from the Wide Field and Planetary Camera (image at left) and from the Space Telescope Imaging Spectrograph (STIS) (images at right). The STIS data show multiple images, each representing the emission from a distinct chemical constituent. (NASA Photo PRC97-14)

WFPC2

as the spacecraft transitioned from night to day conditions. Researchers found ways to work around the jitter, developed software to help correct the fuzzy focus on the images, and concentrated the initial work of the telescope on brighter objects in the universe. But while these adjustments were remarkably innovative and allowed some very good science data to be drawn out of the telescope, they could not completely compensate for the flaw. In order to get the promised scientific use out of the telescope and restore NASA's credibility in the eyes of the scientific community and the American public, the team needed to fix the source of the problem.

In just a few months, the Hubble team came up with a radical idea for a solution. The scientists and engineers proposed

Astronauts practice in a weightless water tank facility for the Solar Maximum repair mission. The experience gained from that 1984 mission helped make the 1993 Hubble servicing mission possible. (NASA Photo S83-42898)

replacing the least-used instrument on the Hubble with a module that would contain a corrective optics system for the remaining three instruments. The Corrective Optics Space Telescope Axial Replacement (COSTAR), as they called it, would contain 10 separate mirrors, ranging in size from a dime to a quarter, that would refocus the light reflected from the primary mirror before it entered the three "axial" instruments.[25] In order to work, these tiny mirrors would have to be accurately polished to 1/50th of a wavelength of white light.

It was a risky proposition. Even if the complicated COSTAR instrument could be built with that degree of accuracy, it would have to be installed in space, and it had to work perfectly. NASA could not afford another failure. Some NASA managers suggested limiting the effort to the less challenging task of replacing the Wide Field/Planetary Camera, which was the instrument that took all the visible light photographs. But team leaders argued that Goddard and NASA owed the scientific community a fully working telescope. The COSTAR project was approved.

With only 80 employees and more experience in large-screen television systems than space instruments, Tinsley Optical Laboratories in Richmond, California, was an unlikely candidate to make the COSTAR mirrors. But it turned out that the processes for building both products were surprisingly similar, and every employee of the small company took on an almost personal responsibility for making sure the mirrors were made correctly.

The Hubble servicing mission became the number one priority at Goddard as well. The team had a target date of June 1993 for the repair mission to take place, with a outside deadline of June 1994. Eventually, the team committed to having the mission ready to launch by 1 December 1993.

To achieve that date, a lot of work had to be done. A problem with the solar arrays had to be diagnosed, and new arrays had to be built. Meanwhile, the telescope had developed problems with its gyros, which also would have to be replaced. To make all these repairs in orbit also would require more Extra-Vehicular Activity (EVA) time on the part of the Shuttle astronauts than any mission to date, and the work would be challenging.

The Goddard-managed recovery team convinced managers at the Johnson Space Center to assign the astronauts for the repair mission a full year earlier than usual, giving them almost 2 years to prepare for the mission. Johnson also agreed to put only veteran Shuttle astronauts on the mission, so that nobody on the mission would be adjusting to space for the first time while the team tried to work on the telescope.

The astronauts shuttled back and forth between Goddard and Johnson, learning the spacecraft's systems and rehearsing the servicing effort as well as every contingency and emergency the managers could envision. They even spent a record 400 hours in Johnson's neutral-buoyancy water tank practicing the five EVA missions the repair would require.

All of this activity, of course, had to be done in the fishbowl of scrutiny following the discovery of the Hubble flaw. By the time the servicing mission was launched, no fewer than 18 external review committees were overseeing the team's efforts.

But on 1 December 1993 the team was ready, as promised, and on December 2nd the Space Shuttle Endeavour thundered off its launch pad on an 11-day mission to retrieve and fix the Hubble telescope. As the astronauts prepared to

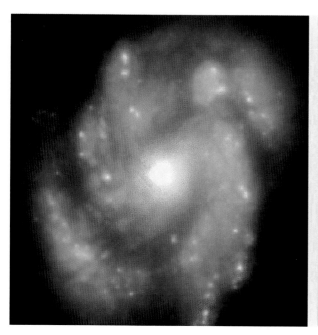 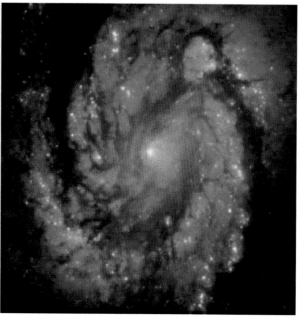

Two images of the spiral galaxy M100 from the Hubble Space Telescope. The image on the left was taken a few days before the first servicing mission. The image on the right, taken after servicing, shows a vast improvement in clarity. (NASA Photo PR94-01)

head home a week and a half later, the mission appeared to have been a success. The proof, however, would lie in the images transmitted back to Earth once the telescope was back in orbit.

Goddard scientists and engineers watching at the Space Telescope Science Institute held their breaths as they waited for the first images, knowing that the consequences of another error would be terrible. As one team manager put it, "We felt like the future of the Agency was riding on this effort. We really did." They need not have worried. A crystal-clear image of a star appeared on the main computer screen, sending cheers and applause through the room. An effort that some experts had given no more than a 50-percent chance of success had succeeded beyond everyone's wildest expectations.

In recognition of the challenge, the effort, and the accomplishment, the Hubble team was given numerous awards. The team was even awarded the 1993 Collier Trophy—recognizing the servicing mission as the greatest aeronautical achievement in the nation that year.

With the flaw repaired, the Hubble Space Telescope finally began fulfilling its long-awaited promise. The images its high-resolution camera and instruments have brought us since 1994 have been nothing short of awe-inspiring. From the towering pillars of starbirth in the Eagle Nebula to the artistically spectacular shock waves from exploding and dying stars, the Hubble has brought the distant universe to our doorstep in brilliant, breath-taking technicolor.

The Hubble provides extraordinarily clear images, illuminating far more detail about a wide variety of phenomena in the solar system, the galaxy, and the universe than scientists ever had before. In 1994, the Hubble captured the collision of a Comet Shoemaker-Levy into the planet Jupiter. It has been able to distinguish the shape of galaxies at distances so far away, and therefore so far back in time, that we can start to see a pattern in how galaxies evolve. It has let us see at least the visible and ultraviolet results from the collisions of galaxies and the death of giant stars.

In fact, the visible and ultraviolet images[26] from the Hubble have been able to give scientists a lot more detail about the life cycle of stars. It has generated clear images of dusty stellar nurseries; newborn stars with potential solar system material massing around them; bright, Sun-like stars in nearby galaxies; swollen giant stars approaching destruction; and the remnants of supernovae at different stages following these stars' explosions.

The gas clouds surrounding smaller dying stars are cool enough that they lend themselves well to analysis in the ultraviolet and visual ranges, and Hubble has produced a virtual catalog of the different shapes these "planetary" nebulae can take. Some nebulae are round, but others are shaped more like hourglasses, butterflies, goblets, rectangles, or streaming jets. Scientists are still puzzling over this phenomenon because, up until their death, all these stars have the same basic round shape.

The Hubble Space Telescope's capabilities were improved even further by another planned servicing mission in 1997. These upgrades included the addition of a Near-Infrared Camera and Multi-Object Spectrometer (NICMOS), which offers much greater detail in the cooler infrared region. Another upgrade is called the Space Telescope Imaging Spectrograph (STIS). Among other things, this instrument is useful in finding possible galactic black holes, because one of the signatures of this phenomenon is a swirling motion of the galaxy surrounding it. As the galaxy swirls, part of it is moving away from us, shifting its light lower in the spectrum, while another part moves toward us, shifting its light higher. The STIS spectrometer can create an extremely detailed cross-section image of a galaxy, measuring shifts in wavelength at 500 different points across the galaxy simultaneously. By comparison, previous spectrometers looking at these celestial bodies could sample only a dozen or so points. Scientists hope the more detailed images provided by the STIS will help identify swirling and other types of galactic movement.

Even before the STIS instrument was put on the Hubble, however, the technology developed for it was put to work here on Earth. The digital imaging technology used in the instrument has provided doctors with a new technique that facilitates non-surgical biopsies on women who may have breast cancer.

Additional servicing missions are planned for the Hubble in 2000 and 2002.

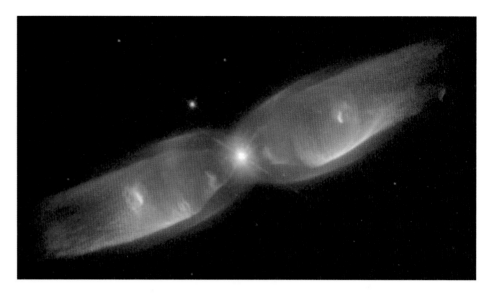

Scientists hope that these improvements will allow the telescope to extend its useful life until at least 2005. A study is currently underway for a "Next Generation Space Telescope" (NGST), which scientists hope will succeed the Hubble. If it is approved, the NGST will have much greater light collecting power than even the Hubble possesses and will be optimized to look at infrared light in the earliest galaxies of the ancient universe.

Of course, the more "invisible" wavelengths are every bit as important in piecing together the puzzle of our universe as those we can see. But the Hubble is particularly popular because we are, in the end, a visual species. The data from the Hubble's instruments have given scientists many valuable new insights about the universe. But the photographs and enhanced infrared and ultraviolet images from the telescope have reached far beyond the scientific community. They have sparked the imagination of millions of people who now gaze up at the night sky with a reawakened sense of curiosity and wonder. For without even a single word of

A Hubble image of a planetary nebulae with striking bipolar structure. (NASA Photo PR97-38)

The STIS captured this text-book case of the Z-shaped spectral signature that reveals the presence of a super massive black hole in galaxy M84. (NASA Photo PRC97-12)

An infrared image of the Egg Nebula, taken by the Near-Infrared Camera and Multi-Object Spectrometer instrument on the Hubble Space Telescope. (NASA Photo PRC97-11)

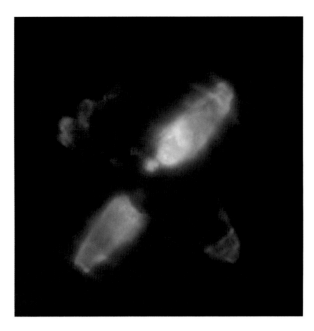

explanation, the Hubble images have made us realize how powerful, beautiful, and mysterious the universe can be.[27]

INTERNATIONAL ULTRAVIOLET EXPLORER

While the Hubble Space Telescope was still in its embryonic planning stages, another satellite project devoted exclusively to exploring the ultraviolet realm was taking shape. The ultraviolet discoveries of the OAO satellites in the 1960s had made scientists eager to explore further into this previously invisible realm of the spectrum with a telescope specifically designed for that purpose.

The satellite was called the International Ultraviolet Explorer (IUE), which was put into orbit in 1978. Although some components came from other places, the spacecraft was constructed in-house at Goddard. Having learned some difficult operating lessons from the larger, more cumbersome OAOs, the scientists decided to design the IUE to have a

geosynchronous orbit. While this would dramatically simplify ground operations for the satellite, because it would be in sight of a ground station all the time, it meant that the spacecraft had to be small and light enough to reach an orbit 23,000 miles above the Earth. It would also require very high-resolution cameras and an extremely precise pointing system, accurate to within a few arc-seconds.

Another unique aspect of the IUE was its development as an international project between NASA, ESA, and the British Science Research Council. The detectors and solar panels were supplied by the Europeans, and the telescope and spacecraft were designed and built by Goddard.

The OAO's star tracker problems also taught Goddard's engineers that a better way was needed to stabilize an astronomy satellite. So they worked with the Bendix Corporation to develop an inertial gyro system for the IUE. The gyro worked so well that the spare was used in the Hubble Space Telescope. In fact, the IUE continued to work flawlessly for 11 years with only two of its initial six gyros, and the team even managed to operate the satellite for the last 6 months of its 19-year life with only one remaining gyro.

Technology also had advanced far enough by the mid-1970s, when the IUE was being built, that it could incorporate a vastly simpler ground computer system. The interface between an experimenter's software system and the satellite's system was designed to be "transparent," so that outside astronomers could use the IUE telescope as easily as they used their own ground-based observatories, making adjustments in real time. This change meant that observers no longer had to be experts in satellite instrumentation. As a result, it opened up a whole new era in space science and generated a lot more support for satellite research in the astronomy community.

The IUE was scheduled to launch in mid-January 1978. Only a couple of weeks before that, however, a short circuit was discovered somewhere in its internal wiring system. On New Year's Eve, the satellite was sitting in many pieces on the floor of Goddard's clean room as engineers and technicians searched for the trouble spot. Even if the problem was

solved quickly, there would not be time to complete another full test on the satellite if it was going to make its launch date. But the technician in charge of the repair solemnly promised the engineers and scientists in charge that the satellite would be fixed and reassembled not only perfectly, but on time. It was, and on 26 January 1978 the IUE satellite was launched into orbit.

Observing time on the IUE was shared between the United States and European partners. Goddard controlled the satellite 16 hours a day, and the Europeans controlled it the remaining 8 hours.

The IUE was originally designed for a 5-year mission. To everyone's surprise, it

Goddard's International Ultraviolet Explorer was one of the most successful satellites in the Center's history. Designed for a 5-year mission, it was a facility used by thousands of astronomers for almost 19 years.

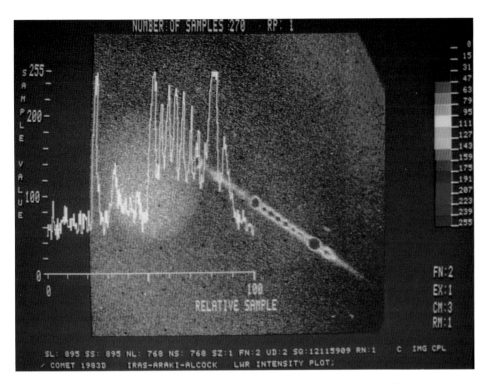

Data depicting Comet 1983D. The ultraviolet spectrum of Comet 1983D, as obtained by the International Ultraviolet Explorer.

kept returning useful data for almost 19 years, adding a tremendous amount to our understanding of our solar system, our galaxy, and the universe.

One very basic and important contribution of the IUE was that it allowed scientists to fill in observations of thousands of celestial objects in a previously unobtainable portion of the spectrum. But there were also some objects and phenomena that could be studied particularly well in ultraviolet wavelengths. The temperature of many of the gas clouds surrounding stars, in between stars, and in between galaxies, for example, means that they create a signature in the ultraviolet range. As a result, the IUE was able to teach scientists a lot about the temperature, density, and behavior of this circumstellar, interstellar, and intergalactic matter. Among other things, IUE data indicated that just outside of our galaxy was a "halo" of hot gas that scientists had not known existed.

By analyzing the gas clouds surrounding the nuclei of active galaxies, the IUE was able to help measure the size, temperature, and behavior of these high-energy objects. In addition, the satellite played a key role in observing the Supernova 1987A that occurred in the nearby Large Magellanic Cloud galaxy. Scientists were not sure, at first, which of two closely located stars in the galaxy had exploded. The IUE accurately detected which star had exploded, which was significant because Supernova 1987A was the closest supernova to occur since the invention of the telescope. Scientists knew that the star that exploded had been one they had observed before, but the two possible candidates were different types of stars. IUE's results told scientists that the exploding star was the "blue supergiant" star—a fact that surprised researchers but provided significant new information about stars and supernova explosions. IUE also continued to help study the Supernova's debris as it expanded from the initial explosion.

The satellite also confirmed that many other stars in the galaxy had chromospheres, just like our own Sun. In addition, it provided important information about how gas flows behave in binary star systems, disproving one previous theory about how matter flowed to and from companion stars.

The IUE satellite taught us many things about events in our own solar system as well. Although radio astronomers previously had found radiation belts around the planet Jupiter, IUE made the first extensive study of auroral activity on the planet.

IUE was also extremely helpful in allowing us to better understand comets. Once, scientists thought comets were little more than dirty ice balls. And the IUE did determine that Halley's comet had tremendous water reserves, spewing off up to 10 tons of water per second during its last flyby of our Sun. But the IUE also detected sulfur emissions from the IRAS-Araki-Alcock comet's nucleus, providing solid evidence that comets were much more complex than scientists had once thought. In fact, quantitative evidence of numerous elements has now been detected in comets, lending support to the idea that comets might be cosmic "Johnny Appleseeds," seeding planets in the galaxy with water and other elements necessary for life. Whether or not this is true may depend on whether comets originate inside or outside our solar system—a question that will need further study of comets to answer.

By the time the IUE was finally shut down in September 1996, it had accommodated almost 4,000 guest observers. Those scientists, in turn, had generated more than 3,500 scientific papers from IUE data and made it the most prolific satellite project in NASA's history.[28]

EXTREME ULTRAVIOLET EXPLORER

As technology progressed even further, it allowed scientists to contemplate telescopes that could observe the universe in more difficult wavelengths, such as the extreme ultraviolet range. Some scientists

believed that there would be no use in investigating this short range between ultraviolet and X-ray wavelengths, because hydrogen and helium atoms in their normal state block these emissions. Because hydrogen and helium atoms are the most plentiful elements in the universe, it might stand to reason that a satellite looking for this type of emission from distant sources might not find very much.

But some scientists argued that from a scientific standpoint, we should observe the universe in all available wavelengths, and that we would not know for sure what could be seen in the extreme ultraviolet world unless we at least made the attempt to look. NASA consequently approved another Explorer project, called the Extreme Ultraviolet Explorer (EUVE). The EUVE satellite was built in-house at Goddard, using instruments developed at the University of California, Berkeley, and launched in 1992.

While the number of extreme ultraviolet sources observable in the universe has, indeed, proven to be small, the satellite has discovered many more than most scientists expected. So far, the EUVE has identified approximately 900 stars and 11 galaxies with radiation in the extreme ultraviolet range. What that means is that there are at least portions of interstellar and intergalactic matter that are hotter or less dense or both than expected, allowing extreme ultraviolet radiation to penetrate them and reach the EUVE telescopes. The EUVE observations also have enabled us to study very hot gases around stars and galaxies, helping us in our ongoing effort to piece together an accurate puzzle of what our universe is and how it operates.[29]

THE HIGH ENERGY UNIVERSE

In the early 1960s, most scientists thought that the most exciting promise of satellite-based astronomy lay in the ultra-violet wavelengths. But by the end of the decade, scientists realized that the higher regions of the spectrum had even more potential for significant and paradigm-changing discoveries. Some of Goddard's most significant contributions to astronomy, in fact, have been in this high-energy astronomy field.

A group of scientists from the Naval Research Laboratory (NRL) began exploring X-rays coming from the Sun in 1948, using short-duration sounding rocket

flights to get above the Earth's X-ray-absorbing atmosphere. The first X-ray source from outside the solar system was discovered in 1962 by a sounding rocket research group headed by Riccardo Giacconi, from American Science and Engineering, and Bruno Rossi, from the Massachusetts Institute of Technology. The researchers thought they were going to look at solar-induced X-rays from the Moon, but they detected another object in the sky emitting X-rays in far greater quantities than the Sun. Because the source was a star in the Scorpio constellation, it was named Sco X-1. Their results, confirmed a month later by the NRL group, cracked open the door to a universe that until then had been completely hidden from view. They also sparked interest in developing follow-on satellite research projects to probe further into this "invisible" universe.

Throughout the 1960s, bizarre new sources of high-energy radiation were found. One particularly puzzling find was an X-ray source in the Crab Nebula, a gas cloud that was the remnant of a supernova explosion that occured almost a thousand years ago.

A supernova is one possible result when a star uses up the nuclear fuel at its core and "dies." The energy from nuclear reactions at the core of a star are what keeps it from collapsing under the weight of its own gravitational field. When those reactions cease, the star will collapse on itself. If it is a small- to medium-sized star, like our own Sun, it will become what is known as a "white dwarf." A white dwarf

A ROSAT X-ray image showing the remnants of Tycho's Supernova of 1572.

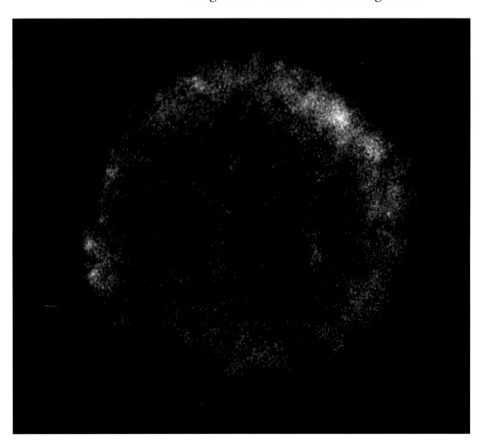

is about 1/100th the size of the original star, which means that our Sun would end up about the size of Earth. That much compression generates a tremendous amount of heat, turning the star "white-hot"—hence the object's name.

A star five times the size of our Sun will collapse with even more force, generating a tremendous "supernova" explosion that propels most of its material out into intergalactic space. This explosion is so powerful that it can generate energy as intense as the light from 10 billion Suns. The shock waves from the explosion can spread as far as 100 light-years, seeding the galaxy with heavier elements and heating the interstellar gas enough to trigger the formation of new stars. The material that is left is compressed so far that the atoms themselves are crushed. The positively-charged protons in the nuclei capture the negatively-charged electrons circling them, becoming neutrons. The resulting object is known as a "neutron" star. The collapsed matter in this kind of star is so great that a particle 1/10th of an inch in diameter would weigh as much as an aircraft carrier.

When an even larger star explodes, the gravitational weight of the remaining material can be so dense that it collapses in on itself indefinitely, creating a strange phenomenon known as a black hole. The gravitational pull of a black hole is so great that neither matter nor light can escape from it. Black holes are still not well understood, but rocket and satellite research over the last 30 years has taught

scientists a great deal more about their existence and behavior.

Astronomers actually had observed white dwarfs as far back as 1862, and had come up for an explanation for the objects by 1933. But until the late 1960s, neutron stars and black holes existed in theory only. The first real evidence of a neutron star was finally found in the Crab Nebula, which had perplexed astronomers ever since they had detected X-ray emissions coming from the cloud in 1962. The X-rays were puzzling because the Crab Nebula was the remnant of a supernova that occurred in 1054 A.D. High-energy emissions from an explosion that long ago should have dissipated by now. So the continuing presence of X-ray emissions was a mystery.

The mystery was solved in 1968 when radio astronomers discovered a very strong, regular, and rapid pulsing signal coming from deep within the Nebula. At first, the odd signals were nicknamed "LGMs," because some people thought they might be "little green men" signaling us from a distant galaxy. But scientists soon realized that the pulsing signals were from a new class of object that was apparently rotating at a rate that would tear most objects apart—30 times a second in the case of the Crab Nebula. In order for something to hold together at that rate, it would have to have a staggeringly high density level. This was the clue that led scientists to the discovery of neutron stars.

Scientists deduced that, in the process of being compressed from a large star into an ultra-dense remnant core in a supernova

This X-ray image shows the Crab Nebula with its intense spinning neutron star, or pulsar, at its core. The white area indicates the position of the pulsar, which emits a high level of X-ray radiation. The yellow area marks the milder X-ray signature across the rest of the nebula.

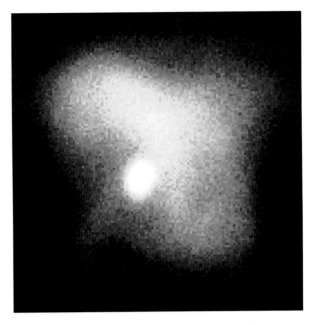

explosion, the normal rotation of the star must be accelerated greatly—in some cases as much as 100 million times. The magnetic field of the star also must be amplified by the compression, creating a stream of strong radio waves that emanated from each pole. Because the star was rotating at such high speed, these signals appeared to us as pulses, leading astronomers to name these objects "pulsars."

The discovery of the pulsar-type of neutron star explained the mysterious high-energy emissions from the Crab Nebula and gave scientists another hint about the complexities and amazing phenomena that lay undiscovered in the "invisible" realm of the high-energy universe. It also made astronomers even more interested in exploring this realm from the unencumbered perspective of space.[30]

UHURU

The first three satellite projects dedicated to high-energy astronomy were Explorers developed and managed by

Goddard. Explorer 42 was the first of the Small Astronomy Satellite (SAS) series, as the three were called. It was launched by a joint team from NASA and the University of Rome, Italy, on 12 December 1970, from a platform off the coast of Kenya. Since the satellite was also launched on Kenya's day of independence, it was named "Uhuru," which is the Swahili word for "freedom."

The Uhuru satellite provided the first detailed and accurate view of the X-ray sky, cataloging 161 X-ray sources with luminosities as great as 1,000 times the strength of our Sun. That catalog was a significant contribution to the astronomical community. In fact, it was cited more than any other scientific paper in the year it was published.[31]

The Uhuru satellite also discovered that many, if not all, X-ray stars were part of binary systems in which a very strong, dense collapsed star was actually pulling matter off of a nearby larger star, producing X-ray emissions in the process. Some of these collapsed stars were neutron stars, but Uhuru made an even more significant breakthrough by studying a particularly strong binary X-ray system called Cygnus X-1. In looking at the satellite data, scientists realized that they had found what would prove to be the first tangible evidence of a black hole. In a black hole, matter is pulled off a companion star and pulled into the hole's immense gravity field. As the matter swirls down into the hole it is compressed, heating it to temperatures of tens of millions or even a billion degrees, creating flashes of X-ray and gamma ray energy before it finally disappears into the black hole.[32]

OTHER X-RAY SATELLITES

Several satellites have pursued X-ray astronomy since Uhuru. In 1975, Goddard launched SAS-3, which looked more closely at some of the X-ray sources mapped by the Uhuru satellite. That work was followed in 1977 by the first of three High Energy Astronomy Observatory (HEAO)

satellites. The HEAO projects were managed by the Marshall Space Flight Center, but Goddard provided the project scientist on the first two HEAO satellites, which focused on X-ray astronomy.

HEAO A, like Uhuru, was a scanning mission that mapped the sky in numerous X-ray frequencies. The second observatory, HEAO B, carried the largest X-ray telescope ever built. Two X-ray telescopes had flown successfully aboard Skylab,

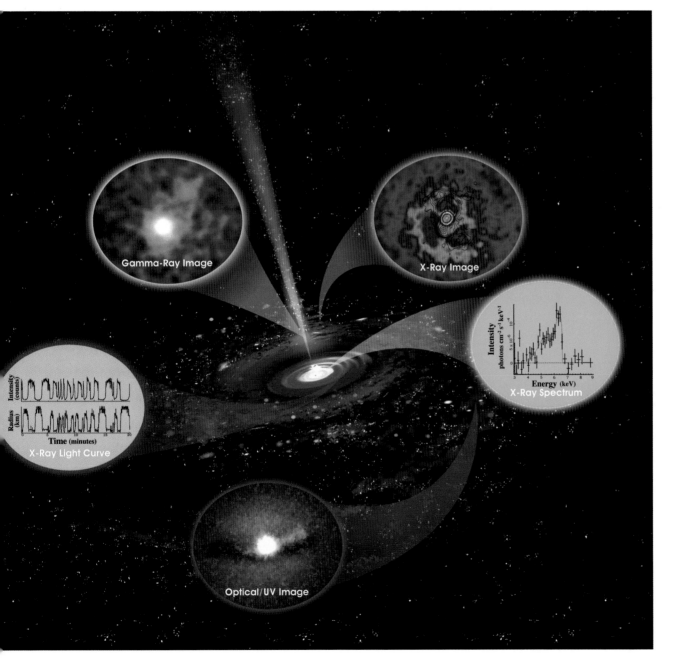

One of the advantages of exploring the universe in numerous regions of the electromagnetic spectrum is that different wavelengths can tell scientists different things about the same object. This image shows a single black hole as it appears in optical/UV, X-ray, and gamma ray wavelengths of the spectrum.

giving scientists the confidence that a focusing X-ray telescope could work on a satellite like HEAO. Since HEAO B's November 1978 launch date was the centennial of physicist Albert Einstein's birth, the satellite was named the "Einstein Observatory." This observatory became an extremely successful project. One of the secondary objectives of project managers was to bring X-ray astronomy into the mainstream of the astronomical community, so the Einstein Observatory was designed to incorporate guest observers. Eventually over 400 guest astronomers used the satellite's telescope.[33]

The results of these satellites have changed our entire view of the cosmos. The HEAO satellites indicated to scientists that all stars are X-ray sources at some level. In addition, because supernovae, neutron stars, and even the matter surrounding black holes emit most of their energy in the X-ray region, these satellites gave astronomers the opportunity to study these incredibly powerful events and objects in the universe for extended periods of time.

X-ray satellites also have found important clues to the structure of both our own Milky Way galaxy and other galaxies in the universe. Before the Einstein Observatory was launched, only three other normal galaxies outside our own had been detected in the X-ray region of the spectrum. By the end of the HEAO project, well over 100 galaxies that gave off X-ray radiation had been identified.

The satellites also found evidence that explosive activity was present in almost all galaxy nuclei, including our own. Some galaxies are more energetic than others, however. Some of the most energetic of these are called "quasars," or "quasi-stellar objects," because they are so distant that they initially appeared to be single stars. These quasars can be detected as far away as 10 billion light-years and are so powerful that one the size of our solar system would put out more energy than 10 trillion of our Suns. The source of this incredible energy is still something of a mystery, but scientists are beginning to find evidence that indicates these galaxies may have tremendous black holes at their centers.

In fact, it is possible that all galaxies begin life as quasars. Early star clusters spiraling toward the center may form a giant star that eventually collapses and forms a black hole. After the black hole at its core devours all the star material near it, the galaxy may settle down, becoming a "normal" galaxy like our own. These quasar galaxies may provide clues to the formation of galaxies in the early universe, because the energy we detect from them originated so far back in time.[34]

Investigations with X-ray satellites also have given us a better understanding of how galaxies interact with one another. Many of the universe's galaxies, it turns out, are clumped together in clusters. Especially in dense clusters, the galaxies can collide with each other. The friction from these collisions may slow a galaxy down, causing it to spiral in toward the center of the cluster where its stars may be torn apart by a larger galaxy there that "feeds" on inward-spiraling galaxies. Over time, this would result in galaxy clusters with a giant galaxy at the center surrounded by much dimmer galaxies. This theory was given a boost when HEAO A found evidence of just this type of galaxy cluster.

This process is occurring in our own galaxy as well. X-ray satellites have shown us that the Milky Way has an active galactic nucleus sending out bright X-ray signals that may be from a black hole. Our galaxy also has experienced collisions with other, smaller galaxies. Scientists recently discovered a small galaxy that had collided with ours in the Sagittarius constellation, for example. The odd thing about this galaxy was that even though scientists estimated it had orbited around that location about 10 times, it was still intact. For a small galaxy not to be ripped apart by the gravitational forces of a larger galaxy with which it collides, it must contain very dense material. It may be that this small galaxy contains a large amount of "dark matter"—one of the great remaining mysteries of the universe.

Dark matter, which may make up as much as 90 percent of the matter in the universe, cannot be observed. But something beyond the matter we can see must exist in space, or even our own spiraling galaxy cluster should fly apart. Dark matter also may provide the answer to whether our universe will continue to expand or will eventually start collapsing back in on itself. Based on the observable matter we know, there is not enough density in our universe for it to stop expanding.

But if there is enough dark matter, with enough mass, the universe actually may have enough density to stop expanding at some point in the distant future.[35]

RECENT X-RAY SATELLITES

Scientists at Goddard and elsewhere are continuing to work together to learn more about how stars and galaxies evolve and behave. Goddard has provided part of the scientific payload on two Japanese satellites designed to further explore the X-ray region of the spectrum. And in 1996, Goddard launched the Rossi X-Ray Timing Explorer (RXTE) satellite to take a more precise look at collapsed stars and massive black holes in quasars and galaxies. The RXTE satellite is the first U.S-sponsored X-ray mission since HEAO B, and it was designed as an observatory satellite, in that 100 percent of its observation time is open to guest observers.

The RXTE set out to find answers to some of the many remaining questions about the X-ray universe, such as the cause of a mysterious X-ray background radiation, similar to the infrared and microwave background radiation explored by the COBE satellite. And although previous missions have identified active galactic nuclei and neutron stars, scientists still are trying to understand the dynamics of these objects.

In the process of trying to better understand these known objects, the RXTE satellite has discovered some even more amazing phenomena. It found a young pulsar spinning twice as fast as any pulsar ever discovered—a remnant of a supernova

4,000 years ago in a nearby galaxy called the Large Magellanic Cloud. This new pulsar is turning at 60 times per second, or twice the rate of the Crab Nebula pulsar, which had been the most energetic pulsar found up until the RXTE's discovery. Scientists estimate that this new pulsar may have been turning as rapidly as 150 times per second when it was created. The magnetic field of the new pulsar, on the other hand, is even weaker than that of the Crab Nebula, leading scientists to wonder if neutron stars might progress through a predictable evolutionary process. When they are created, pulsars appear to rotate at very high speeds and have relatively weak magnetic fields. Over time they slow down, and their magnetic fields appear to increase. Indeed, the magnetic fields of these stars may be the reason they slow down over time.

In exploring this phenomenon, the RXTE satellite also uncovered a neutron star with what appears to be the most intense magnetic field ever found in the universe. This discovery may confirm the existence of a special class of neutron stars called "magnetars," with magnetic fields estimated to be 1,000 trillion times the strength of the Earth's magnetic field. The neutron star associated with this magnetic field is spinning only once every 7.5 seconds, in contrast to faster-rotating neutron stars with weaker magnetic fields. A neutron star born with that great a magnetic field might slow down so quickly that it would be undetectable at the X-ray and radio wave frequencies where most neutron stars are

found. So this discovery might account for the large number of supernovae remnants in the galaxy that do not appear to have neutron stars at their centers. It may also help us understand the rate at which stars die and seed the galaxy with the heavier elements necessary for life as we know it.

There is still much we do not understand, however. So the exploration continues. The Advanced X-Ray Astrophysics Facility (AXAF), a large X-ray telescope observatory with high-resolution instruments at least 100 times more sensitive than those on the first HEAO X-ray telescope, is currently scheduled for launch in 1999. AXAF was originally designed as one of four "great observatories" to explore the universe in all parts of the electromagnetic spectrum. The other three are the planned Space Infrared Telescope Facility (SIRTF), the Hubble Space Telescope, and the Compton Gamma Ray Observatory (GRO). AXAF and SIRTF have been downsized considerably from their original designs, but both should still bring back important clues that will help us better understand our galaxy and our universe.[36]

GAMMA RAY SATELLITES

Some of the most perplexing and exotic phenomena in the universe are those that emit radiation at the highest frequencies of the electromagnetic spectrum. Gamma rays, which are produced by reactions within an atom's nucleus, are produced deep within the core of stars, but they rarely reach the surface. In most cases, we only have found observable gamma rays associated with phenomena such as in the birth or death of a star, or around black holes. But phenomena that create emissions at these extraordinarily high frequencies are very unusual in the universe. Out of 500 pulsars detected in the radio and X-ray regions of the spectrum since 1968, for example, only 6 emit gamma rays.[37]

Yet gamma rays are evidence of some of the most powerful energy events known to scientists, so they are as fascinating as they are mystifying. As we have improved our satellites and instruments, we have begun to understand a little more about what creates these rare, high-energy

sources in the universe. But it is still a strange, perplexing, and exciting frontier.

The gamma ray universe has been explored by scientists with Goddard satellites as far back as 1961, when a gamma ray telescope was put into orbit aboard the Explorer 11 satellite. Explorer 11 detected the first gamma ray sources outside our own solar system and helped rule out one of the major competing theories for the evolution of the universe. According to the "steady-state" theory of the universe, the universe was neither expanding nor contracting, but stretched infinitely into space and time. Celestial bodies moving away from us would be replaced by the forma-

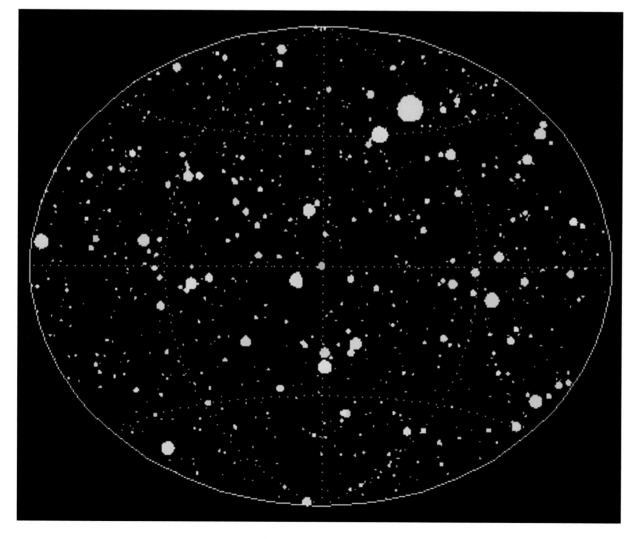

An all-sky image from Goddard's Compton Gamma Ray Observatory mapping the location and intensity of over 800 gamma ray bursts. The cause of these incredibly high-energy events is still a puzzling mystery to scientists.

tion of new matter, which would create new stars and galaxies. Explorer 11, however, found that the intensity of gamma rays in the universe was a thousand times weaker than what should have existed if the steady-state theory were true.[38]

Explorer 11 was an important first step into this high-energy field, even though it located only one or two gamma ray sources during its time in orbit. The next step was taken in 1972, when Goddard launched Explorer 48, which was the second spacecraft in the Small Astronomy Satellite (SAS) series. SAS 2 carried a gamma ray telescope and detected numerous additional gamma ray sources. Even more importantly, it laid the groundwork for a larger gamma ray observatory, HEAO 3. This third High Energy Astronomical Observatory, launched in 1979, conducted the first extensive sky survey of gamma ray sources.

HEAO 3 also provided some important clues about what exists at the center of our galaxy. In addition to a continuous spectrum of gamma rays coming out of our galaxy's nucleus, HEAO 3 detected a spike of gamma ray energy at one particular and precise wavelength. An energy surge at that precise frequency happens when electrons meet anti-electrons, or positrons, and annihilate each other. The spike of energy detected by HEAO 3 told scientists that there must be a strong source of positrons, or "anti-matter" at that location, and the most likely source of these extremely high-energy particles is a black hole. In other words, these results told scientists

An image showing the gamma ray emissions detectable from our own Moon with Goddard's EGRET on board the Compton Gamma Ray Observatory. (NASA Photo PAO_E97_01.JPG)

that there might well be a black hole at the center of our galaxy.[39]

HEAO 3 and SAS 2 were both relatively small satellites with specialized instruments. The next step, then, was to explore the high energy universe across a broad range of the gamma ray portion of the spectrum. This was the mission of Goddard's Compton Gamma Ray Observatory (CGRO), a 17-ton satellite that was launched from the Space Shuttle Atlantis in April 1991. The Compton Observatory was named in honor of Dr. Arthur Holly Compton, an astrophysicist whose Nobel prize-winning discoveries about high-energy processes are central to the techniques used by the observatory's instruments.

The Compton Observatory's instruments were 10 times more sensitive than those on HEAO 3, allowing it to make numerous important contributions to our understanding of gamma ray sources in the universe. One of the most perplexing sources of gamma rays, for example, is something called a "gamma ray burst." These short-lived bursts of high-energy

radiation were first detected by Air Force satellites in the 1960s but have remained a mystery ever since. In a few seconds, one of these bursts can put out more gamma ray energy than our Sun could produce in 1,000 years.

Since its launch, the Compton Observatory has detected more than a thousand of these bursts. It also discovered that the bursts are not limited to our galaxy, but are spread evenly across the sky. This has tremendous significance, because it means the bursts are coming from very far distances. For something to appear that energetic after traveling that far a distance, its initial energy has to be staggeringly high. Scientists now believe that gamma ray bursts may originate from locations as far away as 12 billion light-years, which means they date back almost as far as the universe itself. Perhaps the most mystifying thing about gamma ray bursts, however, is that no known phenomenon could explain a burst of energy that high.

Several theories have been proposed about the source of gamma ray bursts, including the collision of two neutron stars, or the collapse of a massive giant star into black hole. This second theory was given additional weight recently by a group of researchers from the University of Cambridge in the United Kingdom. Massive stars have very short life spans, so they die pretty much where and when they are born. If gamma ray bursts are linked to the death of these stars, they should correlate with the location and near-time of these stars' birth.

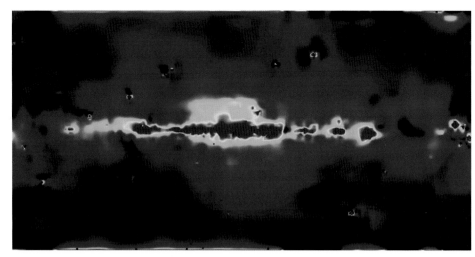

A map of gamma ray emission from the central region of the Milky Way, obtained by the Compton Gamma Ray Observatory.

Gamma ray sources are typically very hard to pinpoint, but an Italian-Dutch satellite called BeppoSAX, launched in 1996, gave scientists the ability to nail down the location of these bursts with much more accuracy. The Cambridge scientists plotted the location of three gamma ray bursts detected so far and found that they were located in star-forming regions. The results are far from conclusive, but this evidence certainly gives some additional credence to the theory that gamma ray bursts may be caused by massive stars falling into black holes. In any event, the Cambridge research indicated that gamma ray bursts are extremely rare events, occurring in any galaxy perhaps as seldom as once every 40 million years.[40]

The gamma ray burst picture got even more complicated when scientists realized that a gamma ray burst detected by the Compton Observatory on 14 December 1997 had put out more energy in a few seconds than any event since the beginning of the universe. For a few seconds, the energy of the burst was as bright as the rest of the universe combined and, in a core region about 100 miles across, it would have created conditions similar to those that existed 1 millisecond after the Big Bang. Scientists estimate that the burst originated about 12 billion light-years from Earth and released hundreds of times more energy than a supernova explosion. Scientists are baffled as to the possible source for such a tremendous burst. All they know is that something obviously exists in the universe that has the ability to produce more energy than any current theory can explain. But this kind of event and mystery is what propels science forward.

Goddard's Compton Observatory also discovered traces of Cobalt 57 that scientists believe was produced by the 1987A Supernova explosion in the Large Magellanic Cloud. This evidence helped confirm that heavier elements in the universe are, indeed, formed in the process of supernovae explosions. In addition, the CGRO satellite has uncovered new objects and phenomena, such as gamma-ray quasars (as opposed to quasars that emit their energy in X-ray wavelengths), identifying a new class of active galactic nuclei.[41]

CONCLUSION

Astronomers have been exploring the heavens for centuries. But the ability to go into the heavens themselves has taken us into a whole new dimension. In the past 40 years, rocket and satellite technology has changed dreams and theory into science and knowledge. Because of the efforts of the people at Goddard and its many industry, university, NASA, and international partners, we now can see into the

Sun to explore how it works and how it affects life here on Earth. We can map the fields and forces surrounding our own planet and probe the atmospheres of planets further out in our solar system. We have uncovered stars, galaxies, and mysterious high-energy phenomena that would have boggled the minds of astronomers even 100 years ago.

In the process, we have found evidence to support some important scientific theories and disprove others. We have peered back to the dawn of time and discovered worlds and events that have forced us to change many of our ideas about the galaxy and universe in which we live. In fact, we have sometimes ended up almost falling over ourselves trying to keep up with new discoveries and information that keep changing the picture of our universe, just as we thought we understood what was going on.

The truth is, the universe is an astoundingly complex and almost infinitely large territory that we may never fully understand. Columbus, Magellan, and Lewis and Clark may have faced the same element of the unknown as Goddard's space scientists, but a continent or an ocean is a much more limited area than a galaxy or universe. The amazing thing is the amount of headway we have actually made into this mysterious and unforgiving territory in only 40 short years.

In some cases, Goddard's efforts have helped scientists find answers about objects or phenomena, such as the existence and boundaries of Earth's magnetosphere or

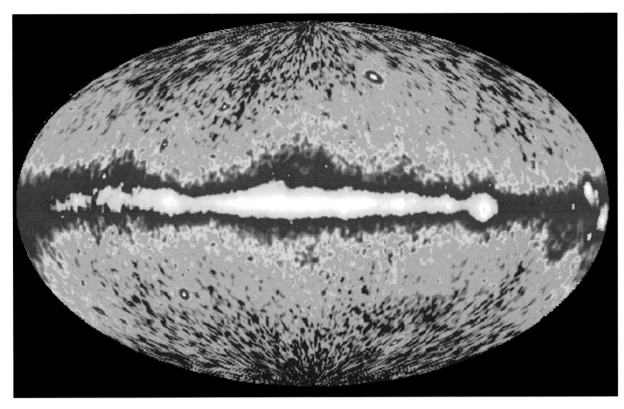

A map of the whole sky in gamma rays. The prominent white band represents emission from the disc of the Milky Way. Bright spots above and below are high-energy sources, such as quasars.

the origins of pulsars. In other areas, the Center's work has uncovered pieces of information that we only know must fit into the puzzle somewhere—we just do not know yet how or where, or even how significant these pieces may turn out to be.

But as Goddard scientists point out, astronomer Tycho Brahe made observations in the late 16th century about the orbits of the planets without being able to make any bigger conclusions about them. A few years later, however, mathematician Johannes Kepler used that information to come up with his laws of planetary motion. Those laws later provided Issac Newton with the basis for his universal law of gravity, which transformed science and made modern cosmology possible. In other words, progress and learning are ongoing, incremental processes that require many building blocks to be in place before a building takes shape. And while we are putting together the pieces, we cannot always see ahead to envision what the building will look like.

Even when a building appears or an "ah-ha" moment occurs, it is still not the end of the cycle. We continue to build, because we continue to be curious, and there is always something new to learn. This is one of the most wonderful things about life as we know it. The universe we live in is so large and so intricate that as long as our curiosity and spirit of adventure remain alive, there will always be new territory to explore and new wonders to uncover. One of the marvels of space, we have discovered, is that it is not simply a new or final frontier. It is an endless frontier, with the ability to inspire both our minds and our souls with the power of its elements, the depth of its mysteries, and the beauty of its music.

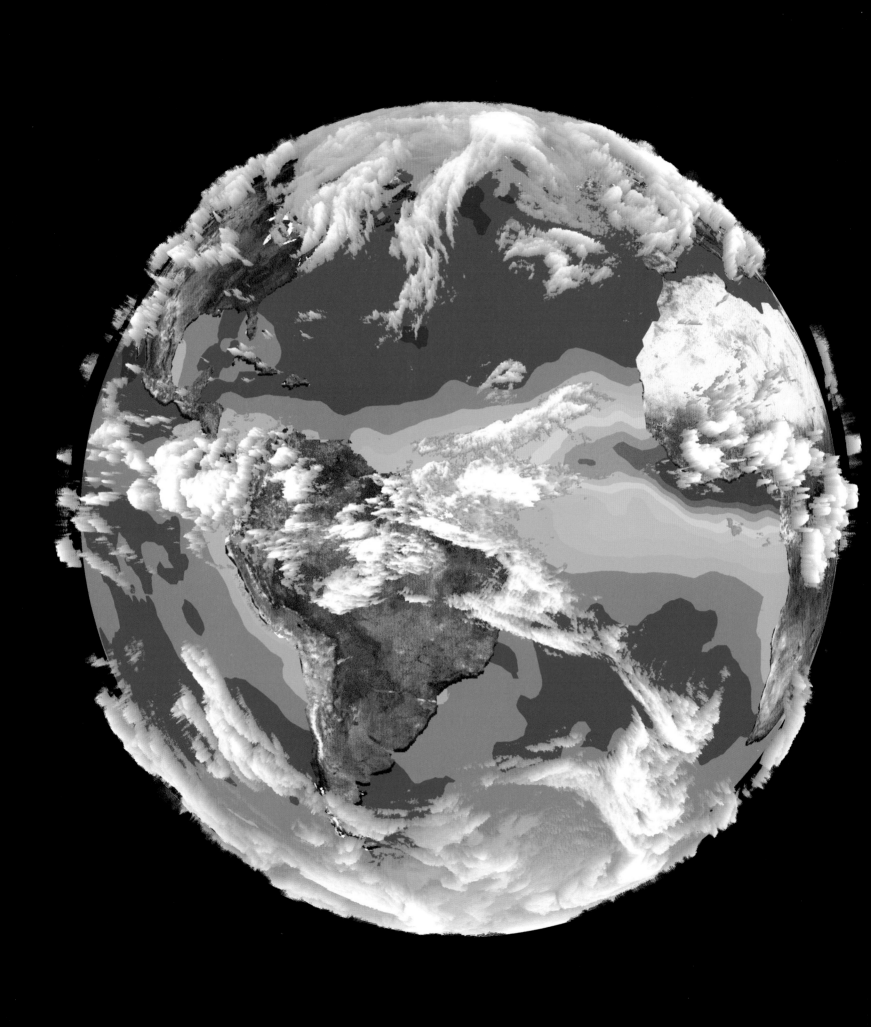

CHAPTER 5:
Exploring the Earth

When scientists first began using rockets for research, their eyes were focused upward, on the mysteries that lay beyond our atmosphere and our planet. But they soon realized that this new technology also could give them a unique vantage point from which to look back at Earth.

Scientists working with V-2 and early sounding rockets for the Naval Research Laboratory (NRL) made the first steps in this direction almost 10 years before Goddard was formed. The scientists put aircraft gun cameras on several rockets in an attempt to determine which way the rockets were pointing. When the film from one of these rockets was developed, it had recorded images of a huge tropical storm over Brownsville, Texas. Because the rocket

This image of Earth was created using data from four different satellites. It shows fires burning on land areas (red dots) and a large aerosol cloud over the Atlantic ocean formed by the burning biomass in Africa. It also indicates dust and cloud cover around the globe. Satellite data and images such as this one are beginning to give us a more comprehensive view of the Earth's interrelated systems and climate.

Otto Berg's montage photo, taken from a gun camera on board an early research rocket, was perhaps the first weather photo ever taken from space. Note the storm clouds in the upper portion of the image.

was spinning, the image was not a neat, complete picture. Otto Berg, the scientist who had modified the camera to take the photo, took the separate images home and pasted them together on a flat board. He then took the collage to *Life* magazine, which published what was arguably one of the earliest weather photos ever taken from space.[1]

Commercial industry and the military recognized the unique possibilities that space also offered for communication several years before NASA was organized. Project RAND[2] had published various reports in the early 1950s outlining the potential benefits of satellite-based communication relays, and by 1959 both AT&T and Hughes had conducted internal company studies on the commercial viability of communication satellites.[3]

These rudimentary seeds, already sown by the time Goddard opened its doors, grew into an amazing variety of communication, weather, and other remote-sensing satellite projects at the Center that have revolutionized many aspects of our lives. They have taught us

significant and surprising things about the planet we inhabit. Our awareness of large-scale crop and forest conditions, ozone depletion, greenhouse warming, and El Niño weather patterns has increased dramatically because of our ability to look back on Earth from space. Satellites have allowed us to measure the shape of the Earth more accurately, track the movement of tectonic plates, and analyze portions of the atmosphere and areas of the world that are hard to reach from the ground.

In addition, the "big picture" perspective that satellites offer has allowed scientists to begin investigating the dynamics between different individual processes and the development and behavior of global patterns and systems. Ironically, we had to develop the ability to leave our planet before we could begin to understand it fully.

GEODESY

From the very first days of the space program, scientists realized that satellites could offer an important side-benefit to researchers interested in mapping the gravity field and shape of the Earth, and Goddard played an important role in this effort. The field of geodesy, or the study of the Earth's gravitational field and its relationship to the solid structure of the planet, dates back to the third century B.C., when the Greek astronomer Eratosthenes combined astronomical observation with land measurement to try to prove that the Earth was round. Later astronomers and scientists used other methods of triangulation to estimate the exact size of the Earth.

Astronomers also used the Moon, or stars with established locations, to try to map the shape of the Earth and exact distances between points more precisely. But satellites offered a new twist to this methodology.

From the beginning, Goddard's endeavor to track and characterize the orbit of the first satellites was innately scientific, because the Earth's shape and gravity field affected the orbit of satellites. From that orbital data, scientists could infer information about the Earth's gravity field, which is affected by the distribution of its mass. They discovered that the Earth is not perfectly round, and its mass is not perfectly distributed. In some places, the land or ocean topography results in either more or less dense mass accumulation. The centrifugal force of the Earth's rotation combines with gravity and these mass concentrations to create bulges and depressions in the planet. In fact, although we think of the Earth as round, Goddard's research showed us that it is really slightly pear-shaped.

Successive Goddard satellites enabled scientists to gather much more precise information about the Earth's shape as well as exact positions of points on the planet. In fact, within 10 years, scientists had learned as much again about global positioning, the size and shape of the Earth, and its gravity field as their predecessors had learned in the previous 200 years.

Laser reflectors on Goddard satellites launched in 1965, 1968, and 1976, for example, allowed scientists to make much more precise measurements between points, which enabled them to determine the exact location or movement of objects. The laser reflectors developed for Goddard's Laser GEOdynamics (LAGEOS) satellite, launched in 1976, could determine movement or position within a few centimeters, which allowed scientists to track and analyze tectonic plate movement and continental drift. Among other things, the satellite data told scientists that the continents seem to be inherently rigid bodies, even if they contain divisive bodies of water such as the Mississippi River, and that continental plate movement appears to occur at a constant rate over time. Plate movement information provided by satellites has helped geologists track the dynamics that lead up to earthquakes, which is an important step in predicting these potentially catastrophic events.

The satellite positioning technique used for this plate tectonic research was the precursor to the Global Positioning System (GPS) technology that now uses a

A technician working on reflectors for one of Goddard's laser geodynamic satellites.

constellation of satellites to provide precise three-dimensional navigation for aircraft and other vehicles. Although a viable commercial market is developing for GPS technology today, the greatest commercial application of space has remained the field of communication satellites.[4]

COMMUNICATION SATELLITES

Despite all the talk about the commercial possibilities of space, the only area that has proven substantially profitable since 1959 is communication satellites, and Goddard played an important role in developing the early versions of these spacecraft. The industry managers who were conducting research studies and contemplating investment in this field in 1959 could not have predicted the staggering explosion of demand for communications that has accompanied the so-called "Information Age." But they saw how dramatically demand for telephone service had increased since World War II, and they recognized potential in other communications technology markets, such as better or broader transmission for television and radio signals. As a result, several companies were willing to invest their own money, if necessary, to develop communication satellites.

The Department of Defense (DOD) actually had been working on communication satellite technology for a number of years, and it wanted to keep control of what it considered a critical technology. So when NASA was organized, responsibility for communication satellite technology development was split between the new

The world's first communication satellite was an inflatable mylar sphere called "Echo" that simply reflected transmissions back to Earth. The spacecraft was readily visible to the eye. (NASA Photo G-63-3202)

space agency and the DOD. The DOD would continue responsibility for "active" communication satellites, which added power to incoming signals and actively transmitted the signals back to ground stations. NASA's role initially was limited to "passive" communication satellites, which relied on simply reflecting signals off the satellite to send them back to Earth.[5]

ECHO

NASA's first communication satellite, consequently, was a passive spacecraft called "Echo." It was based on a balloon design by an engineer at NASA's Langley Research Center and developed by Langley, Goddard, JPL, and AT&T. Echo was, in essence, a giant mylar balloon, 100 feet in diameter, that could "bounce" a radio signal back down to another ground station a long distance away from the first one.

Echo I, the world's first communication satellite, was put into orbit successfully on 12 August 1960. Soon after launch, it reflected a pre-taped message from President Dwight Eisenhower across

the country and other radio messages to Europe, demonstrating the potential of global radio communications via satellite. It also generated a lot of public interest, because the sphere was so large that it could be seen from the ground with the naked eye as it passed by overhead.

Echo I had some problems, however. The sphere seemed to buckle somewhat, hampering its signal-reflecting ability. So in 1964, a larger and stronger passive satellite, Echo II, was put into orbit. Echo II was made of a material 20 times more resistant to buckling than Echo I and was almost 40 feet wider in diameter.

Echo II also experienced some difficulties with buckling. But the main reason the Echo satellites were not pursued further was not because of these problems. It was simply that the concept was eclipsed by much better technology—active communication satellites.[6]

SYNCOM, TELSTAR, AND RELAY

By 1960, Hughes, RCA, and AT&T were all advocating the development of different types of active communication satellites. Hughes felt strongly that the best system would be based on geosynchronous satellites. Geosynchronous satellites are in very high orbits—22,300 miles above the ground. This high orbit allows their orbital speed to match the rotation speed of the Earth, which means they can remain essentially stable over one spot, providing a broad range of coverage 24 hours a day. Three of these satellites, for example, can provide cover-

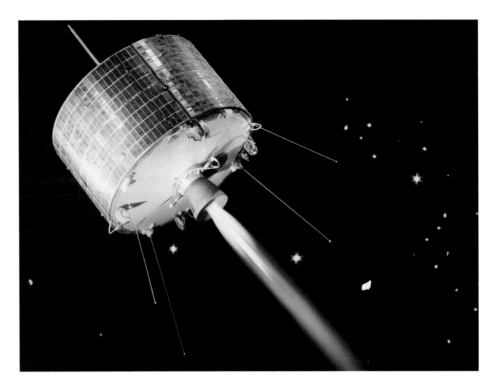

age of the entire world, with the exception of the poles.

The disadvantage of using geosynchronous satellites for communications is that sending a signal up 22,300 miles and back causes a time-delay of approximately a quarter second in the signal. Arguing that this delay would be too annoying for telephone subscribers, both RCA and AT&T supported a bigger constellation of satellites in medium-Earth orbit, only a few hundred miles above the Earth.[7]

DOD had been working on its own geosynchronous communication satellite, but the project was running into significant development problems and delays. NASA had been given permission by 1960 to pursue active communication satellite technology as well as passive systems, so DOD approached NASA about giving Hughes a sole-source contract to develop an experimental geosynchronous satellite. The result was Syncom, a geosynchronous

The Syncom satellite proved that high-altitude, geosynchronous spacecraft could still be used effectively for communications. (NASA Photo G-63-3266)

satellite design built by Hughes under contract to Goddard.

Hughes already had begun investing its own money and effort in the technology, so Syncom I was ready for Goddard to launch in February 1963—only 17 months after the contract was awarded. Syncom I stopped sending signals a few seconds before it was inserted into its final orbit, but Syncom II was launched successfully 5 months later, demonstrating the viability of the system. The third Syncom satellite, launched in August 1964, transmitted live television coverage of the Olympic Games in Tokyo, Japan, to stations in North America and Europe.

Although the military favored the geosynchronous concept, it was not the only technology being developed. In 1961, Goddard began working with RCA on the "Relay" satellite, which was launched on 13 December 1962. Relay was designed to demonstrate the feasibility of medium-orbit, wide-band communications satellite technology and to help develop the ground

The Relay satellite, which Goddard helped RCA build and launch, was a medium-altitude orbit satellite design. (NASA Photo G-63-3970)

station operations necessary for such a system. It was a very successful project, transmitting even color television signals across wide distances.

AT&T, meanwhile, had run into political problems with NASA and government officials who were concerned that the big telecommunications conglomerate would end up monopolizing this potentially powerful technology. But when NASA chose to fund RCA's Relay satellite instead of AT&T's design, AT&T decided to use its own money to develop a medium-orbit communications satellite, which it called Telstar. NASA would launch the satellite, but AT&T would reimburse NASA for the costs involved. Telstar 1 was launched on 10 July 1962, and a second Telstar satellite followed less than a year later. Both satellites were very successful, and Telstar 2 demonstrated that it could even transmit both color and black and white television signals between the United States and Europe.

In some senses, Relay and Telstar were competitors. But RCA and AT&T, who were both working with managers at Goddard, reportedly cooperated very well with each other. Each effort was seen as advancing the technology necessary for this new satellite industry to become viable, and both companies envisioned the potential long-term profit that industry could offer.

By 1962, it was clear that satellite communications technology worked and would be extremely profitable. Fearful of the powerful monopoly satellites could offer a single company, Congress passed the Satellite Communications Act, setting up a

consortium of existing communications car-
riers to run the satellite communications
industry. Individual companies could bid to
sell satellites to the consortium, but no single company would own the system. NASA
would launch the satellites for Comsat, as
the consortium was called, but Comsat
would run the operations.

In 1964, the Comsat consortium was
expanded further with the formation of the
International Telecommunications Satellite
Organization, commonly known as
"Intelsat," to establish a framework for
international use of communication satellites. These organizations had the responsibility for choosing the type of satellite technology the system would use. The work of
RCA, AT&T, and Hughes proved that
either medium-altitude or geosynchronous
satellites could work. But in 1965, the consortium finally decided to base the international system on geosynchronous satellites
similar to the Syncom design.[8]

Applications Technology Satellites

Following its role in developing the
prototype satellites, Goddard stepped back
from operational communication satellites
and focused on developing advanced technology for future systems. Between 1966
and 1974, Goddard launched six
Applications Technology Satellites (ATSs)
to research advanced technology for communications and meteorological spacecraft.
The ATS spacecraft were put into geosynchronous orbits where they investigated
microwave and millimeter wavelengths for

Goddard's sixth Applications Technology Satellite undergoes final prelaunch testing at Cape Canaveral, Florida. (NASA Photo G-74-7446)

communication transmissions, methods for
aircraft and marine navigation and communications, and various control technolo-
gies to improve geosynchronous satellites.

Four of the spacecraft were highly successful and provided valuable data for
improving future communication satellites.
The sixth ATS spacecraft, launched on
30 May 1974, even experimented with
transmitting health and education television
to small, low-cost ground stations in remote
areas. It also tested a geosynchronous satellite's ability to provide tracking and data
transmission services for other satellites.
Goddard's research in this area, and the
expertise the Center developed in the process, made it possible for NASA to develop
the Tracking and Data Relay Satellite
System (TDRSS) the agency still uses today.[9]

After ATS-6, NASA transferred
responsibility for future communication

satellite research to the Lewis Research Center. Goddard, however, maintained responsibility for developing and operating the TDRSS.[10]

METEOROLOGICAL SATELLITES

Statistically, the United States has the world's most violent weather. In a typical year, the U.S. will endure some 10,000 violent thunderstorms, 5,000 floods, 1,000 tornadoes, and several hurricanes.[11] Improving weather prediction, therefore, has been a high priority of meteorologists for a very long time.

The early sounding rocket flights first indicated some of the possibilities space flight might offer in terms of understanding and forecasting the weather, and they prompted the military to pursue development of a meteorological satellite. The Advanced Research Projects Agency (ARPA)[12] had a group of scientists and engineers working on this project at the U.S. Army Signal Engineering Laboratories in Ft. Monmouth, New Jersey, when NASA was first organized. Recognizing the country's history of providing weather services to the public through a civilian agency, the military agreed to transfer the research group to NASA. These scientists and engineers became one of the founding units of Goddard in 1958.

TELEVISION AND INFRARED OBSERVATION SATELLITE

Early meteorology satellite and violent storms pioneer.

These early Goddard researchers worked on a project called the Television and Infrared Observation Satellite (TIROS). When it was launched on 1 April 1960, it became the world's first meteorological satellite, returning thousands of images of cloud cover and spiraling storm systems. Goddard's Explorer VI satellite recorded some crude cloud cover images before TIROS I was launched, but as the first spacecraft dedicated to meteorological data gathering, the TIROS satellite transmitted the first really good cloud cover photographs.[13]

Despite its name, the first TIROS carried only television cameras. The second TIROS satellite, launched in November 1960, also included an infrared instrument, which gave it the ability to detect cloud cover even at night.

The TIROS capabilities were limited, but the satellites still provided a tremendous service in terms of weather forecasting. One of the biggest obstacles meteorologists faced was the local, "spotty" nature of the data

they could obtain. Weather balloons and ocean buoys could collect data in their immediate area only. Huge sections of the globe, especially over the oceans, were dark areas where little meteorological information was available. This made forecasting a difficult task, especially for coastal areas.

Sounding rockets offered the ability to take measurements at all altitudes of the atmosphere, which helped provide temperature, density, and water vapor information. But sounding rockets, too, were limited in their scope of coverage. Satellites offered the first chance to get a "big picture" perspective on weather patterns and storm systems as they traveled around the globe.

Because weather forecasting was an operational task usually managed by the Weather Bureau, there was some disagreement about who should have responsibility for designing and operating this new class of satellite. Some at Goddard felt that NASA should take the lead, because the new technology was satellite-based. But the Weather Bureau was paying for the satellites and wanted control over the type of spacecraft and instruments they were funding. The final agreement was for NASA to conduct research on advanced meteorological satellite technology and manage the building, launching, and testing of operational weather satellites. The Weather Bureau would have final say over operational satellite design, however, and would take over management of spacecraft operations after the initial test phase was completed.[14]

The TIROS satellites continued to improve throughout the early 1960s.

Although the spacecraft were officially research satellites, they also provided the Weather Bureau with a semioperational weather satellite system from 1961 to 1965. TIROS III, launched in July 1961, detected numerous hurricanes, tropical storms, and weather fronts around the world that conventional ground networks missed or would not have seen for several more days.[15] TIROS IX, launched in January 1965, was the first of the series launched into a polar orbit, rotating around the Earth in a north-south direction. This orientation allowed the satellite to cross the equator at the same time each day and provided coverage of the entire globe, including the higher latitudes and polar regions, as its orbit precessed around the Earth.

Scientists also improved the coverage of the later TIROS satellites by changing the location of the spacecraft's camera. The TIROS satellites were designed like a wheel of cheese. The wheel spun around but, like a toy top or gyroscope, the axis of the wheel kept pointing in the same direction as the satellite orbited the Earth. The cameras were placed on the satellite's axis, which allowed them to take continuous pictures of the Earth when that surface was actually facing the planet. Like dancers doing a do-si-do, however, the surface with the cameras would be pointing parallel to or away from the Earth for more than half of the satellite's orbit. TIROS IX (and the operational TIROS satellites), put the camera on the rotating section of the wheel, which was kept facing perpendicular to the Earth throughout its orbit. This made the satellite operate more like a dancer twirling around while circling a partner. While the camera could only take pictures every few seconds, when the section of the wheel holding the camera rotated past the Earth, it could continue taking photographs throughout the satellite's entire orbit.

NIMBUS/ESSA/NOAA

In 1964, Goddard took another step in developing more advanced weather satellites when it launched the first Nimbus spacecraft. NASA had originally envisioned the larger and more sophisticated Nimbus as the design for the Weather Bureau's operational satellites. The Weather Bureau decided that the

Goddard test and evaluation personnel conduct vibration testing of a Nimbus research weather satellite.
(NASA Photo G-67-2656)

Nimbus spacecraft were too large and expensive and opted to stay with the simpler TIROS design for the operational system. So the Nimbus satellites were used as research vehicles to develop advanced instruments and technology for future weather satellites. Between 1964 and 1978, Goddard developed and launched a total of seven Nimbus research satellites.

In 1965, the Weather Bureau was absorbed into a new agency called the Environmental Science Services Administration (ESSA). The next year, NASA launched the first satellite in ESSA's operational weather system. The satellite was designed like the TIROS IX spacecraft and was designated "ESSA 1." As per NASA's agreement, Goddard continued to manage the building, launching, and testing of ESSA's operational spacecraft, even as the Center's scientists and engineers worked to develop more advanced technology with separate research satellites.

The ESSA satellites were divided into two types. One took visual images of the Earth with an Automatic Picture Transmission (APT) camera system and transmitted them in real time to stations around the globe. The other type recorded images that were then transmitted to a central ground station for global analysis. These first ESSA satellites were deployed in pairs in "Sun-synchronous" polar orbits around the Earth, crossing the same point at approximately the same time each day.

In 1970, Goddard launched an improved operational spacecraft for ESSA using "second generation" weather satellite technology. The Improved TIROS Operational System (ITOS), as the design was called initially, combined the functions of the previous pairs of ESSA satellites into a single spacecraft and added a day-and-night scanning radiometer. This improvement meant that meteorologists could receive global cloud cover information every 12 hours instead of every 24 hours.

Soon after ITOS 1 was launched, ESSA evolved into the National Oceanic and Atmospheric Administration (NOAA), and successive ITOS satellites were redesignated as NOAA 1, 2, 3, etc. This designation system for NOAA's polar-orbiting satellites continues to this day.

In 1978, NASA launched the first of what was called the "third generation" of polar-orbiting satellites. The TIROS-N design was a much bigger, three-axis-stabilized spacecraft that incorporated much more advanced equipment. The TIROS-N series of instruments, used aboard operational NOAA satellites today, provided much more accurate sea-surface temperature information, which is necessary to predict a phenomenon like an El Niño weather pattern. They also could identify snow and sea ice and could provide much better temperature profiles for different altitudes in the atmosphere.

While the lower-altitude polar satellites can observe some phenomena in more detail because they are relatively close to the Earth, they cannot provide the continuous "big picture" information a geosynchronous satellite can offer. So for the past

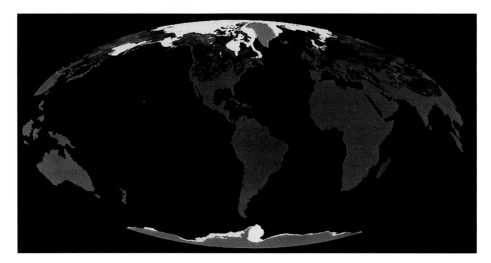

25 years, NOAA has operated two weather satellite systems—the TIROS series of polar-orbiting satellites at lower altitudes, and two geosynchronous satellites more than 22,000 miles above the Earth.[16]

Satellite imagery showing snow and sea ice cover at the north and south poles of the Earth.

ATS/SMS/GOES

While polar-orbiting satellites were an improvement over the more equatorial-orbiting TIROS satellites, scientists realized that they could get a much better perspective on weather systems from a geosynchronous spacecraft. Goddard's research teams started investigating this technology with the launch of the first Applications Technology Satellite (ATS-1) in 1966. Because the ATS had a geosynchronous orbit that kept it "parked" above one spot, meteorologists could get progressive photographs of the same area as often as every 30 minutes. The "satellite photos" showing changes in cloud cover, which we now almost take for granted during nightly newscasts, are made possible by geosynchronous weather satellites. Those cloud movement images also allowed meteorologists to infer wind currents and speeds. This information is particularly useful in

The polar-orbiting ITOS satellites were an improved version of the original TIROS weather satellites.

determining weather patterns over areas of the world such as oceans or the tropics, where conventional aircraft and balloon methods cannot gather data easily.

Goddard's ATS III satellite, launched in 1967, included a multicolor scanner that could provide images in color, as well. Shortly after its launch, ATS III took the first color image of the entire Earth, a photo made possible by the satellite's 22,300-mile-high orbit.[17]

In 1974, Goddard followed its ATS work with a dedicated geosynchronous weather satellite called the Synchronous Meteorological Satellite (SMS). Both SMS-1 and SMS-2 were research prototypes, but they still provided meteorologists with practical information as they tested new technology. In addition to providing continuous coverage of a broad area, the SMS satellites collected and relayed weather data from 10,000 automatic ground stations in 6 hours, giving forecasters more timely and detailed data than ever before.

The Synchronous Meteorological Satellite was the first geosynchronous weather satellite. This design evolved into the GOES series of spacecraft.

Goddard launched NOAA's first operational geostationary[18] satellite, designated the Geostationary Operational Environmental Satellite (GOES), in October 1975. That satellite has led to a whole family of GOES spacecraft. As with previous operational satellites, Goddard managed the building, launching, and testing of the GOES spacecraft.

The first seven GOES spacecraft, while geostationary, were still "spinning" designs like NOAA's earlier operational ESSA satellites. In the early 1980s, however, NOAA decided that it wanted the new series of geostationary GOES spacecraft to be three-axis-stabilized, as well, and to incorporate significantly more advanced instruments. In addition, NOAA decided to award a single contract directly with an industry manufacturer for the spacecraft and instruments, instead of working separate instrument and spacecraft contracts through Goddard.

Goddard typically developed new instruments and technology on research satellites before putting them onto an operational spacecraft for NOAA. The plan for GOES 8,[19] however, called for incorporating new technology instruments directly into a newly designed spacecraft with an operational mission. Meteorologists across the country were going to rely on these new instruments for accurate weather forecasting information, which put a tremendous amount of added pressure on the designers. But the contractor selected to build the instruments underestimated the cost and complexity of developing the

GOES 8 instruments. In addition, Goddard's traditional "Phase B" design study, which would have generated more concrete estimates of the time and cost involved in the instrument development, was eliminated on the GOES 8 project. The study was skipped in an attempt to save time, because NOAA was facing a potential crisis with its geostationary satellite system.

NOAA wanted to have two geostationary satellites up at any given point to cover adequately both coasts of the country. GOES 4 had failed in 1982, after two years in orbit. The GOES 5 satellite then failed in 1984, leaving only one geostationary satellite, GOES 6, in operation. The early demise of GOES 4 and GOES 5 left NOAA uneasy about how long GOES 6 would last, prompting "streamlining" efforts on the GOES 8 spacecraft design. The problem became even more serious in 1986 when the launch vehicle for the GOES G spacecraft, which would have become GOES 7, failed after launch. Another GOES satellite was launched successfully in 1987, but the GOES 6 spacecraft failed in January 1989, leaving the United States again with only one operational geostationary weather satellite.

By 1991, when the GOES 8 project could not predict a realistic launch date, because working instruments for the spacecraft still had not been developed, Congress began to investigate the issue. The GOES 7 spacecraft was aging, and managers and elected officials realized that it was entirely possible that the country

A computer-generated image of Hurricane Fran, using data from the GOES weather satellites. (NASA Photo PAO H96_01.JPG)

might soon find itself without any geostationary satellite coverage at all.

To buy the time necessary to fix the GOES 8 project and alleviate concerns about coverage, NASA arranged with the Europeans to "borrow" one of their Eumetsat geostationary satellites. The satellite was allowed to "drift" further west so that it sat closer to the North American coast, allowing NOAA to move the GOES 7 satellite further west.

Meanwhile, Goddard began to take a more active role in the GOES 8 project. A bigger GOES 8 project office was established at the Center, and Goddard brought in some of its best instrument experts to work on the project, both at Goddard and at the contractor's facilities. After all, Goddard had some of the best meteorological instrument-building expertise in the country. But because Goddard was not directly in charge of the instrument subcontract, the Center had been handicapped in making that knowledge and experience available to the beleaguered contractor.

The project was a sobering reminder of the difficulties that could ensue when, in an effort to save time and money, designers attempted to streamline a development project or combine research and operational functions into a single spacecraft. But in 1994, the GOES 8 spacecraft was launched successfully, and the results have been impressive. Its advanced instruments performed as advertised, improving the spacecraft's focusing and atmospheric sounding abilities and significantly reducing the amount of time the satellite needed to scan any particular area.[20]

EARTH RESOURCES SATELLITES

As meteorological satellite technology developed and improved, Goddard scientists realized that the same instruments used for obtaining weather information could be used for other purposes. Meteorologists could look at radiation that traveled up from the Earth's surface to determine facts like water vapor content and temperature profiles at different altitudes in the atmosphere. But those same emissions also could reveal potentially valuable information about the Earth's surface, as well.

Objects at a temperature above absolute zero emit radiation, many of them at precise and unique wavelengths in the electromagnetic spectrum. So by analyzing the emissions of any object, from a star or comet to a particular section of forest or farmland, scientists can learn important facts about its chemical composition.

Instruments on the Nimbus spacecraft had the ability to look at reflected solar radiation from the Earth in several different wavelengths. As early as 1964, scientists began discussing the possibilities of experimenting with this technology to see what it might reveal about not only the atmosphere, but also resources on Earth.

The result was the Earth Resources Technology Satellite (ERTS), launched in 1972 and later given the more popular name "Landsat 1." The spacecraft was based on a Nimbus satellite, with a multichannel radiometer to look at different wavelength bands where the reflected energy from surfaces such as forests, water, or different crops would fall. The satellite instruments also had much better resolution than the Nimbus instruments. Each swath of the Earth covered by the Nimbus scanner was 1500 miles wide, with each pixel in the picture representing 5 miles. The polar-orbiting ERTS satellite instrument could focus in on a swath only 115 miles wide, with each pixel representing about 73 yards. This resolution allowed scientists to view a small enough section of land, in enough detail, to conduct a worthwhile analysis of what it contained.

Images from the ERTS/Landsat satellite, for example, showed scientists a 25-mile-wide geological feature near Reno, Nevada, that appeared to be a previously undiscovered meteor crater. Other images collected by the satellite were useful in discovering water-bearing rocks in Nebraska, Illinois, and New York and determining that water pollution drifted off the Atlantic coast as a cohesive unit, instead of dissipating in the ocean currents.

The success of the ERTS satellite prompted scientists to explore this use of satellite technology further. They began working on instruments that could achieve pixel resolutions as high as 4½ yards, but were told to discontinue that research because of national security concerns. If a civilian satellite provided such detailed data, it might allow foreign countries to find out critical information about military installations or other important targets in the United States. This example illustrates one of the ongoing difficulties with Earth resource satellite research. The fact that the same information can be used for both scientific and practical purposes often creates complications with who should be responsible for the work and how and where the information will be used.

Consequently, the follow-on satellite, "Landsat 2," was limited to the same levels of resolution as Landsat 1. More recent Landsat spacecraft, however, have been able to improve instrument resolution further.[21]

Landsat 2 was launched in January 1975 and looked at land areas for even more variables than its ERTS predecessor, integrating information from ground stations with data obtained by the satellite's instruments. Because wet land and green crops reflect solar energy at different wavelengths than dry soil or brown plants, Landsat imagery enabled researchers to look at soil moisture levels and crop health over wide areas, as well as soil temperature, stream flows, and snow depth. This

data has been used by the U.S. Department of Agriculture, the U.S. Forest Service, the Department of Commerce, the Army Corps of Engineers, the Environmental Protection Agency, and the Department of the Interior, as well as agencies from foreign countries.[22]

The Landsat program clearly was a success, particularly from a scientific perspective. It proved that satellite technology could determine valuable information about precious natural resources, agricultural activity, and environmental hazards. The question was who should operate the satellites. Once the instruments were developed, the Landsat spacecraft were going to be collecting the same data, over and over, instead of exploring new areas and technology. One could argue that by examining

A Landsat image of the Muir glacier in southeastern Alaska taken in September 1986. The red color indicates areas of vegetation.

the evolution of land resources over time, scientists were still exploring new processes and gathering new scientific information about the Earth. But that same information was being used predominantly for the practical purposes of natural resource management, agricultural and urban planning, and monitoring environmental hazards. NASA had never seen its role as providing ongoing, practical information, but no other agency had the expertise or charter to operate land resource satellites.

As a result, NASA continued to manage the building, launch, and space operation of the Landsat satellites until 1984. Processing and distributing the satellite's data was managed by the Department of the Interior, through an Earth Resources Observation System (EROS) Data Center built by the U.S. Geological Survey in Sioux Falls, South Dakota, in 1972.

In 1979, the Carter Administration developed a new policy in which the Landsat program would be managed by NOAA and eventually turned over to the private sector. The first Reagan Administration put that policy into effect in 1984, soliciting commercial bids for operating the system, which at that point consisted of two operational satellites. Landsat 4 had been launched in 1982 and Landsat 5 was launched in 1984. Ownership and operation of the system was turned over to the EOSAT Company officially in 1985, which sold the images to anyone who wanted them, including the government. At the same time, responsibility for overseeing the program was transferred from NASA to NOAA. Under the new program guidelines, the next spacecraft in the Landsat program, Landsat 6, would also be constructed independently by industry.

This move soon manifested two drawbacks. The first was that the market for Landsat images did not compare with that surrounding the communication satellite industry. The EOSAT Company found itself struggling to stay afloat. Prices for images jumped from the $200 per image that EROS had charged to $4,000 per shot, and EOSAT still found itself bordering on insolvency.

As a private company, EOSAT also was concerned with making a profit, not archiving data for the good of science or the government. Government budgets would not allow the purchase of thousands of archival images at $4,000 each, so the EROS Data Center only bought a few

A Landsat image of Salt Lake City and a portion of the Great Salt Lake in Utah.

selected images each year. As a result, many of the scientific or archival benefits the system could have created were lost.

In 1992, the Land Remote Sensing Policy Act reversed the 1984 decision to commercialize the Landsat system, noting the scientific, national security, economic, and social utility of the Landsat images. Landsat 6 was launched the following year, but the spacecraft failed to reach orbit and ended up in the Indian Ocean.

This launch failure was discouraging, but planning for the next Landsat satellite was already underway. Goddard had agreed to manage the design of a new data ground station for the satellite, and NASA and DOD initially agreed to share responsibility for managing the satellite development. But the Air Force subsequently pulled out of the project and, in May 1994, management of the Landsat system was turned over to NASA, the U.S. Geological Survey (USGS), and NOAA. At the same time, Goddard assumed sole management responsibility for developing Landsat 7.

The only U.S. land resource satellites currently in operation are Landsat 4 and 5, which are both degrading in capability. Landsat 5, in fact, is the only satellite still able to transmit images. The redesigned Landsat 7 satellite is scheduled for launch by mid-1999, and its data will once again be made available though the upgraded EROS facilities in Sioux Falls, South Dakota. Until then, scientists, farmers, and other users of land resource information must rely on Landsat 5 images through EOSAT, or turn to foreign companies for the information.

The French and the Indians have created commercial companies to sell land resource information from their satellites, but both companies are heavily subsidized by their governments while a market for the images is developed. A viable commercial market probably could be developed in the United States. But it seems that the demand would need to grow substantially on its own or would require government subsidy before a commercialization effort could succeed. The issue of scientific versus practical access to the information also would have to be resolved.

Regardless of how the organization of the system is eventually structured, Landsat imagery has proven itself an extremely valuable tool for not only natural resource management, but also for urban planning and agricultural assistance. Former NASA Administrator James C. Fletcher even commented in 1975 that if he had one space-age development to save the world, it would be Landsat and its successor satellites.[23] Without question, the Landsat technology has enabled us to learn much more about the Earth and its land-based resources. And as the population and industrial production on the planet increase, learning about the Earth and potential dangers to it has become an increasingly important priority for scientists and policy makers alike.[24]

ATMOSPHERIC RESEARCH SATELLITES

One of the main elements scientists are trying to learn about the Earth is the composition and behavior of its atmosphere. In fact, Goddard's scientists have been investigating the dynamics of the Earth's atmosphere for scientific and meteorological purposes since the inception of the Center. Explorers 17, 19, and 32, for example, all researched various aspects of the density, composition, pressure, and temperature of the Earth's atmosphere. Explorers 51 and 54, also known as "Atmosphere Explorers," investigated the chemical processes and energy transfer mechanisms that control the atmosphere.

Another goal of Goddard's atmospheric scientists was to understand and measure what was called the "Earth Radiation Budget." Scientists knew that radiation from the Sun enters the Earth's atmosphere. Some of that energy is reflected back into space, but most of it penetrates the atmosphere to warm the surface of the Earth. The Earth, in turn, radiates

energy back into space. Scientists knew that the overall radiation received and released was about equal, but they wanted to know more about the dynamics of the process and seasonal or other fluctuations that might exist. Understanding this process is important because the excesses and deficits in this "budget," as well as variations in it over time or at different locations, create the energy to drive our planet's heating and weather patterns.

The first satellite to investigate the dynamics of the Earth Radiation Budget was Explorer VII, launched in 1959. Nimbus 2 provided the first global picture of the radiation budget, showing that the amount of energy reflected by the Earth's atmosphere was lower than scientists had thought. Additional instruments on Nimbus 3, 5, and 6, as well as operational TIROS and ESSA satellites, explored the dynamics of this complex process further. In the early 1980s, researchers developed an Earth Radiation Budget Experiment (ERBE) instrument that could better analyze the short-wavelength energy received from the Sun and the longer wavelength energy radiated into space from the Earth. This instrument was put on a special Earth Radiation Budget Satellite (ERBS) launched in 1984, as well as the NOAA 9 and NOAA 10 weather satellites.

This instrument has provided scientists with information on how different kinds of clouds affect the amount of energy trapped in the Earth's atmosphere. Lower, thicker clouds, for example, reflect a portion of the Sun's energy back into space, creating a

The Earth Radiation Budget Satellite was launched in 1984 to investigate the balance of solar radiation in the Earth's atmosphere.

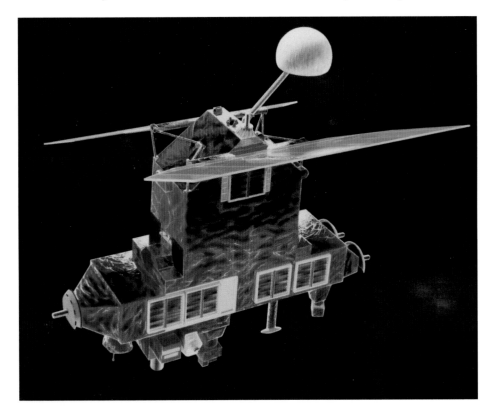

In a single pass across Hurricane Alley, the Tropical Rainfall Measuring Mission provided graphic information: tropical storm Howard and hurricanes Isis, Vearl, and Danielle.

cooling effect on the surface and atmosphere of the Earth. High, thin cirrus clouds, on the other hand, let the Sun's energy in, but trap some of the Earth's outgoing infrared radiation, reflecting it back to the ground. As a result, they can have a warming effect on the Earth's atmosphere. This warming effect can, in turn, create more evaporation, leading to more moisture in the air. This moisture can trap even more radiation in the atmosphere, creating a warming cycle that could influence the long-term climate of the Earth.

Because clouds and atmospheric water vapor seem to play a significant role in the radiation budget of the Earth as well as the amount of global warming and climate change that may occur over the next century, scientists are attempting to find out more about the convection cycle that transports water vapor into the atmosphere. In 1997, Goddard launched the Tropical Rainfall Measuring Mission (TRMM) satellite into a near-equatorial orbit to look more closely at the convection cycle in the tropics that powers much of the rest of the world's cloud and weather patterns. The TRMM satellite's Clouds and the Earth's Radiant Energy System (CERES) instrument, built by NASA's Langley Research Center, is an improved version of the earlier ERBE experiment. While the satellite's focus is on convection and rainfall in the lower atmosphere, some of that moisture does get transported into the upper atmosphere, where it can play a role in changing the Earth's radiation budget and overall climate.[25]

OZONE

An even greater amount of atmospheric research has been focused on a once little-known chemical compound of three oxygen atoms called ozone. Ozone, as most Americans now know, is a chemical in the upper atmosphere that blocks incoming ultraviolet rays from the Sun, protecting us from skin cancer and other harmful effects caused by ultraviolet radiation.

The ozone layer was first brought into the spotlight in the 1960s, when designers began working on the proposed Supersonic Transport (SST). Some scientists and environmentalists were concerned that the jet's high-altitude emissions might damage the ozone layer, and the Federal Government funded several research studies to evaluate the risk. The cancellation of the SST in 1971 shelved the issue, at least temporarily, but 2 years later a much greater potential threat emerged.

In 1973, two researchers at the University of California, Irvine, came up with the astounding theory that certain man-made chemicals, called chlorofluorocarbons (CFCs), could damage the atmosphere's ozone layer. These chemicals were used widely in everything from hair spray to air-conditioning systems, which meant that the world might have a dangerously serious problem on its hands.

In 1975, Congress directed NASA to develop a "comprehensive program of research, technology, and monitoring of phenomena of the upper atmosphere" to evaluate the potential risk of ozone damage further. NASA already was conducting atmospheric research, but the congressional mandate supported even wider efforts. NASA was not the only organization looking into the problem, either. Researchers around the world began focusing on learning more about the chemistry of the upper atmosphere and the behavior of the ozone layer.

Goddard's Nimbus 4 research satellite, launched in 1970, carried an instrument to analyze ultraviolet (UV) rays that were "backscattered," or reflected, from different altitudes in the Earth's atmosphere. Different wavelengths of UV radiation should be absorbed by the ozone at different levels in the atmosphere. By analyzing the amount of UV radiation present in different wavelengths, researchers could develop a profile of how thick or thin the ozone layer was at different altitudes and locations.

In 1978, Goddard launched the last and most capable of its Nimbus-series satellites. Nimbus 7 carried an improved version of this experiment, called the Solar Backscatter Ultraviolet (SBUV) instrument. It also carried a new sensor called the Total Ozone Mapping Spectrometer (TOMS). As opposed to the SBUV, which provided a vertical profile of ozone in the atmosphere, the TOMS instrument generated a high-density map of the total amount of ozone in the atmosphere.

A similar instrument, called the SBUV-2, has been put on weather satellites since the early 1980s. For a number of years, the Space Shuttle periodically flew a Goddard instrument called the Shuttle Solar Backscatter Ultraviolet (SSBUV) experiment that was used to calibrate the SBUV-2 satellite instruments to ensure the continued accuracy of readings. In the last couple of years, however, scientists have developed data-processing methods of calibrating the instruments, eliminating the need for the Shuttle experiments.

Yet it was actually not a NASA satellite that discovered the "hole" that finally developed in the ozone layer. In May 1985, a British researcher in Antarctica published a paper announcing that he had detected an astounding 40-percent loss in the ozone layer over Antarctica the previous winter. When Goddard researchers reviewed their TOMS data from that time period, they discovered that the data indicated the exact same phenomenon. Indeed, the satellite indicated an area of ozone layer thinning, or "hole,"[26] the size of the continental United States.

Ironically, it was because the anomaly was so drastic that researchers had missed it. The TOMS data analysis software was programmed to flag grossly anomalous data points, which were assumed to be errors. Nobody expected the ozone loss to be as great as it was, so the data points over the area where the loss had occurred looked like problems with the instrument or its calibration.

Once they verified the Nimbus 7 data, Goddard's researchers generated a visual map of the area over Antarctica where the ozone loss had occurred. In fact, the ability to generate visual images of the ozone layer and its "holes" have been among the significant contributions NASA's ozone-related satellites have made to the public

debate over the issue. Data points are hard for most people to fully understand. But for non-scientists, a visual image showing a gap in a protective layer over Antarctica or North America makes the problem not only clear, but somehow very real.

The problem then became one of determining what was causing the loss of ozone. This was a particularly sticky issue, because it related directly to legislation and restrictions that would be extremely costly for industry. By 1978, the Environmental Protection Agency (EPA) had moved to ban

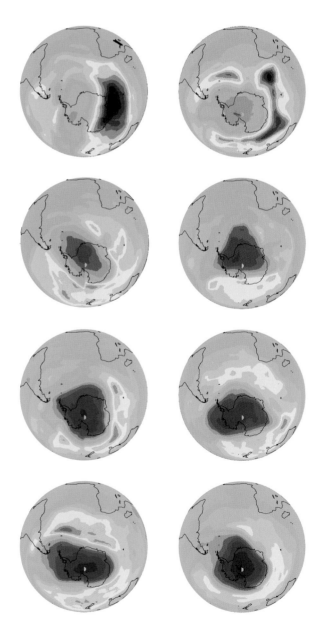

This series of Total Ozone Mapping Spectrometer maps shows the development of an ozone "hole" over Antartica. Red indicates areas of thicker ozone; blues and violets indicate areas of ozone thinning.

the use of CFCs in aerosols. By 1985, the United Nations Environmental Program (UNEP) was calling on nations to take measures to protect the ozone and, in 1987, 43 nations signed the "Montreal Protocol," agreeing to cut CFC production 50 percent by the year 2000.

The CFC theory was based on a prediction that chlorofluorocarbons, when they reached the upper atmosphere, released chlorine and fluorine. The chlorine, it was suspected, was reacting with the ozone to form chlorine monoxide—a chemical that is able to destroy a large amount of ozone in a very short period of time. Because the issue was the subject of so much debate, NASA launched numerous research efforts to try to validate or disprove the theory. In addition to satellite observations, NASA sent teams of researchers and aircraft to Antarctica to take *in situ* readings of the ozone layer and the ozone "hole" itself. These findings were then supplemented with the bigger picture perspective the TOMS and SBUV instruments could provide.

The TOMS instrument on Nimbus 7 was not supposed to last more than a couple of years. But the information it was providing was considered so critical to the debate that Goddard researchers undertook an enormous effort to keep the instrument working, even as it aged and began to degrade. The TOMS instrument also had not been designed to show long-term trends, so the data processing techniques required significant improvement to give researchers that kind of information.

The Upper Atmosphere Research Satellite was launched in 1991 to take an intensive look at components and processes in the Earth's upper atmosphere.

In the end, Goddard was able to keep the Nimbus 7 TOMS instrument operating for almost 15 years, which provided ozone monitoring until Goddard was able to launch a replacement TOMS instrument on a Russian satellite in 1991.[27]

A more comprehensive project to study the upper atmosphere and the ozone layer was launched in 1991. The satellite, called the Upper Atmosphere Research Satellite (UARS), was one result of Congress's 1975 mandate for NASA to pursue additional ozone research. Although its goal is to try to understand the chemistry and dynamics of the upper atmosphere, the focus of UARS is clearly on ozone research. Original plans called for the spacecraft to be launched from the Shuttle in the mid-1980s, but the Challenger accident delayed its launch until 1991.

Once in orbit, the more advanced instruments on board the UARS satellite were able to map chlorine monoxide levels in the stratosphere. Within months, the satellite was able to confirm what the Antarctic

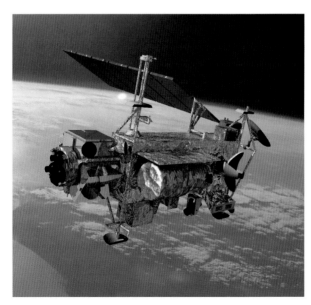

aircraft expeditions and Nimbus 7 satellite had reported—that there was a clear and causal link between levels of chlorine, formation of chlorine monoxide, and levels of ozone loss in the upper atmosphere.

Since the launch of UARS, the TOMS instrument has been put on several additional satellites to ensure that we have a continuing ability to monitor changes in the ozone layer. A Russian satellite called Meteor 3 took measurements with a TOMS instrument from 1991 until the satellite ceased operating in 1994. The TOMS instrument also was incorporated into a Japanese satellite called the Advanced Earth Observing System (ADEOS) that was launched in 1996. ADEOS, which researchers hoped could provide TOMS coverage until the next scheduled TOMS instrument launch in 1999, failed after less than a year in orbit. Fortunately, Goddard had another TOMS instrument ready for launch on a small NASA satellite called an Earth Probe, which was put into orbit with the Pegasus launch vehicle in 1996. Researchers hope that this instrument will continue to provide coverage and data until the next scheduled TOMS instrument launch.

All of these satellites have given us a much clearer picture of what the ozone layer is, how it interacts with various other chemicals, and what causes it to deteriorate. These pieces of information are essential elements in developing a strategy to protect one of our most precious natural resources.

Using the UARS satellite, scientists have been able to track the progress of

CFCs up into the stratosphere and have detected the buildup of chlorine monoxide over North America and the Arctic as well as Antarctica. Scientists also have discovered that ozone loss is much greater when the temperature of the stratosphere is cold. In 1997, for example, particularly cold stratospheric temperatures created the first Antarctic-type of ozone hole over North America.

Another factor in ozone loss is the level of aerosols, or particulate matter, in the upper atmosphere. The vast majority of aerosols come from soot, other pollution, or volcanic activity. Goddard's scientists have been studying the effects of these particles in the atmosphere ever since the launch of the Nimbus 1 spacecraft in 1964. Goddard's 1984 Earth Radiation Budget Satellite (ERBS), which is still operational, carries a Stratospheric Aerosol and Gas Experiment (SAGE II) that tracks aerosol levels in the lower and upper atmosphere. The Halogen Occultation Experiment (HALOE) instrument on UARS also measures aerosol intensity and distribution.

The light green to bold orange colors in this UARS satellite image show the increase in atmospheric sulfur dioxide levels that followed the June 1991 eruption of Mt. Pinatubo in the Philippines.

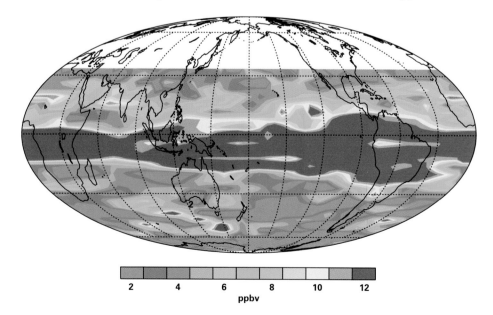

In 1991, both UARS and SAGE II were used to track the movement and dispersal of the massive aerosol cloud created by the Mt. Pinatubo volcano eruption in the Philippines. The eruption caused stratospheric aerosol levels to increase to as much as 100 times their pre-eruption levels, creating spectacular sunsets around the world but causing some other effects, as well. These volcanic clouds appear to help cool the Earth, which could affect global warming trends, but the aerosols in these clouds seem to increase the amount of ozone loss in the stratosphere.

The good news is that the atmosphere seems to be beginning to heal itself. In 1979 there was no ozone hole. Throughout the 1980s, while legislative and policy debates raged over the issue, the hole developed and grew steadily larger. In 1989, most U.S. companies finally ceased production of CFC chemicals and, in 1990, the United Nations strengthened its Montreal Protocol to call for the complete phaseout of CFCs by the year 2000. Nature is slow to react to changes in our behavior but, by 1997, scientists finally began to see a leveling out and even a slight decrease in chlorine monoxide levels and ozone loss in the upper atmosphere.[28]

Continued public interest in this topic has made ozone research a little more complicated for the scientists involved. Priorities and pressures in the program have changed along with Presidential administrations and congressional agendas and, as much as scientists can argue that data is simply data, they cannot hope to please everyone in such a politically charged arena. Some environmentalists argue that the problem is much worse than NASA describes, while more conservative politicians argue that NASA's scientists are blowing the issue out of proportion.[29]

But at this point a few things are clearer. The production of CFC chemicals was, in fact, harming a critical component of our planet's atmosphere. It took a variety of ground and space instruments to detect and map the nature and extent of the problem. But the perspective offered by Goddard's satellites allowed scientists and the general public to get a clear overview of the problem and to map the progression of events that caused it. This information has had a direct impact on changing the world's industrial practices which, in turn, have begun to slow the damage and allow the planet to heal itself. The practical implications of Earth-oriented satellite data may make life a little more complicated for the scientists involved, but no one can argue the significance or impact of the work. By developing the technology to view and analyze the Earth from space, we have given ourselves an invaluable tool for helping us understand and protect the planet on which we live.

OCEANOGRAPHIC SATELLITES

One of the biggest advantages to remote sensing of the Earth from satellites stems from the fact that the majority of the Earth's surface area is extremely difficult to study from the ground. The world's oceans cover 71 percent of the Earth's surface and comprise 99 percent of its living area. Atmospheric convective activity over the tropical ocean area is believed to drive a significant amount of the world's weather. Yet until recently, the only way to map or analyze this powerful planetary element was with buoys, ships, or aircraft. But these methods could only obtain data from various individual points, and the process was extremely difficult, expensive, and time-consuming.

Satellites offered oceanographers a tremendous advantage. A two-minute ocean-color satellite image for example, contains more measurements than a ship traveling 10 knots could make in a decade. This ability has allowed scientists to learn a lot more about the vast open stretches of ocean that influence our weather, our global climate, and our everyday lives.[30]

Although Goddard's early meteorological satellites were not geared specifically toward analyzing ocean characteristics, some of the instruments could provide information about the ocean as well as the atmosphere. The passive microwave sensors that allowed scientists to "see" through clouds better, for example, also let them map the distribution of sea ice around the world. Changes in sea ice distribution can indicate climate changes and affect sea levels around the world, which makes this an important parameter to monitor. At the same time, this information has allowed scientists to locate open passageways for ships trying to get through the moving ice floes of the Arctic region.

By 1970, NOAA weather satellites had instruments that could measure the temperature of the ocean surface in areas where there was no cloud cover, and the Landsat satellites could provide some information on snow and ice distributions. But since the late 1970s, much more sophisticated ocean-sensing satellite technology has emerged.[31]

The Nimbus 7 satellite, for example, carried an improved microwave instrument that could generate a much more detailed picture of sea ice distribution than either

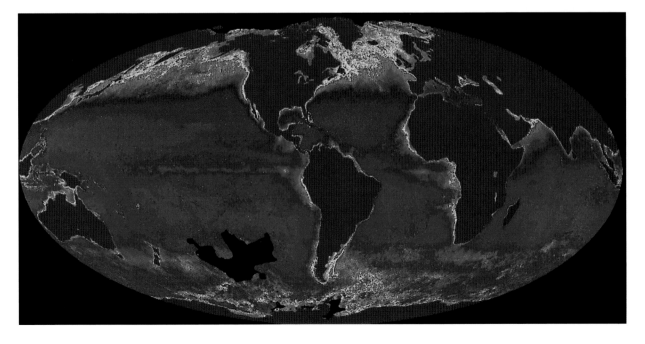

Goddard's Nimbus 7 satellite carried a Coastal Zone Color Scanner, which detected the distribution of phytoplankton around the world. Phytoplankton is a critical component of the global carbon cycle and its distribution has important implications for global climate change predictions.

the earlier Nimbus or Landsat satellites. Nimbus 7 also carried the first Coastal Zone Color Scanner (CZCS), which allowed scientists to map pollutants and sediment near coastlines. The CZCS also showed the location of ocean phytoplankton around the world. Phytoplankton are tiny, carbon dioxide-absorbing plants that constitute the lowest rung on the ocean food chain. So they generally mark spots where larger fish may be found. But because phytoplankton bloom where nutrient-rich water from the deep ocean comes up near the surface, their presence also gives scientists clues about the ocean's currents and circulation.

Nimbus 7 continued to send back ocean-color information until 1984. Scientists at Goddard continued working on ocean-color sensor development

This image from the Costal Zone Color Scanner depicts ocean temperatures in the Atlantic Ocean off North America. Reds are warmest, and blues and violets are coolest. Swirls indicate eddies in the Gulf Stream.

throughout the 1980s, and a more advanced coastal zone ocean-color instrument was launched on the Sea-viewing Wide Field-of-view Sensor (SeaWiFS) satellite in 1997. In contrast to most scientific satellites, SeaWiFS was funded and launched by a private company instead of by NASA. Most of the ocean-color data the satellite provides is purchased by NASA and other research institutions, but the company is selling some data to the fishing industry, as well.[32]

Since the launch of the Nimbus 7 and TIROS-N satellites in 1978, scientists have been able to get much better information on global ocean surface temperatures. Sea surface temperatures tell scientists about ocean circulation, because they can use this information to track the movement of warmer and cooler bodies of water. Changes in sea surface temperatures also indicate the development of phenomena such as El Niño climate patterns. In fact, one of the most marked indications of a developing El Niño condition, which can cause heavy rains in some parts of the world and devastating drought in others, is an unusually warm tongue of water moving eastward from the western equatorial Pacific Ocean.

NOAA weather satellites have carried instruments to measure sea surface temperature since 1981, and NASA's EOS AM-1 satellite, scheduled for launch in 1999, incorporates an instrument that can measure those temperatures with even more precision. The launch of Nimbus 7 also gave researchers the ability to look at surface winds, which help drive ocean circulation.

With Nimbus 7, however, scientists had to infer surface winds by looking at slight differentiations in microwave emissions coming from the ocean surface. A scatterometer designed specifically to measure surface winds was not launched until the Europeans launched ERS-1 in 1991. Another scatterometer was launched on the Japanese ADEOS spacecraft in 1996. Because ADEOS failed less than a year after launch, Goddard researchers have begun an intensive effort to launch another scatterometer, called QuickSCAT, on a NASA spacecraft. JPL project managers are being aided in this effort by the Goddard-developed Rapid Spacecraft Procurement Initiative, which will allow them to incorporate the instrument into an existing small spacecraft design. Using this streamlined process, scientists hope to have QuickSCAT ready for launch in 1999.[33]

In the 1970s, researchers at the Wallops Flight Facility also began experimenting with radar altimetry to determine sea surface height, although they were pleased if they could get accuracy within a meter. In 1992, however, a joint satellite project between NASA and the French Centre National d'Etudes Spatiales (CNES) called TOPEX/Poseidon put a much more accurate radar altimeter into orbit. Goddard managed the development of the TOPEX radar altimeter, which can measure sea surface height within a few centimeters. In addition to offering useful information for maritime weather reports, this sea level data tells scientists some important things about ocean movement.

The first Earth Observing System satellite under construction. (NASA Photo G98-019-008)

For one thing, sea surface height indicates the buildup of water in one area of the world or another. One of the very first precursors to an El Niño condition, for example, is a rise in ocean levels in the western equatorial Pacific, caused by stronger-than-normal easterly trade winds. Sea level also tells scientists important information about the amount of heat the ocean is storing. If the sea level in a particular area is low, it means that the area of warm, upper-level water is shallow. Therefore, colder, deeper water can reach the surface there, driving ocean circulation and bringing nutrients up from below, leading to the production of phytoplankton. The upwelling of cold water also will cool down the sea surface temperature, reducing the amount of water that evaporates into the atmosphere.

All of these improvements in satellite capabilities gave oceanographers and scientists an opportunity to integrate onsite surface measurements from buoys or ships with the more global perspective available from space. As a result, we are finally beginning to piece together a more complete picture of our oceans and the role they play in the Earth's biosystems and climate. In fact, one of the most significant results of ocean-oriented satellite research was the realization that ocean and atmospheric processes were intimately linked to each other. To understand the dynamics of the ocean or the atmosphere, we needed to look at the combined global system they comprised.[34]

EL NIÑO AND GLOBAL CHANGE

The main catalyst that prompted scientists to start looking at the oceans and atmosphere as an integrated system was the El Niño event of 1982-83. The rains and drought associated with the unusual weather pattern caused $8 billion in damage, leading to several international research programs to understand and predict the phenomenon better. The research efforts, including measurements by ships, aircraft, ocean buoys, and satellites, continues today. By 1996, scientists had begun to understand the warning signals and patterns of a strong El Niño event. They also had the technology to track atmospheric wind currents and cloud formation, ocean color, and sea surface temperatures, sea surface levels, and sea surface winds, which let them accurately predict the heavy rains and severe droughts that occurred at

This image of the sea surface temperature anomaly during the 1982-83 El Niño event was created from satellite data.

points around the world throughout the 1997-98 winter.

The reason the 1982-83 El Niño event prompted a change to a more integrated ocean-atmospheric approach is that the El Niño phenomenon does not exist in the ocean or the atmosphere by itself. It is the coupled interactions between the two elements that cause this periodic weather pattern to occur. The term El Niño, which means "The Child," was coined by fishermen on the Pacific coast of Central America, who noticed a warming of their coastal ocean waters, along with a decline in fish population, near the Christ Child's birthday in December. But as scientists have discovered, the sequence of events that causes that warming begins many months earlier, in winds headed the opposite direction.

In a normal year, strong easterly trade winds blowing near the equator drag warmer, upper-level ocean water to the western edge of the Pacific Ocean. That buildup of warm water causes convection

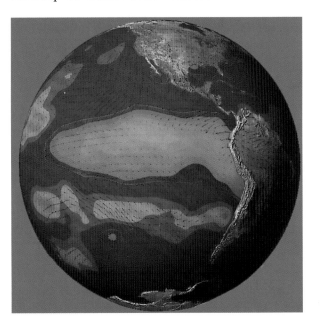

up into the tropical atmosphere, leading to rainfall along the Indonesian and Australian coastlines. It also leads to upwelling of colder, nutrient-rich water along the eastern equatorial Pacific coastlines, along Central and South America. In an El Niño year, however, a period of stronger-than-normal trade winds that significantly raises sea levels in the western Pacific is followed by a sharp drop in those winds. The unusually weak trade winds allow the large buildup of warm water in the western tropical Pacific to flow eastward along the equator. That change moves the convection and rainfall off the Indonesian and Australian coasts, causing severe drought in those areas and, as the warm water reaches the eastern edge of the Pacific Ocean, much heavier than normal rainfall occurs along the western coastlines of North, Central, and South America. The movement of warm water toward the eastern Pacific also keeps the colder ocean water from coming up to the surface, keeping phytoplankton from growing and reducing the presence of fish further up on the food chain.

In other words, an El Niño is the result of a change in atmospheric winds, which causes a change in ocean currents and sea-level distribution, which causes a change in sea surface temperature, which causes a change in water vapor entering the atmosphere, which causes further changes in the wind currents, and so on, creating a cyclical pattern. Scientists still do not know exactly what causes the initial change in atmospheric winds, but they

now realize that they need to look at a global system of water, land, and air interactions to find the answer. And satellites play a critical role in the ability to do that.

An El Niño weather pattern is the biggest short-term "coupled" atmospheric and oceanographic climate signal on the planet after the change in seasons, which is why it prompted researchers to take a more interdisciplinary approach to studying it. But scientists are beginning to realize that many of the Earth's climatic changes or phenomena are really coupled events that require a broader approach to understand them. In fact, the 1990s have seen the emergence of a new type of scientist who is neither oceanographer nor atmospheric specialist, but is a kind of amphibious researcher focusing on the broader issue of climate change.[35]

GLOBAL WARMING

One of the other important topics these researchers are currently trying to assess is the issue of global warming. Back in 1896, a Swedish chemist named Svante Arrhenius predicted that the increasing carbon dioxide emissions from the industrial revolution would eventually cause the Earth to become several degrees warmer. The cause of this warming is what has become known as the "greenhouse effect." In essence, carbon dioxide and other "greenhouse gases," such as water vapor, allow the short-wavelength radiation from the Sun to pass through the atmosphere, warming the Earth. But the gases absorb the longer-wavelength energy traveling back from the Earth into space, radiating part of that energy back down to the Earth again. Just as the glass in a green-house allows the Sun through but traps the heat inside, these gases end up trap-ping a certain amount of heat in the Earth's atmosphere, causing the Earth to become warmer.

The effect of this warming could be small or great, depending on how much the temperature actually changes. If it is only a degree or two, the effect would be relatively small. But a larger change in cli-mate could melt polar ice, causing the sea level to rise several feet and wiping out numerous coastal communities and resources. If the warming happened rapidly, vegetation might not have time to adjust to the climate change, which could affect the world's food supply as well as timber and other natural resources.

This satellite image depicts the global water vapor levels—an important factor in global warming studies.

The critical question, then, is how dangerous is global warming. And the answer depends on numerous factors. One, obviously, is the amount of carbon dioxide and other emissions we put into the air—a concern that has driven efforts to reduce our carbon dioxide-producing fossil fuel consumption. But the amount of carbon dioxide in the air also depends on how much can be absorbed again by plant life on Earth—a figure that scien-tists use satellites to compute. Landsat images can tell scientists how much defor-estation is occurring around the world and how much healthy plant life remains to absorb carbon dioxide. Until recently, the amount of carbon dioxide absorbed by the world's oceans was unknown. The ocean-color images of SeaWiFS are help-ing to fill that gap, because the phyto-plankton this satellite tracks are a major

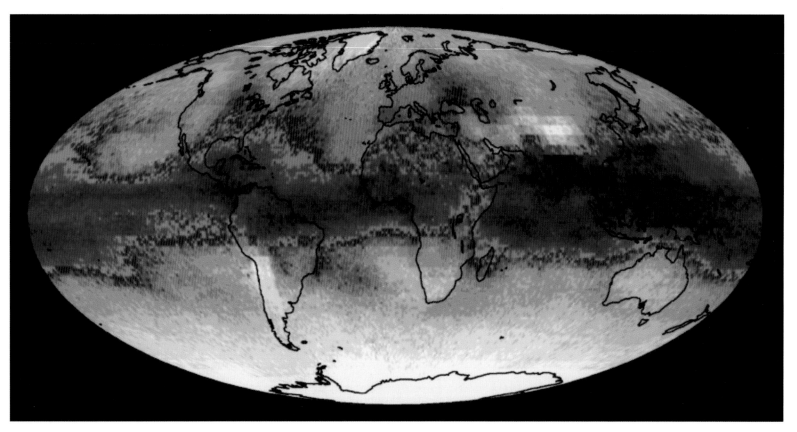

source of carbon dioxide absorption in the oceans.

Another part of the global warming equation is the amount of water vapor in the atmosphere—a factor driven by ocean processes, especially in the heat furnace of the tropics. As a result, scientists are trying to learn more about the transfer of heat and water vapor between the ocean and different levels of the atmosphere, using tools such as Goddard's TRMM and UARS satellites.

All of these numbers and factors are fed into atmospheric and global computer models, many of which have been developed at the Goddard Institute for Space Studies (GISS) in New York City. These models then try to predict how our global climate may change based on current emissions, population trends, and known facts about ocean and atmospheric processes.

While these models have been successful in predicting short-term effects, such as the global temperature drop after the Mt. Pinatubo volcano eruption, the problem with trying to predict global change is that it is a very long-term process, with many factors that may change over time. We have been studying the Earth in bits and pieces, and for only a short number of years. In order to understand which climate changes are short-term variations and which are longer trends of more permanent change, scientists needed to observe and measure the global, integrated climate systems of planet Earth over a long period of time. This realization was the impetus for NASA's Mission to Planet Earth.[36]

EARTH SCIENCE ENTERPRISE

In some senses, the origins of what became NASA's "Mission to Planet Earth" (MTPE) began in the late 1970s, when we began studying the overall climate and planetary processes of other planets in our solar system. Scientists began to realize that we had never taken that kind of "big picture" look at our own planet, and that such an effort might yield some important and fascinating results. But an even larger spur to the effort was simply the development of knowledge and technology that gave scientists both the capability and an understanding of the importance of looking at the Earth from a more global, systems perspective.

Discussions along these lines were already underway when the El Niño event of 1982-83 and the discovery of the ozone "hole" in 1985 elevated the level of interest and support for global climate change research to an almost crisis level. Although the MTPE was not announced as a formal new NASA program until 1990, work on the satellites to perform the mission already was underway. In 1991, Goddard's UARS satellite became the first official MTPE spacecraft to be launched.

Although the program has changed its name to the Earth Science Enterprise, suffered several budget cuts, and refocused its efforts from overall global change to a narrower area of global climate change (leaving out changes in solid land masses), the basic goal of the program echoes what was initiated in 1990. In essence, the Earth Science program aims to integrate satellite, aircraft, and ground-based instruments to monitor 24 interrelated processes and parameters in the planet's oceans and atmosphere over a 15-year period.

Phase I of the program consisted of integrating information from satellites such as UARS, the TOMS Earth probe, TRMM, TOPEX/Poseidon, ADEOS, and SeaWiFS with Space Shuttle research payloads, research aircraft, and ground station observations. Phase II is scheduled to begin in 1999 with the launch of Landsat 7 and the first in a series of Earth Observing System (EOS) satellites. The EOS spacecraft are large research platforms with many different instruments to look at various atmospheric and ocean processes that affect natural resources and the overall global climate. They will be polar-orbiting satellites, with orbital paths that will allow the different satellites to take measurements at different times of the day. EOS AM-1 is scheduled for launch in 1999. EOS PM-1 is scheduled for launch late in the year 2000. The first in an EOS altimetry series of satellites will study the role of oceans, ocean winds, and ocean-atmosphere interactions in climate systems. These spacecraft will launch in the same timeframe. An EOS CHEM-1 satellite, which will look at the behavior of ozone and greenhouse gases, measure pollution, and study the effect of aerosols on global climate, is scheduled for launch in 2002.

There is still much we do not know about our own planet. Indeed, the first priority of the Earth Science Enterprise satellites is to try to fill in the gaps in what we

know about the behavior and dynamics of our oceans and our atmosphere. Then scientists can begin to look at how those elements interact and assess their impact on global climate and climate change. Only then will we really know how great a danger global warming is, or how much our planet can absorb the man-made elements we are creating in increasing amounts.[37]

This is an ambitious task. But until the advent of satellite technology, the job would have been impossible even to imagine. Satellites have given us the ability to map and study large sections of the planet that would be difficult to cover from the planet's surface. Surface and aircraft measurements also play a critical role in these studies. But satellites were the breakthrough that gave us the unique ability to stand back far enough from the trees to see the complete and complex forest in which we live.

CONCLUSION

For centuries, humankind has stared at the stars and dreamed of traveling among them. We imagined ourselves zipping through asteroid fields, transfixed by spectacular sights of meteors, stars, and distant galaxies. Yet when the astronauts first left the planet, they were surprised to find themselves transfixed not by distant stars, but by the awe-inspiring view their spaceship gave them of the place they had just left—a dazzling, mysterious planet they affectionately nicknamed the "Big Blue Marble." As our horizons expanded into the universe, so did our perspective and understanding of the place we call home. As an astronaut on an international Space Shuttle crew put it, "The first day or so we all pointed to our countries. The third or fourth day we were pointing to our continents. By the fifth day we were aware of only one Earth."[38]

Satellites have given this perspective to all of us, expanding our horizons and deepening our understanding of the planet we inhabit. If the world is suddenly a smaller place, with cellular phones, paging systems, and Internet service connecting friends from distant lands, it is because satellites have advanced our communication abilities far beyond anything Alexander Graham Bell ever imagined. If we have more than a few hours' notice of hurricanes or storm fronts, it is because weather satellites have enabled meteorologists to better understand the dynamics of weather systems and track those systems as they develop around the world. If we can detect and correct damage to our ozone layer or give advance warning of a strong El Niño winter, it is because satellites have helped scientists better understand the changing dynamics of our atmosphere and our oceans.

We now understand that our individual "homes" are affected by events on the far side of the globe. From both a climatic and environmental perspective, we have realized that our home is indeed "one Earth," and we need to look at its entirety in order to understand and protect it. The practical implications of this information sometimes make the scientific pursuit of this understanding more complicated than

our explorations into the deeper universe. But no one would argue the inherent worth of the information or the advantages satellites offer.

The satellites developed by Goddard and its many partners have expanded both our capabilities and our understanding of the complex processes within our Earth's atmosphere. Those efforts may be different from our search for space-time anomalies or unexplainable black holes, but they are perhaps even more important. After all, there may be millions of galaxies and planets in the universe. But until we find a way to reach them, this planet is the only one we have. And the better we understand it, the better our chances are of preserving it—for ourselves, and also for the generations to come.

Earthrise, as seen by the Apollo astronauts on the Moon. Ironically, it has only been since we left our planet that we have really begun to understand it.

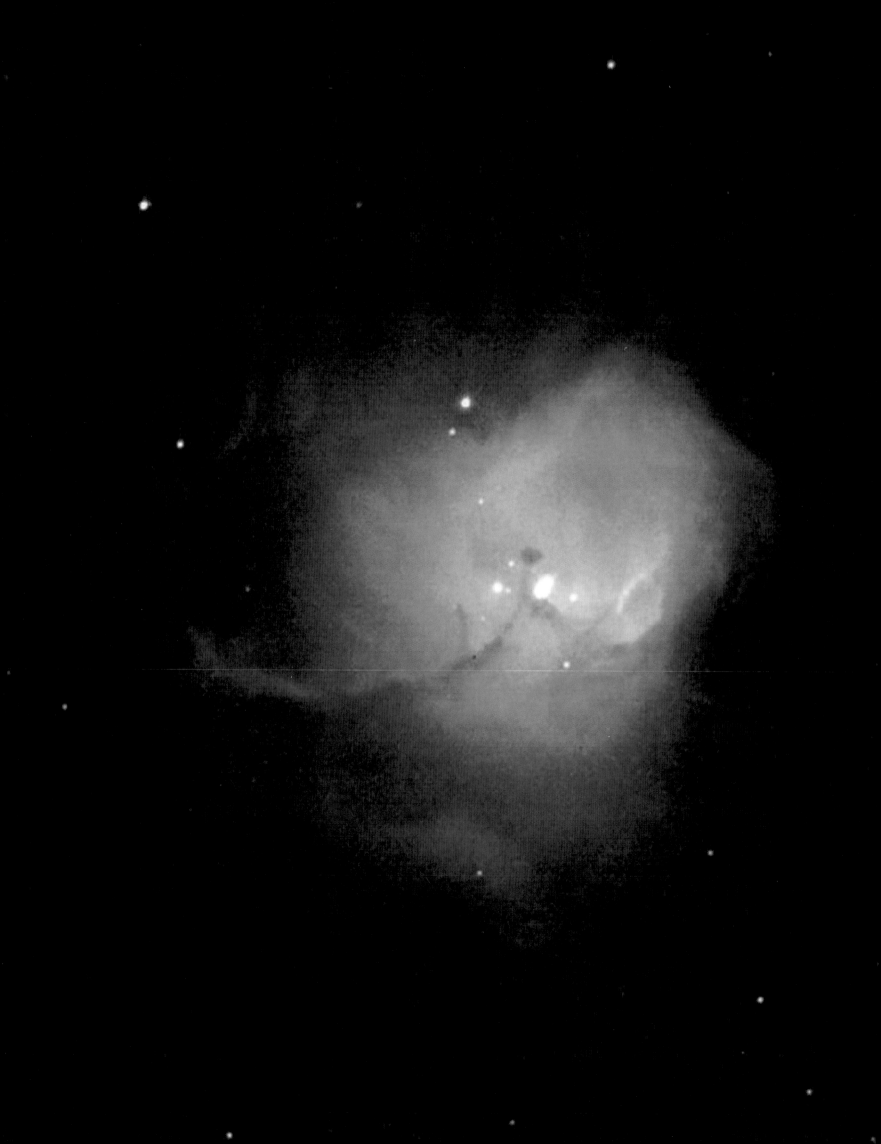

CHAPTER 6:

The Endless Frontier

A cluster of young stars and the glowing nebula around them are about 200,000 light-years from Earth in the small Magellanic Cloud.

When the Goddard Space Flight Center opened its doors in 1959, we were standing on the brink of a great new adventure—one that would change our lives and vastly expand our understanding of the world and universe in which we live. The journey would not be an easy one. It would involve many thousands of people, in many different locations, and the cooperation of countries around the world. It would require enormous ingenuity, a tremendous investment of time and money, and the sacrifice of human lives. The people who undertook this endeavor had to have the determination to persevere through failure and frustration; the dedication to devote hours, months, and years to a single effort; and the vision to imagine not only creative solutions, but also the results that would make the effort worthwhile.

Because it was created at the dawn of the space age and has lived through the many changing tides and eras of NASA, Goddard in many ways parallels the history of the U.S. space program itself. It began in a scramble to catch up with the Russians after the launch of Sputnik, pulling scientists and engineers from numerous military and civilian research institutions into a hybrid organization that could master the challenges of space flight and exploration. The effort was funded by a Nation suddenly worried about its prestige and its military security. Yet President Eisenhower made it very clear that the exploration of this new territory was to be a civilian effort. Despite the fact that it was the height of the Cold War, NASA and Goddard were formed with the directive that "the activities in space should be devoted to peaceful purposes for the benefit of all mankind."[1]

The challenges this group of researchers faced were so extensive that even the people who organized NASA initially failed to realize how complex the effort would be. Goddard, it was thought, could manage all the tasks necessary for the scientific and human exploration of space. This notion soon changed, but it left Goddard with a unique legacy of diversity. Goddard remained one of the only places in the world where the entire cycle of a space project could be completed, from theory to launch to final analysis of the data received. The Center also has another

distinction within NASA. In an agency dedicated primarily to the engineering challenge of traveling into space, Goddard is dedicated to science.[2]

These two distinguishing characteristics of Goddard—its wide diversity of projects and responsibilities, and its role in conducting scientific research—have created unique and impressive strengths within the Center. Goddard's blend of science and engineering has given it the ability not only to conceive of experiments, but also to design the technology and equipment necessary to execute those ideas. This in-house satellite-building capability, which stressed innovative thinking and design, led to the development of numerous valuable concepts and spacecraft. These included the highly successful Explorer series, the concept of modular satellites that could be serviced in space, and the

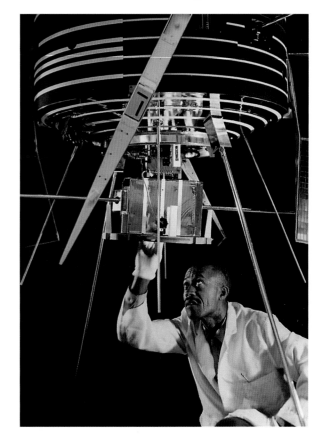

A technician checks Goddard's Radio Astronomy Explorer satellite prior to its launch on 4 July 1968.

new state-of-the-art Small Explorer class of research satellites. The blend of science and engineering at the same Center also gave Goddard's scientists and engineers the ability to work closely together to design and build the wide variety of complex instruments that made Goddard's scientific achievements possible.

At the same time, Goddard's diversity and wide range of responsibilities created a unique set of challenges for the Center throughout its history. Scientific research was not the exclusive domain of NASA, which meant that Goddard managers constantly had to balance conflicting internal needs and priorities with the needs of a greater, international research community. Goddard's work in the areas of Earth science and "applications" was sometimes even more complex, because NASA's role in these areas was unclear. In addition, no matter how much scientists argue that data is simply data, research on our planet is often complicated by the inescapable practical ramifications of what that research uncovers.

Yet many of Goddard's challenges simply reflected the larger challenges inherent in this new realm of space exploration. If managing Goddard's many satellite projects was a complex task, it was because space flight itself was an incredibly complex and expensive endeavor that required the cooperation of many people. A small team of design engineers might get a new airplane off the ground, but to get a spacecraft into orbit required the combined efforts of an army of professionals and support staff at NASA Centers, universities, private industry, and in countries around the world. Striking the right balance between the sometimes conflicting needs and priorities of such a diverse group of people and organizations was a difficult thing to do.

THE EVOLVING SPACE AGE: GODDARD'S FIRST FORTY

The challenges facing Goddard's first scientists and engineers were mostly technical ones. Limited launch vehicle capability meant that satellites had to be extremely small and lightweight. Large amounts of data had to be processed and transmitted to the ground with very little power. Launch vehicles themselves were unreliable, causing Goddard to build back-up models for each of its satellites. And all of this was being attempted when computers were in their infancy, and telephone service was still unreliable with many ground tracking stations.

Today, technology has advanced beyond anything those pioneers could even have imagined. In some cases, these advances have allowed the design of much larger and more complex satellites. In 1959, the first Explorer satellite carried into orbit by a Jupiter C rocket was a slender cylinder that was about 70 inches long and weighed 22 pounds. In 1991, the Compton Gamma Ray Observatory launched by the Space Shuttle was 70 feet long and weighed more than 17 tons. Tracking systems also advanced from many different ground stations around the world

Students prepare a Get-Away-Special can experiment to be carried in the cargo bay of the Space Shuttle.

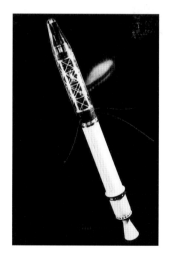

Explorer I took the United States into space for the first time when it was launched successfully on 1 February 1958.

to a network of geosynchronous tracking and data relay satellites.

New technology—some of which was developed at Goddard—also resulted in advancements such as solid-state tape recorders and computers that are a fraction of the size and weight of their predecessors, but hold many times more memory and power. Ironically, these advances have allowed building once again small, easily launched satellites that are still vastly more capable and can store data reliably enough that it can be retrieved by a simple network of ground stations.

Advances in computer and spacecraft technology have created a new era in the type and amount of data satellites can gather, as well. From the days when scientists had to decipher simple audio tones from satellites passing overhead, we have

The Polar satellite under construction. Polar was one of several satellites included in the International Solar-Terrestrial Program effort to look at Sun-Earth connections.

satellites sending back breathtaking images of distant galaxies and complex streams of data from the inside of the Sun. The new EOS satellites are scheduled to transmit a terabyte of data every day, creating a whole new challenge in data processing and storage. Once the problem was trying to get enough data. Today the challenge is to manage the large volume.

Technology has also improved the usefulness of satellites to the general scientific community. In the early days, the only people who could get useful data from physics or astronomy satellites were the scientists who had designed the instruments. By the mid-1970s, Goddard's engineers were able to build astronomy satellites with "transparent" software that could allow guest observers to use the platforms as easily as a ground telescope, opening up space science to a much broader community of researchers.

These advances in technology have allowed us to expand the horizons of our world. When Goddard was founded, scientists were simply trying to find out what lay beyond our immediate atmosphere. Today, Goddard's satellites have reached back to the dawn of time and cracked open doors to invisible and distant reaches of the universe, answering some of our most basic questions and uncovering new worlds and phenomena we never even dreamed existed.

We have discovered not only radiation belts and a magnetosphere that surround our planet, but also a complex relationship between the Sun and the Earth that begins

A montage of some of Goddard's launch vehicles and satellites from the 1980s.

with even more complex reactions and events within the Sun itself. We have learned much more about the composition and behavior of comets, leading scientists to wonder whether these cosmic ice balls might be capable of seeding a galaxy with elements necessary for life as we know it.

We have developed the capability to look at our galaxy and the distant universe in parts of the electromagnetic spectrum that are blocked by the Earth's atmosphere. From this perspective, we have discovered that the universe is a vastly more complex and fascinating place than we ever imagined it was. We have discovered pulsars, quasars, neutron stars, and other, more mystifying, phenomena such as

gamma ray bursts and black holes. We have found echoes of our genesis in the distant glow of the universe, and evidence of primordial elements from a time when the stars were young. We have found ourselves witnessing the birth, life, and death of stars in distant galaxies, giving us a window to our own past, present, and future.

At the same time, we have discovered that our view from space has given us an entirely new perspective on our home planet Earth. Our satellites have allowed extensively improved global communications, reliable weather prediction, and monitoring of valuable natural resources. They also have allowed scientists to learn much more about the complex systems that make life possible here on Earth, as well as potential threats to the health of those systems. If global warming, ozone, and El Niño climate patterns are now household terms and concerns, it is largely because of spacecraft Goddard helped put into space and atmospheric models the Center's scientists developed from those satellites' data.

Satellite technology made it possible to turn theories and dreams into science and knowledge, rejuvenating the field of science itself. In the process, it has also created whole new disciplines of scientists. The advent of sounding rocket and satellites created space physicists who could delve into solar physics and "fields and particles" research around Earth and other planets in the solar system. Years later, the results from various Earth-oriented satellites would lead to the creation of climatologists—scientists who combined atmospheric and oceanographic research to look at the interrelated systems that affect global climate changes here on Earth.

A computer-enhanced image of Hurricane Linda created from GOES satellite data.

THE NEW MILLENNIUM: GODDARD'S NEXT FORTY

Today, Goddard stands at the threshold of a new millennium and a new era of space exploration. The Center has grown and evolved dramatically in its first 40 years, but so has the world. And the challenges faced by those trying to explore the mysteries of that world and the universe beyond it have changed, as well. Once, constraints of technology drove Goddard's scientists and engineers to be extremely creative and innovative in their methods. The need for innovation and flexibility is as great today as it ever was, but the driving force is economic, not technological. In a post-Cold War world of shrinking budgets, scientists and engineers simply need to find ways to do more for less.

The players involved in the exploration of space also have evolved and changed. When Goddard was founded, no one really knew how to build a satellite.

Today, industry has matured greatly, making it possible to consider new kinds of relationships and agreements. Indeed, one of the legacies of Goddard's 40 years of effort is the expertise its scientists, engineers, and technicians developed and passed on to the Center's industry partners in their many joint efforts. This shared experience is one of the reasons industry has developed the ability to do some of the tasks once reserved for NASA alone.

At the cutting edge of technology and knowledge, change is the only constant. And as with any other development at Goddard over the past 40 years, the changes the Center faces today are a kind of scientific research in and of themselves. If history is any guide, it will take numerous attempts and adjustments before the correct mix of method and structure is found. It is even possible that, in the ever-changing world of technology and scientific exploration, the "correct" approach or mix may never be achieved. But the willingness to try new approaches is what allowed Goddard's early employees to overcome the enormous challenges and obstacles they faced in conquering even the basics of space flight. Indeed, many would argue that an openness to new ideas or approaches is critical for any scientific progress to occur at all.

In the 1960s, Goddard's employees were driven by a collective enthusiasm for exploration and a belief that their efforts were going to make a difference not only to science, but also to the security and life of American citizens. It is harder to keep

A small part of the Hubble Deep Field South. One of the deepest views of space ever made.

that level of enthusiasm without the direct external threat the Russians provided. But the need for that innovation and enthusiasm is as great as it ever was.

If we are to continue to explore our own planet and the universe in which we live, we have to keep our spirit of innovation alive and find ways to make the best use of people's talents, time, and energy. It is not an easy task. And in some cases, it may be hard to explain the economic value of the effort. But it is our curiosity about the world beyond the horizon that brought us out of the caves and has driven civilization forward ever since. Indeed, our curiosity and thirst for knowledge are part of what make us human. We may not be able to express this fact in dollars and cents on a balance sheet. But we sense almost instinctively that our minds, imaginations, and souls need sustenance every bit as much as our bodies. If we cease our search for new lands and ideas, if we stop trying to expand our minds and inspire our imaginations, we stagnate; and a life force within us begins to die.

As we move into a new millennium, the data satellites generate will increase in quality and quantity, generating a need for new data processing and archive centers like this EOSDIS facility at Goddard.

Yet to learn more about our world and to keep new ideas flowing through our minds, we need people willing to undertake the challenge of stepping into the unknown and exploring a territory that is as demanding and unforgiving as it ever was. Some things have not changed in the past 40 years. Space is still a new and unknown frontier, as full of risk, challenge, and frustration as it was the day we began to explore it. And that exploration is still a complex and expensive endeavor that requires the cooperation of many different people, institutions, and countries.

The technical obstacles may not be as great as they once were, but the goalposts have moved. Getting into space is no longer sufficient. The task now is to go further and to do it with fewer resources. To accomplish this task requires people with the same dedication, enthusiasm, and passion that made the first successful satellites

possible. And this, more than any other single accomplishment or project, is the legacy of the Goddard Space Flight Center. For 40 years, whether it has been in ramshackle warehouses, the muddy swampland of Beltsville, or the neat buildings that now adorn its sprawling campus, Goddard has been a place of enthusiasm, innovation, and dogged determination to develop satellites that could improve our lives and bring the universe within our reach.

The sagas of the Apollo and Space Shuttle astronauts may be better known, but the researchers, administrative support staff, and other support personnel at Goddard have experienced their own share of adventure in 40 years of space exploration. The control room at Goddard was every bit as tense as Mission Control at Cape Canaveral or the Johnson Space Center, whether or not any particular spacecraft had people on board. Setting up and maintaining the worldwide network to track satellites and the Apollo missions involved unique challenges, from coping with political unrest to making use of makeshift telegraph lines across miles of Australian outback territory.

There were technicians and support personnel who frantically trouble-shot computer tracking systems or pieced together satellites that developed problems shortly before launch. There were engineers who spent sleepless nights coordinating the repair of the Hubble Space Telescope. There were scientists who were willing to devote 10 or 15 years of their career to a single research project, knowing the spacecraft might blow up 2 minutes after launch. There were disappointments, failures, and even tragedies.

Success came at a price. And the price was dedication. Sometimes, it was simply the refusal to give up, and the willingness to risk failure in the hope of finding out something worthwhile. But for 40 years, it has been this intangible, unquantifiable element of passion and dedication that has enabled Goddard to make its invaluable contribution to space science and to American society.

The world is more complex than it ever was. And so is the field of space flight. There are new pressures, new constraints, and new relationships. Forty years after its founding, one of Goddard's biggest challenges remains maintaining a balance between project teams and the Centerwide population, scientists and engineers, internal and external communities,

industry and government, U.S. and international efforts, and the cost, schedule, and reliability of the projects it undertakes. At the same time, it needs to keep the flexibility and willingness to consider new approaches and ideas, the passion for exploration, and the enthusiasm for innovation that made space flight possible in the first place.

Our journeys into space comprise the greatest adventure the human race ever has undertaken. We watched, transfixed, as the Echo satellite moved across the night sky and Neil Armstrong became the first human to set foot on the Moon. We find ourselves moved beyond words by images from the Hubble Space Telescope that make us hear and feel the music of the spheres and the power of cosmos. Each new discovery reminds us once again that the universe is a truly majestic and mysterious realm. Our explorations in space keep the wondering child inside us alive, as we take step after step into a magical, technicolor world we only know is far more vast and complex than the land we call home.

And yet, our journeys into space have given us a whole new perspective on home, as well. Viewed from space, we are all residents of a single planet Earth, and we have begun to realize how interconnected we all really are.

The effort that has brought us this perspective has not been easy, but no exploration ever is. We have mapped certain portions of this unforgiving cosmic territory and have begun to venture into others. Along the way, we have achieved spectacular successes and endured heart-breaking setbacks. But we are still only scratching the surface of the mysteries that lie in this strange new frontier. There is no single list of questions left to answer about our planet, our solar system or our universe, because the more we learn, the more we realize how much there is left to learn. As we discover answers to one question, we find clues to another we had not yet thought to ask.

Over the past 40 years, we have discovered that space is not only a new frontier, but also an endless one. And exploring it will continue to be one of our greatest ongoing challenges and adventures—a quest of the mind, the imagination, and the human spirit to improve our lives, preserve our home planet, and expand our understanding of ourselves and the vast, mysterious, and powerful universe in which we live.

The Hubble Space Telescope opened a window to wonders of the universe that still lie waiting to be discovered and explored. Under the Hubble's lens, this nearby galaxy shows itself to be comprised of numerous distinctive elements, including clumpy gas clouds, darkened dust lanes, and young luminous central star clusters.

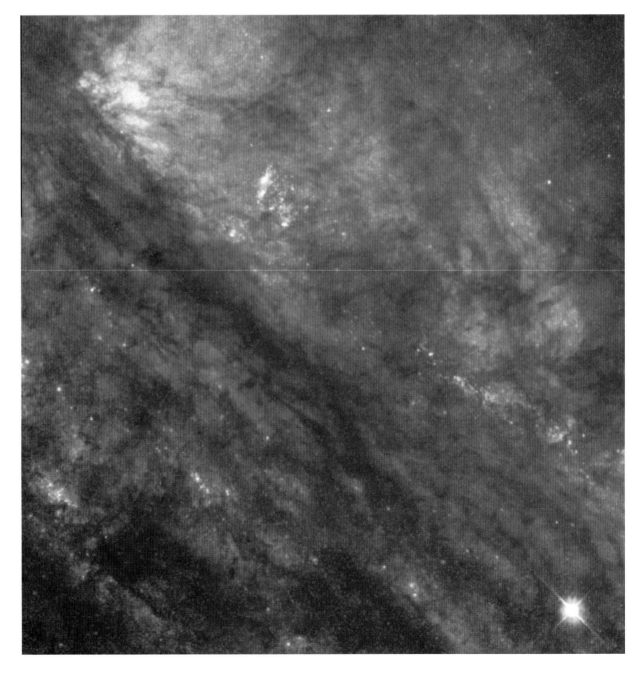

References

CHAPTER 1

1   Alfred Rosenthal, *Venture Into Space* (Washington, D.C.: National Aeronautics and Space Administration, NASA SP-4301, 1968), 20-21; Homer G. Newell, *Beyond the Atmosphere* (Washington, D.C.: National Aeronautics and Space Administration, NASA SP-4211, 1980), 55-56.

2   When President Eisenhower originally proposed the civilian space agency, it was called the National Aeronautics and Space Agency, but the name was later changed to the National Aeronautics and Space Administration. Shirley Thomas, *Men of Space* (New York: Chilton Books, 1965), 84.

3   Newell, *Beyond the Atmosphere*, 408.

4   Today, NASA refers to this part of its mission as human space flight. But in the early days, the astronaut program was known both formally and informally as the "manned space flight program." So in some instances I use the term "manned space flight" when referring to this part of NASA in a historical context, even though that term is now outdated.

5   Newell, *Beyond the Atmosphere*, 246; Samuel Keller, interview with author, Washington, D.C., 15 October 1997.

6   According to Homer G. Newell, "on 22 July 1965 (NASA Associate Administrator Robert) Seamans removed Goett from the directorship ... with the concurrence of both (James) Webb and (Hugh) Dryden." Newell, *Beyond the Atmosphere*, 256; Harry J. Goett, interview with author, Los Altos Hills, California, 13 February 1998.

7   Thomas, *Men of Space*, 94.

8   Christopher Kraft, as quoted in Kathleen M. Mogan, Frank P. Mintz, ed., *Keeping Track: A History of the GSFC Tracking and Data Acquisition Networks: 1957 to 1991* (Greenbelt, MD: NASA Publication, undated), 104.

9   Andre Gide, as quoted in Julia Cameron, *The Artist's Way: A Spiritual Path to Higher Creativity* (New York: G. P. Putnam's Sons, 1992), p. 199.

CHAPTER 2

1   John C. Mather and John Boslough, *The Very First Light* (New York: Basic Books, 1996), 12-13.

2   Homer G. Newell, *Beyond the Atmosphere* (Washington, D.C.: National Aeronautics and Space Administration, NASA SP-4211, 1980), 25-26.

3   Alfred Rosenthal, *Venture Into Space* (Washington, D.C.: National Aeronautics and Space Administration, NASA SP-4301, 1968), 6-13.

4   Newell, *Beyond the Atmosphere*, 31-32.

5   William R. Corliss, *NASA Sounding Rockets, 1958-1968* (Washington, D.C.: National Aeronautics and Space Administration, NASA SP-4401, 1971), 29; Newell, *Beyond the Atmosphere*, 51.

6   William R. Corliss, "The Evolution of the Satellite Tracking and Data Network (STADAN)," Goddard Historical Note Number 3, X-202-67-26 (Greenbelt, Maryland: Goddard Space Flight Center, January 1967), 12.

7 Rosenthal, *Venture Into Space*, 16; Newell, *Beyond the Atmosphere*, 31, 54.

8 Newell, *Beyond the Atmosphere*, 55-56; Rosenthal, *Venture Into Space*, 20-22; Robert Rosholt, *An Administrative History of NASA, 1958-1963* (Washington, D.C.: National Aeronautics and Space Administration, NASA SP-4101, 1966), 3-8; John W. Townsend, Jr., interview with author, Cabin John, Maryland, 15 October 1997.

9 For more detailed information on the formation of NASA, see Rosholt, *An Administrative History of NASA, 1958-1963*, and Newell, *Beyond the Atmosphere*, 87-99.

10 Rosholt, *An Administrative History of NASA, 1958-1963*, 13.

11 Rosenthal, *Venture Into Space*, 22; John E. Naugle, *First Among Equals* (Washington, D.C., National Aeronautics and Space Administration, 1991), 13-14; J. H. Capshew, "Within Goddard's Orbit: Satellites, Space Research and NASA," unpublished manuscript, 28 September 1989, Chapter 2, 12.

12 The Army had successfully launched a Jupiter C missile into space and retrieved its nose cone after re-entry sometime before the beginning of November 1957 (Rosenthal, *The Early Years*, 126); Naugle, *First Among Equals*, 6; Dr. Frank B. McDonald, "IMPs, EGOs, and Skyhooks," *Journal of Geophysical Research*, Vol. 101, A5, 1 May 1996, 10,523; John C. Clark, phone interview with author, 18 May 1998.

13 Alfred Rosenthal, ed. *NASA Space Missions Since 1958* (Washington D.C.: National Aeronautics and Space Administration, 1982), 1-14; "NASA Major Launch Record," Launch summary, 1958-1992, unpublished document, prepared by Chao Yang, Goddard Space Flight Center Library, 1997.

14 John W. Townsend, Jr., Interview, 15 October 1997.

15 "Press release by Senator J. Glenn Beall, Maryland, at Washington D.C. Office, 1 August 1958," from NASA Headquarters History Office Archives.

16 Rosenthal, *Venture Into Space*, 284-85.

17 Alfred Rosenthal, *The Early Years*, (Washington, D.C.: National Aeronautics and Space Administration, undated), 17-20, 27-28; Rosenthal, *Venture Into Space*, 27-28; Rosholt, *An Administrative History of NASA*, 47; Capshew, "Within Goddard's Orbit, Chapter 3, 5-12; John W. Townsend, Jr., interview, 15 October 1997.

18 Rosenthal, *Venture Into Space*, 286-289; T. Keith Glennan, Memorandum, 1 May 1959, from NASA Headquarters History Office archives.

19 Rosenthal, *Venture Into Space*, 209.

20 McDonald, "IMPs, EGOs, and Skyhooks," 10,523-10,524; Rosenthal, *Venture Into Space*, 290-291; John W. Townsend, Jr., interview, 15 October 1997; Roland Van Allen, interview with author, GSFC, Greenbelt, Maryland, 6 October 1997; Memorandum, from John W. Townsend, Jr. to T. Keith Glennan, 6 March 1959, from NASA Headquarters History Office archives.

21 Townsend, Jr., interview, 15 October 1997; Roland Van Allen, interview, 6 October 1997; Frank McDonald, "IMPs, EGOs, and Skyhooks," 10,523-10,524; Frank McDonald, phone interview with author, 5 May 1998.

22 Rosenthal, *The Early Years*, 28.

23 John W. Townsend, Jr., interview, 15 October 1997; Samuel Keller, interview with author, Washington, D.C., 15 October 1997.

24 Alberta Moran, interview with author, GSFC, Greenbelt, MD, 10 July 1997.

25 The Space Science Board name was changed to the Space Studies Board around 1989. The Board contributes ideas for missions,

but does not make decisions about which experiments are selected for the missions.

26 John E. Naugle, *First Among Equals*, 37, 51-53, 57-59, 67-69, 82-85.

27 *NASA Space Missions Since 1958*, 135, 112, 28.

28 John E. Naugle, *First Among Equals*, 61.

29 John W. Townsend, Jr., interview, 15 October 1997; Frank McDonald, interview, 16 October 1997; Les Meredith and Dave Blanchard, interview with author, GSFC, Greenbelt, Maryland, 21 October 1997.

30 Samuel Keller, interview, 15 October 1997; John New, interview with author, Lanham, Maryland, 15 October 1997.

31 Frank McDonald, interview, 16 October 1997; John W. Townsend, Jr., interview, 15 October 1997.

32 Newell, *Beyond the Atmosphere*, 114-115; Rosenthal, *An Administrative History of NASA*, 248-49.

33 Robert Jastrow, interview with author, Los Angeles, California, 11 February 1998; Robert Jastrow, *The Enchanted Loom*, (New York: Simon & Shuster, 1981), 9; "Establishment of an Institute for Space Studies," Memorandum, from Robert Jastrow to the Director of Space Flight Programs, with initialled note "approved subject to attached memo by Dr. Glennan" by Abe Silverstein, 13 December 1960, from NASA Headquarters History Office archives; Newell, *Beyond the Atmosphere*, 237-240.

34 John W. Townsend, Jr., interview, 15 October 1997; John C. Clark, phone interview with author, 18 May 1998.

35 *NASA Space Missions Since 1958*, 75, 87,

36 *NASA Space Missions Since 1958*, 29, 32, 96, 100, 107; Andrew J. Butrica, ed., *Beyond the Ionosphere* (Washington, D.C.: National Aeronautics and Space Administration, 1997), 104.

37 Newell, *Beyond the Atmosphere*, 109.

38 Newell, *Beyond the Atmosphere*, 251-157; Harry J. Goett, interview with author, Los Altos Hills, California, 13 February 1998; George Pieper, interview with author, GSFC, Greenbelt, Maryland, 14 October 1997; John W. Townsend, Jr., interview, 15 October 1997.

39 A Reduction in Force, or RIF, is the formal term for layoffs of civil servants. (George Pieper, interview, 19 November 1997, comments, 31 August 1998.)

40 Frank Ceppolina, interview with author, GSFC, Greenbelt, Maryland, 12 January 1998.

41 Wallace H. Tucker, *The Star Splitters: The High Energy Astronomy Observatories* (Washington, D.C.: National Aeronautics and Space Administration, 1984); Margorie Townsend, interview with author, Washington, D.C., 22 November 1997; Nancy Roman, phone interview with author, 27 January 1998; *NASA Space Missions Since 1958*, 454-455, 513-516.

42 Nancy Roman, phone interviews with author, 27 January 1998 and 23 February 1998; Jesse Mitchell, phone interview with author, 4 March 1998; Albert Opp, phone interview with author, 25 February 1998; John C. Clark, phone interview with author, 18 May 1998; George Pieper, interview with author, Greenbelt, Maryland, 19 November 1997.

43 In a sense, support for funding any NASA project is affected by national priorities. But the Earth Science research results themselves were more likely to be used as a basis for regulation or legislation than space science results, and therefore, as the scientists relate, were more often attacked by both sides of any related policy debate, particularly with regard to environmental issues. This link to legislation or regulation gave Earth Science projects an additional element of complexity that Space Science projects typically did not have.

44 Robert Cooper, interview with author, Greenbelt, Maryland, 20 October 1997; Vincent V. Salomonson, interview, 19 November 1997; Robert Price, interview, 16 January 1998; John M. Klineberg, interview with author, Palo Alto, California, 26 November 1997; John C. Clark, phone interview with author, 18 May 1998; W. Henry Lambright, "Administrative Entrepreneur-ship and Space Technology: The Ups and Downs of 'Mission to Planet Earth,'" *Public Administration Review*, Vol. 54, No. 3, March/April 1994, 97-104.

45 Jim Gravura, phone interview with author, 3 March 1998.

46 "Compton Gamma-Ray Observatory: Exploring the Mysteries of Time," Fact Sheet, from GSFC Public Affairs Office files.

47 Wallops underwent several name changes over the years. In 1946, it became the "Pilotless Aircraft Research Division (PARD)" of Langley. When the NACA became NASA in 1958, it became an independent NASA Center and was renamed the Wallops Island Station. When it was absorbed into Goddard in 1982, it was renamed once again, as the Wallops Flight Facility. James Hansen, *Engineer in Charge* (Washington, D.C.: National Aeronautics and Space Administration, NASA SP-4305, 1987), 267-270, 567; Arnold Torres, Ray Stanley and Keith Koehler, interview with author, Wallops Island, 23 October 1997; Harold D. Wallace, Jr., *Wallops Station and the Creation of an American Space Program*, (Washington, D.C.: National Aeronautics and Space Administration, NASA SP-4311, 1997), 6-16.

48 Goddard Space Flight Center organizational charts, from the GSFC Library.

49 Goddard Space Flight Center organizational charts, from the GSFC Library, Greenbelt, Maryland; Dave Shrewsberry, interview with author, GSFC, Greenbelt, Maryland, 15 January 1998; Jon Busse, phone interview with author, 3 March 1998; Arnold Torres, Ray Stanley and Keith Koehler, interview, 23 October 1997; Tom Young, interview with author, GSFC, Greenbelt, Maryland, 18 November 1997.

50 Charles Gunn, interview with author, Falls Church, Virginia, 15 January 1998; John C. Clark, interview, 18 May 1998.

51 Dave Shrewsberry, interview with author, GSFC, Greenbelt, Maryland, 15 January 1998; "NASA's Small Explorer Program: Faster, Better, Cheaper," Fact Sheet FS-96(07)-014, from GSFC Public Affairs Office files, July 1996.

52 John C. Mather, *The Very First Light*, xvii.

53 Bill Robie, *For the Greatest Achievement*, (Washington, D.C.: Smithsonian Institution Press, 1993), frontispiece.

54 W. Henry Lambright, "Administrative Entrepreneurship and Space Technology: The Ups and Downs of 'Mission to Planet Earth,'" *Public Administration Review*, Vol. 54, No. 2, March/April 1994, 100.

55 Robert Price, interview with author, GSFC, Greenbelt, Maryland, 16 January 1998; Vincent V. Salomonson, interview with author, GSFC, Greenbelt, Maryland, 20 October 1997; W. Henry Lambright, "Administrative Entrepreneurship and Space Technology: The Ups and Downs of 'Mission to Planet Earth,'" *Public Administration Review*, Vol. 54, No. 2, March/April 1994, 97-104.

56 Orlando Figueroa, interview with author, GSFC, Greenbelt, Maryland, 14 January 1998; W. Brian Keegan, interview with author, GSFC, Greenbelt, Maryland, 21 November 1997; Joseph H. Rothenberg, interview with author, NASA HQ, Washington, D.C., 15 January 1998; Stephen Holt, interview with author, GSFC, Greenbelt, Maryland, 14 January 1998.

57 Arnold Torres, Ray Stanley and Keith Koehler, interview, 23 October 1997.

58 Tom Young, interview, 18 November 1997.

59 Tom Huber, interview with author, GSFC, Greenbelt, Maryland, 20 November 1997; Joseph H. Rothenberg, interview, 15 January 1998; "Response to Initial Set of NASA Advisory Council Questions for GSFC," 15 September 1997, Viewgraphs, from Joseph H. Rothenberg files; James Adams, telephone interview with author, 16 July 1998.

60 "Space Operations Management," Memorandum from Daniel S. Goldin to Directors, NASA Field Installations, 18 October 1995, from the files of Arthur J. Fuchs, GSFC; Arthur J. Fuchs, interview with author, GSFC, Greenbelt, Maryland, 12 January 1998.

61 Arnold Torres, Ray Stanley and Keith Koehler, interview, 23 October 1997.

62 Antonio J. Busalacchi, phone interview with author, 28 February 1998; Arnold Torres, Ray Stanley and Keith Koehler, interview, 23 October 1998.

CHAPTER 3

1 Alfred Rosenthal, ed., *NASA Space Missions Since 1958*, (Washington, D.C.: National Aeronautics and Space Administration, 1982), 435; Alfred Bester, *The Life and Death of a Satellite*, (Boston: Little, Brown and Co., 1966), 60-61.

2 John Boeckel, interview with author, GSFC, Greenbelt, Maryland, 17 October 1997; Margorie Townsend, interview with author, Washington, D.C., 22 November 1997; John New, interview with author, Lanham, Maryland, 15 October 1997; Homer G. Newell, *Beyond the Atmosphere*, 144-149; Frank McDonald, interview with author, GSFC, Greenbelt, Maryland, 16 October 1997.

3 Karen Kaplan, "Outer Space Outage Signals Growing Dependence on Satellites," *Los Angeles Times*, 21 May 1998, A1, A31.

4 John Boeckel, interview, 17 October 1997.

5 John Boeckel, interview, 17 October 1997; Roland Van Allen with author, GSFC, Greenbelt, Maryland, interview, 16 October 1997; John New, interview, 15 October 1997; Margorie Townsend, interview, 22 November 1997; Bester, *The Life and Death of a Satellite*, 74-76.

6 John W. Townsend, Jr., interview with author, Cabin John, Maryland, 15 October 1997.

7 Harry J. Goett, interview with author, Los Altos Hills, California, 13 February 1998; John W. Townsend, Jr., interview with author, 15 October 1997; John Boeckel, interview, 17 October 1997; John New, interview, 15 October 1997; Homer G. Newell, *Beyond the Atmosphere*, 165-170.

8 A good example of this danger was SeaSat A —a satellite Goddard did not build, but which the Center was handling through its tracking and data network. Three months after its launch in June 1978, the spacecraft developed problems. Engineers realized it was ailing when it passed over Goddard's ground tracking station. They frantically began trouble-shooting the problem, but by the time the spacecraft came within range of the next ground station that could uplink commands to fix it, the satellite's batteries had gone dead. *NASA Space Missions Since 1958*, 700-701; Robert Cooper, interview with author, Greenbelt, Maryland, 20 October 1997; Robert Price, interview with author, GSFC, Greenbelt, Maryland, 16 January 1998; Tom Huber, interview with author, GSFC, Greenbelt, Maryland, 20 November 1997.

9 Nancy Roman, phone interview with author, 23 February 1998; Frank McDonald, interview with author, GSFC,

Greenbelt, Maryland, 16 October 1997; John New, interview, 15 October 1997; Frank McDonald, "IMPs, EGOs and Skyhooks," *Journal of Geophysical Research*, Vol. 101, No. A5, 10,526; Goddard Space Flight Center Organizational Charts, from the GSFC Technical Library, Greenbelt, Maryland.

10 John New, interview, 15 October 1997.

11 John New, interview, 15 October 1997; Harry J. Goett, interview, 13 February 1998.

12 Homer G. Newell, *Beyond the Atmosphere*, 159-160, 170.

13 Alfred Bester, *Life and Death of a Satellite*, 177-180.

14 Jon Busse, phone interview with author, 3 March 1998.

15 Arnold Torres, Ray Stanley and Keith Koehler, interview with author, Wallops Island, Virginia, 23 October 1997; Jon Busse, interview, 3 March 1998, William R. Corliss, *NASA Sounding Rockets 1958-1968* (Washington, D.C.: National Aeronautics and Space Administration, NASA SP-4401, 1971), 2-3.

16 "NASA Sounding Rocket Launch Vehicles," Fact Sheet, from Suborbital Projects Directorate files, Wallops Island, Virginia.

17 Arnold Torres, Ray Stanley and Keith Koehler, interview, 23 October 1997.

18 Arnold Torres, Ray Stanley and Keith Koehler, interview, 23 October 1997; Scientific Balloon and Aircraft Fact Sheets, from GSFC Public Affairs Office files.

19 Homer G. Newell, *Beyond the Atmosphere*, 133-134; *NASA Space Missions Since 1958*, 3-17; Charles Gunn, interview with author, Falls Church, Virginia, 16 January 1998.

20 John W. Townsend, Jr., interview with author, Cabin John, Maryland, 15 October 1997; Charles Gunn, interview, 16 January 1998.

21 Charles Gunn, interview, 16 January 1998; "The Delta Expendable Launch Vehicle," Fact Sheet, from GSFC Public Affairs Office files.

22 Don Margolies and Jim Barrowman, interview with author, GSFC, Greenbelt, Maryland, 13 January 1998; Dave Shrewsberry, interview with author, GSFC, Greenbelt, Maryland, 15 January 1998; "Science Research with the Spartan," "The Hitchhiker Project," "Shuttle Small Payloads Capabilities," "NASA's Get Away Special Program," Fact Sheets/Booklets from GSFC Special Payloads Division and Public Affairs Office files; "Get Away Special (GAS) Flight History," Memorandum, from Susan Olden to Dave Shrewsberry, et al., 9 December 1997.

23 For more information on the IGY, see Chapter 2.

24 This number is approximate because the network was never static. New stations continued to be added and others closed as the tracking needs developed and changed. Information on minitrack network from: William R. Corliss, "The Evolution of the Satellite Tracking and Data Network (STADAN)," Goddard Historical Note Number 3, X-202-67-26 (Greenbelt, Maryland: Goddard Space Flight Center, January 1967) 1-41; Kathleen M. Mogan and Frank P. Mintz, ed., *Keeping Track: GSFC Tracking and Data Acquisition Networks: 1957 to 1991* (Greenbelt, Maryland: Goddard Space Flight Center, undated), 5-14, 79-81.

25 Verne Stelter, interview with author, GSFC, Greenbelt, Maryland, 20 October 1997.

26 *Keeping Track*, 89, 104.

27 *Keeping Track*, 41, 101.

28 Verne Stelter, interview, 20 October 1997; *Keeping Track*, 38-41.

29 *Keeping Track*, 39; "NASA Major Launch Record," from GSFC Library files.

30 Verne Stelter, interview, 20 October 1997; *Keeping Track*, 96.

31 The name of the network was changed from the Mercury Space Flight Network to the Manned Space Flight Network at the beginning of the Gemini program.

32 Keeping Track, 42-49, 57-66.

33 John C. Clark, phone interview with author, 18 May 1998; Verne Stelter, interview, 20 October 1997; Marjorie Townsend, interview, 22 November 1997; *Keeping Track,* 104.

34 *Keeping Track,* 56; GSFC Organizational Charts, from the GSFC Library files.

35 *Keeping Track,* 61.

36 Verne Stelter, interview, 20 October 1997; Peter Bracken, interview with author, GSFC, Greenbelt, Maryland, 17 October 1997; Dale Harris, interview with author, GSFC, Greenbelt, Maryland, 19 November 1997; Arthur J. Fuchs, interview with author, GSFC, Greenbelt, Maryland, 12 January 1998; *Keeping Track,* 70-75.

37 Roland Van Allen, interview with author, GSFC, Greenbelt, Maryland, 16 October 1997; Peter Bracken, interview, 17 October 1997; Rick Obenschain, interview with author, GSFC, Greenbelt, Maryland, 20 November 1997; "Product Levels - Layman's Definitions," Email Memorandum, from H. K. Ramapriyan to Rick Obenschain, 24 November 1997.

38 Stephen Holt, interview with author, GSFC, Greenbelt, Maryland, 14 January 1998; Rick Obenschain, interview, 20 November 1997; "EOS Data and Information System (EOSDIS) Overview," viewgraphs, from Rick Obenschain files; "The Earth Observing System Data and Information System," Fact Sheet, from GSFC Public Affairs Office files.

CHAPTER 4

1 K.C. Cole, "Study of Black Holes Backs Einstein's Theory of Gravity," *Los Angeles Times,* 7 November 1997, A-1, A-32-33, (referencing research with Goddard's Rossi X-ray Timing Explorer (RXTE).

2 Homer G. Newell, *Beyond the Atmosphere* (Washington, D.C.: NASA SP-4211,1980), 39, 82-84, 329.

3 These missions included Explorers 7, 13, 16, and 23. For specific launch dates, see Appendix A.

4 Frank McDonald, interview with author, GSFC, Greenbelt, Maryland, 16 October 1997; Stephen P. Maran, email comments, 14 July 1998; "Advanced Composition Explorer," booklet, from Don Margolies' files, GSFC.

5 Frank McDonald originally named the series Interplanetary Monitoring Probes, but it was soon changed from Probes to Platforms.

6 Frank McDonald, interview, 16 October 1997; George Pieper, phone interview with author, 20 July 1998, comments, 31 August 1998; John W. Townsend, Jr., phone interview with author, 28 August 1998.

7 Frank McDonald, interview, 16 October 1997; Frank McDonald, "IMPs, EGOs, and Skyhooks," *Journal of Geophysical Research,* Vol. 101, No. A5, 1 May 1996, 10,521-10,530; "NASA Major Launch Record," from GSFC Library files; Alfred Rosenthal, ed., *NASA Space Missions Since 1958* (Washington, D.C.: National Aeronautics and Space Administration, 1982).

8 Newell, *Beyond the Atmosphere,* 338-340.

9 *NASA Space Missions Since 1958,* 135, 179, 212, 270, 306, 382; John C. Clark, phone interview with author, 18 May 1998; Alfred Rosenthal, *Venture Into Space,* (Washington, D.C.: National Aeronautics and Space Administration, 1968), 47, 231,-232; Tom Huber, interview with author, GSFC, Greenbelt, Maryland, 20 November 1997;

Robert Bordeaux, interview with author, Fulton, Maryland, 21 October 1997. (For more information on the Rapid Spacecraft Procurement Initiative, see Chapter 2.)

10 *NASA Space Missions Since 1958*, 675, 710; Frank McDonald, "IMPs, EGOs, and Skyhooks," 10,528.

11 "Advanced Composition Explorer," GSFC Booklet, from Don Margolies' files, 9-19; "Our Sun: A Look Under the Hood," Fact Sheet, from GSFC Public Affairs Office files; Dick Thompson, "Eyes on the Storm-Tossed Sun," *Time*, 8 September 1997, 68-69.

12 John M. Klineberg, interview with author, Palo Alto, California, 24 November 1997; "The Geotail Mission," "Polar Satellite Will Study Effects of Solar Plasma," "ISTP Unites Scientists for Study of Sun-Earth System," "Wind Spacecraft to Study Solar Breeze," Fact Sheets, from GSFC Public Affairs Office files; Solar and Heliospheric Observatory (SOHO) Fact Sheet/Educational Aide, from SOHO project office files; "Advanced Composition Explorer (ACE)," Booklet, from Don Margolies' files; "GGS Polar Mission Profile," Booklet, produced by Lockheed Martin Astro Space, Princeton, New Jersey, undated.

13 "SMEX Project History," Fact Sheet, from SMEX project Web Page; "FAST Satellite Probes Mysteries of the Aurora," Fact Sheet, from GSFC Public Affairs Office files.

14 Newell, *Beyond the Atmosphere*, 363-369; Stephen P. Maran, interview with author, GSFC, Greenbelt, Maryland, 14 January 1998; "Our Sun: A Look Under the Hood," NASA Fact Sheet FS-1997-01-002-HQ-S, January 1997, from GSFC Public Affairs Office files.

15 *NASA Space Missions Since 1958*, 178.

16 For more information on Multi-mission Modular Spacecraft, see Chapter 3.

17 Arthur J. Fuchs, interview with author, GSFC, Greenbelt, Maryland, 17 October 1997; Frank Ceppolina, interview with author, GSFC, Greenbelt, Maryland, 12 January 1998; *Major NASA Satellite Missions and Key Participants*, Vol. IV—1984 and 1985 (Greenbelt, Maryland: Goddard Space Flight Center, 1985), 10-15.

18 Stephen P. Maran, interview, 14 January 1998; *NASA Missions Since 1958*, 746-748; Stephen P. Maran, "A New Look at Old Sol," *Natural Science*, June 1997, 154-161; "Heat Source of Sun's Corona Said Found by SOHO Satellite," Press Release, from the Royal Astronomical Society, 27 March 1998; "SOHO Data on Coronal Ejections May Tell Where Solar Wind Begins," Press Release, from the Royal Astronomical Society, 27 March 1998; "Tiny Explosions, Size of Earth, Said Found on Sun by SOHO Satellite," Press Release, from the Royal Astronomical Society, 26 January 1998; Dick Thompson, "Eyes on the Storm-Tossed Sun," *Time*, 8 September 1997, 68-69; R. Cowen, "Deepening Insight into Solar Outbursts," *Science News*, Vol. 152, 20-27 December 1997, 390; R. Cowen, "Spacecraft Probes Beneath Sun's Surface," *Science News*, Vol 152, 6 September 1997, 150; Alexander Hellemans, "SOHO Probes the Sun's Turbulent Neighborhood," *Science*, Vol. 277, 25 July 1997, 479; David Ehrenstein, "SOHO Traces the Sun's Hot Currents," *Science*, Vol. 277, 5 September 1997, 1438; Randy Showstack, "Scientists Unveil New Theory and Findings About Solar Eruptions," *EOS*, 16 December 1997, 581; "New Satellite Shows Sun in Stunning Detail," Press Release, from NASA HQ, 29 May 1998; "Our Sun: A Look Under the Hood," Fact Sheet, January 1997, from GSFC Public Affairs Office files; "Advanced Composition Explorer," GSFC Booklet, from Don Margolies' files; "Transition Region and Coronal Explorer," Fact Sheet, from GSFC TRACE project web page;

"Spartan 201: NASA's Mission to Explore the Sun's Corona," Fact Sheet, from GSFC Spartan project web page; "The Ulysses Mission - A Deep Space Voyage to High Latitudes over the Solar Pole," Fact Sheet, from the Ulysses/NASA internet web page; "SOHO Illuminates the Sun," Fact Sheet/Educational Reference Guide, from SOHO project office files, GSFC.

19 *NASA Space Missions Since 1958*, 321-326, 547-548; Dave Blanchard, interview with author, GSFC, Greenbelt, Maryland, 22 October 1997; John C. Clark, phone interview with author, 18 May 1998; "SWAS Spacecraft Probes Mysteries of Star Formation," Fact Sheet FS-96(07)-012, July 1996, from GSFC Public Affairs Office files; Wallace H. Tucker, *The Star Splitters* (Washington, D.C.: National Aeronautics and Space Administration, 1984), 6-7, 91.

20 John C. Mather, interview with author, GSFC, Greenbelt, Maryland, 24 October 1997; John C. Mather and John Boslough, *The Very First Light*, (New York: Basic Books, 1996), 113-114; John C. Mather, "Cosmic Background Explorer Observes the Primeval Explosion," GSFC Booklet, undated.

21 John C. Mather, interview, 24 October 1997; Stephen Holt, interview with author, GSFC, Greenbelt, Maryland, 14 January 1998; Mather, *The Very First Light*; "COBE: Revealing Secrets of the Big Bang, Fact Sheet, from GSFC Public Affairs Office files; "Astronomers Discover an Infrared Background Glow in the Universe," NASA Press Release, 9 January 1998.

22 John W. Townsend, Jr., interview with author, Cabin John, Maryland, 15 October 1997; Nancy Roman, phone interview with author, 23 February 1998; George Pieper, interview with author, GSFC, Greenbelt, Maryland, 14 October 1997; John Boeckel, interview with author, GSFC, Greenbelt, Maryland, 17 October 1997; Tom Huber, interview with author, GSFC, Greenbelt,

Maryland, 20 November 1997; *NASA Space Missions Since 1958*, 202-203, 340-341, 452, 517-518.

23 For more discussion on how and why the Hubble program was set up the way it was, see Chapter 2.

24 Perkin-Elmer is now called Raytheon Optical Systems.

25 "Axial" refers to the four instruments located in long modules along the "axis" of the telescope. The Wide Field/Planetary Camera, in contrast, was a wedge-shaped instrument that was located below these instruments, in the lower part of the cylindrical-shaped telescope.

26 Phenomena observed in ultraviolet and infrared wavelengths do not initially appear as a nice, pretty picture. Scientists take the data and enhance it with different colors to visually represent the contrasting intensities and patterns indicated.

27 Joseph H. Rothenberg, interview with author, NASA HQ, Washington, D.C., 15 January 1998; Frank Ceppolina, interview, 12 January 1998; John M. Klineberg, interview with author, Palo Alto, California, 26 November 1997; Tom Huber, interview with author, GSFC, Greenbelt, Maryland, 20 November 1997; George Pieper, interviews with author, GSFC, Greenbelt, Maryland, 14 October 1997 and 19 November 1997; Nancy Roman, phone interview with author, 23 February 1998; *Hubble Space Telescope 1st Servicing Mission Reference Guide*, published for NASA by Lockheed Missiles & Space Company, Inc., Sunnyvale, California, 1993; *Hubble Space Telescope 2nd Servicing Mission Media Reference Guide*, published for NASA by Lockheed Martin Missiles & Space, Sunnyvale, California, 1997; "NASA Embarks on Historic Hubble First Servicing Mission," *Goddard News*, Special Edition, HST 1993; "Hubble Space Telescope

Second Servicing Mission (SM-2)," Hubble Facts, Fact Sheet FS-96(12)-025-GSFC, from GSFC Public Affairs Office files; "Hubble Space Telescope New and Improved," *Starcatcher*, from the Space Telescope Science Institute, Baltimore, Maryland, undated; "Planetary Nebula Gallery," Educational Resource Material EW-1997(12)-008-GSFC, published by GSFC, Greenbelt, Maryland, 1997; "Stars," Educational Resource Material EW-1997(02)-001-GSFC, published by GSFC, Greenbelt, Maryland, 1997; Kathy Sawyer, "Images of Stars' Dazzling Deaths Radiate a Message of Rebirth," *Washington Post*, 22 December 1997, A3; Gloria B. Lubkin, "Stellar Techniques in Mammography," *Physics Today*, June 1995, 21-22; K.C. Cole, "Hubble Finds Biggest Star Yet," *The Los Angeles Times*, 8 October 1997, B2, B8.

28 Tom Huber, interview, 20 November 1997; Nancy Roman, phone interview, 23 February 1998; Les Meredith, interview with author, GSFC, Greenbelt, Maryland, 21 October 1997; George Pieper, interviews with author, 14 October 1997 and 19 November 1997; Yoji Kondo, telephone interview with author, 24 June 1998; Yoji Kondo, "Space Astronomy and IUE," written comments, 17 April 1998; "The International Ultraviolet Explorer (IUE)," Fact Sheet NF-189, June 1993, from GSFC Public Affairs Office; Jim Sahli, "IUE 'Lights Out'," *Goddard News*, November 1996, 5, 7.

29 Yoji Kondo, telephone interview with author, 24 June 1998; "EUVE: Probing a Newly Opened Window," Fact Sheet, undated, from GSFC Public Affairs Office; "EUVE Operations," Fact Sheet, March 1992, from GSFC Public Affairs Office.

30 Tucker, *The Star Splitters*, 7-8; 85; 99; 111-117; Newell, *Beyond the Atmosphere*, 357-363; Steve Holt, interview, 14 January 1998; Nancy Roman, phone interview, 23

February 1998; Edward K. L. Upton, interview with author, Los Angeles, California, 12 April 1998.

31 Tucker, *The Star Splitters*, 24.

32 Margorie Townsend, interview with author, Washington, D.C., 22 November 1997; Tucker, *The Star Splitters*, 24; 129-132.

33 *NASA Space Missions Since 1958*, 664-665, 720-721; Tucker, *The Star Splitters*, 27, 79-81.

34 Tucker, *The Star Splitters*, 103, 133-135, 147-150; "Medal Awarded to Early Black Hole Investigator, Donald Lynden-Bell," Press Release, from the Astronomical Society of the Pacific, 18 May 1998; "X-Ray Timing Explorer Clocks High-Energy Universe," NASA Facts Online Fact Sheet, from GSFC Internet World Wide Web pages.

35 Tucker, *The Star Splitters*, 151-164; "Forecast for the Universe is Stormy, Professor Says," Press Release, from the University of Missouri, 16 April 1998; "Invader Galaxy Apparently Contains Much Dark Matter," Press Release, from the Johns Hopkins University, 13 February 1998; "Mysterious Glow from Colliding Galaxies," Press Release, from the Massachusetts Institute of Technology, 23 February 1998.

36 Stephen Holt, interview with author, 14 January 1998; Stephen P. Maran, interview with author, GSFC, Greenbelt, Maryland, 14 January 1998; "Strongest Known Magnetic Field? Magentar Said Discovered," Press Release from the University of Alabama, Huntsville, 20 May 1998; "Record-Setting Pulsar Said Found by NASA's RXTE Satellite," Press Release from the Los Alamos National Laboratory, 26 January 1998; Tucker, *The Star Splitters*, 81, 113; "X-Ray Timing Explorer Clocks High Energy Universe," NASA Facts Online Fact Sheet, June 1995, from GSFC Internet

World Wide Web pages; "ASCA (Astro D): February 1993," Fact Sheet, undated, from GSFC Laboratory for High Energy Astrophysics World Wide Web pages.

37 "Compton Gamma-Ray Observatory: Exploring the Mysteries of Time," Fact Sheet FS96(07)-015, July 1996, from GSFC Public Affairs Office files.

38 Mather, *The Very First Light*, 48-49; "Goddard Projects Summary August 1959 - December 1967," GSFC Booklet, undated, 8-9.

39 Tucker, *The Star Splitters*, 138-139.

40 Ralph A. M. J. Wijers, et al., "Gamma Ray Bursts from Stellar Remnants: Probing the Universe at High Redshift," *Monthly Notices of the Royal Astronomical Society*, 294, 11 February 1998, L13-L-17; "Gamma Ray Bursts Said to Come from Very Early Universe," Press Release, from the Royal Astronomical Society, 6 February 1998.

41 Stephen P. Maran, interview, 14 January 1998; Al Opp, telephone interview with author, 25 February 1998; "Compton Gamma Ray Observatory (CGRO)," Fact Sheet, 4 June 1997, from GSFC Laboratory for High Energy Astrophysics World Wide Web pages; "Compton Gamma-Ray Observatory: Exploring the Mysteries of Time," Fact Sheet, July 1996, from GSFC Public Affairs Office files; "Compton Gamma-Ray Observatory: Exploring the Mysteries of Time," NASA Facts On Line NF-180-June 1993, from GSFC World Wide Web pages; "Most Energetic Event in Universe Said to be Detected," Press Release, 30 April 1998, from the California Institute of Technology; "Most Powerful Explosion Since the Big Bang," NASA Headquarters Press Release, 5 May 1998.

CHAPTER 5

1 Rough photographs of Earth taken from Viking rockets at altitudes of 60-70 miles actually appeared in the October 1950 issue of *National Geographic* (Seeing the World from 80 Miles Up," *National Geographic*, 98:511-28, October 1959). The photos in Life magazine came a year later but were broader in coverage because they were taken from an altitude of 135 miles. (*Life*, 31:165-66, 15 October 1951); Les Meredith, interview with author, GSFC, Greenbelt, Maryland, 21 October 1997.

2 Project Rand would later become the non-profit, research and development-oriented RAND Corporation.

3 Andrew J. Butrica, ed., *Beyond the Ionosphere: Fifty Years of Satellite Communication*, (Washington, D.C.: National Aeronautics and Space Administration, 1997), 96-103.

4 Homer G. Newell, *Beyond the Atmosphere: The Early Years of Space Science*, (Washington, D.C.: National Aeronautics and Space Administration, 1980), 186-200, 332-3; Vincent V. Salomonson and Louis S. Walter, "The Contributions of Spaceborne Observing Systems to the Understanding of the Solid Earth and Land Surface Processes," Proceedings of the Symposium on the State of Earth Science from Space: Past, Progress, Future Prospects, Space Policy Institute of George Washington University, published in a compendium by the American Institute for Physics (G. Asrar, ed.), May 1994, 3-18; Paul Lowman, interview with author, GSFC, Greenbelt, Maryland, 17 October 1997; Alfred Rosenthal, *NASA Space Missions Since 1958*, (Washington, D.C.: National Aeronautics and Space Administration, 1982), 182, 301, 648-9.

5 *Beyond the Ionosphere*, 100.

6 "The Goddard Space Flight Center Family of Satellites," GSFC Booklet, April 1963 from Roland Van Allen's files; *NASA Space Missions Since 1958*, 32, 120; *Beyond the*

Ionosphere, 99-105; Al Jones, phone interview with author, 23 February 1998.

7   This debate about which approach to take for communication satellites continues to this day. Numerous companies are currently investing in a new round of extremely high capability satellite systems that will vastly improve mobile phone and communications service, but they are taking three different approaches. Hughes is pursuing a geostationary orbit for its system, which will need 8 satellites. Two other companies are planning medium-Earth orbits for their networks, which will require 10-12 spacecraft. Several other companies are planning networks of low-Earth orbiting satellites, which will consist of anywhere from 28 to 840 satellites. Al Jones, phone interview, 23 February 1998; William J. Cook, "1997: A New Space Odyssey," *US News & World Report*, Vol. , 3 March 1997, 45-52.

8   *Beyond the Ionosphere*, 100-124; Al Jones, phone interview, 23 February 1998; John W. Townsend, Jr., interview with author, Cabin John, Maryland, 15 October 1997; Harry J. Goett, interview with author, Los Altos Hills, California, 13 February 1998; *NASA Space Missions Since 1958*, 81, 96, 100, 102, 107, 118, 129.

9   For more information on TDRSS, see Chapter 3.

10 Al Jones, interview, 23 February 1998; *NASA Space Missions Since 1958*, 234, 249, 285, 328, 409, 571; L. J. Allison, ed., "Meteorological Satellites," NASA TM 80704, June 1980, 7-8; *Keeping Track*, 71-73, 107.

11 "Our Atmosphere," Fact Sheet, undated, from GSFC Public Affairs Office files.

12 This agency has, at different times, been known as both "ARPA," for the "Advanced Research Projects Agency," and "DARPA," for the "Defense Advanced Research Projects Agency." At the time referenced here, the agency was known as ARPA.

13 William Bandeen, interview with author, GSFC, Greenbelt, Maryland, 19 November 1997; *NASA Space Missions Since 1958*, 15, 21-23, 29.

14 John W. Townsend, Jr., interview, 15 October 1997; William Bandeen, interview, 19 November 1997; John C. Clark, phone interview with author, 18 May 1998; Harry J. Goett, interview, 13 February 1998.

15 United States Department of Commerce Press Release, WB 61-20, 13 November 1961, from the files of William Bandeen.

16 William Bandeen, interview, 19 November 1997; John W. Townsend, Jr., interview with author, Cabin John, Maryland, 15 October 1997; "TIROS I Plus Ten," *ESSA*, Vol. 5, No. 1, January 1970, 17-23; L. J. Allison, ed., "Meteorological Satellites," NASA TM 80704, June 1980, 1-7.

17 Guenter Warnecke and Wendell S. Sunderlin, "The First Color Picture of the Earth Taken from the ATS-3 Satellite," *Bulletin of the American Meteorological Society*, Vol. 49, No. 2, February 1968, 75-83.

18 The difference between geosynchronous and geostationary satellites is small. A geostationary satellite will remain in exactly the same spot as the Earth rotates. A geosynchronous satellite will remain in *approximately* the same spot, but its orbit will oscillate slightly north to south around the equator. How much the orbit varies depends on the satellite.

19 The satellite actually became known as GOES-8 after it was successfully launched. Satellites are typically referred to with letter designations in development and only given numerical designations once they reach orbit. I refer to this project as GOES 8 throughout to avoid confusion, since that is how the satellite is now known.

20 Rick Obenschain, interview with author, GSFC, Greenbelt, Maryland, 20 November

1997; Vincent V. Salomonson, interview with author, GSFC, Greenbelt, Maryland, 19 November 1997; William Bandeen, interview, 19 November 1997; William Bandeen, phone interview, 1 July 1998; John M. Klineberg, interview with author, Palo Alto, California, 26 November 1997; Jim Greaves, phone interview with author, 1 July 1998; GOES 8 project report and Launch Date records, undated, from Jim Greaves files.

21 William Bandeen, interview, 19 November 1997; Les Meredith, interview, 21 October 1997; John Boeckel, interview with author, GSFC, Greenbelt, Maryland, 17 October 1997; Rudy Hanel, interview with author, Brookeville, Maryland, 24 October 1997; Vincent V. Salomonson, interview, 19 November 1997; Lewis J. Allison, et al., "Remote Sensing of the Atmosphere from Environmental Satellites, GSFC Report X-901-77-132 Preprint, June 1977, 25-26; *NASA Space Missions Since 1958*, 511-512.

22 *NASA Space Missions Since 1958*, 594-95.

23 "Landsat: Time Present, Time Past, and Now Time Future," Booklet NP-1997 (09)-025-GSFC, from Darrell Williams files.

24 William Bandeen, interview, 19 November 1997; Les Meredith, interview, 21 October 1997; John Boeckel, interview, 17 October 1997; Rudy Hanel, interview, 24 October 1997; Rick Obenschain, interview, 20 November 1997; Vincent V. Salomonson, interview, 19 November 1997; Donald T. Lauer, Stanley A. Morain, and Vincent V. Salomonson, "The Landsat Program: Its Origins, Evolution, and Impacts," *Photogrammetric Engineering & Remote Sensing*, Vol. 53, No. 7, July 1997, 831-838.

25 Mark Schoeberl, interview with author, GSFC, Greenbelt, Maryland, 16 January 1998; William R. Bandeen, "Experimental Approaches to Remote Atmospheric Probing in the Infrared from Satellites,"

GSFC Report X-622-68-146 preprint, May 1968, 1-2; "Clouds and the Energy Cycle," Fact Sheet NF-207, January 1994, from GSFC Public Affairs Office files; *NASA Space Missions Since 1958*, 23, 227, 253, 330, 364; *Major NASA Satellite Missions and Key Participants*, Vol. IV - 1984 and 1985, (Greenbelt, Maryland, Goddard Space Flight Center, 1986), 25-26; Dr. Edward J. Hurley and Ruthie Jones, "Nimbus 7: Observing the Atmosphere and Oceans," GSFC Booklet, December 1983, from William Bandeen files, 12-13; "Tropical Rainfall Measuring Mission," Fact Sheet FS-1997(03)-003-GSFC, April 1997, from GSFC Public Affairs Office files; "TRMM Mission Summary," Fact Sheet, from TRMM project web pages; "A Global Eye on Tropical Rainfall: The Tropical Rainfall Measuring Mission (TRMM)," Booklet, undated, from GSFC Public Affairs Office files.

26 Although popularly known as a "hole" in the ozone layer, the phenomenon being researched is actually just a thinning in the layer. There is no place where the ozone is completely gone.

27 Mark Schoeberl, interview, 16 January 1998; W. Henry Lambright, "NASA, Ozone and Policy-Relevant Science: The Accelerative Process," NSF Report DIR-9009827, November 1993, 1-26; Dr. Edward J. Hurley and Ruthie Jones, "Nimbus 7," 22-25; "Ozone: What is It and Why Do We Care About It?" Fact Sheet NF-198, December 1993, from GSFC Public Affairs Office files; "NASA's Ozone Studies," Fact Sheet NF-208, February 1994, from GSFC Public Affairs Office files, "Shuttle Solar Backscatter Ultraviolet (SSBUV) Instrument," Fact Sheet 193, September 1995, from GSFC Public Affairs Office files; Claire L. Parkinson, *Earth From Above: Using Color-Coded Satellite Images to Examine the Global Environment*

(Sausalito, CA: University Science Books, 1997), 17-32.

28 Mark Schoeberl, interview, 16 January 1998; "UARS," Booklet, 1998, from Mark Schoeberl files; "Upper Atmosphere Research Satellite," Fact Sheet, January 1994, from NASA Facts On Line, NASA GSFC Web pages; "Total Ozone Mapping Spectrometer/Earth Probe," Fact Sheet, 22 September 1997, from NASA Facts On Line, NASA GSFC Web pages; "Volcanoes and Global Climate Change," Fact Sheet NF 220, March 1994, from GSFC Public Affairs Office files; "Upper Atmosphere Research Satellite (UARS)," Fact Sheet NF-208, January 1994, from GSFC Public Affairs Office files; W. Henry Lambright, "NASA, Ozone and Policy-Relevant Science," 22-31, Kathy Pedelty, "UARS' Amazing Journey," *Earth Science News*, Vol. 2, No. 1, Spring/Summer 1997, 2-3, 12.

29 Mark Schoeberl, interview, 16 January 1998.

30 "Our Oceans," Fact Sheet, from data compiled from the Smithsonian Institution's Ocean Planet exhibition and from Peter Benchley and Judith Gradwohl, *Ocean Planet: Writings and Images of the Sea* (New York: Harry N. Abrams Inc.), undated, from GSFC Public Affairs Office files.

31 "Antonio J. Busalacchi, phone interview with author, 28 February 1998; "Polar Ice," Fact Sheet NF 212, February 1994, from GSFC Public Affairs Office files, Lewis J. Allison, et al., "Remote Sensing of the Atmosphere from Environmental Satellites," 20-21, 33; Claire L. Parkinson, *Earth From Above*, 33-53.

32 For more information on the SeaWiFS project structure, see Chapter 2.

33 For more information on the Rapid Spacecraft Procurement Initiative, see Chapter 2; Jim Adams, phone interview with author, 16 July 1998.

34 Antonio J. Busalacchi, interview, 28 February, 1998; Vincent V. Salomonson, interview, 19 November 1997; Dorothy Zukor, interview with author, GSFC, Greenbelt, Maryland, 19 November 1997; Claire L. Parkinson, *Earth From Above*, 77-93; Lewis J. Allison, et al., "Remote Sensing of the Atmosphere from Environmental Satellites," 20, 35-37; Dr. Edward J. Hurley and Ruthie Jones, "Nimbus 7," 1-13; "TOPEX-Poseidon: At-A-Glance," Fact Sheet, undated, from TOPEX/Poseidon Web pages. "Sea-viewing Wide Field-of-view Sensor (SeaWiFS)," Fact Sheet FS-97(03)-004-GSFC, May 1997, from GSFC Public Affairs Office Files.

35 Antonio J. Busalacchi, interview, 28 February, 1998; Claire L. Parkinson, *Earth From Above*, 77-84; Dorothy Zukor, interview, 19 November 1997; "Space Based Observation of Anomalies in the Equatorial Pacific," Fact Sheet, undated, from GSFC World Wide Web pages, "El Niño," Fact Sheet NF 211, Rev. April 1996, from GSFC Public Affairs Office files; "El Niño," Fact Sheet, undated, from TOPEX/Poseidon Prime Mission Results Introduction Web pages; "ENSO Primer," Fact Sheet, undated, from GSFC Web pages.

36 Mark Schoeberl, interview, 16 January 1998; Antonio J. Busalacchi, interview, 28 February 1998; "Biosphere," Fact Sheet NF-223, March 1994, from GSFC Public Affairs Office files; "The Greenhouse Effect," Fact Sheet NF-182, June 1993, from GSFC Public Affairs Office files; "Global Warming," Fact Sheet NF-222, March 1994, from GSFC Public Affairs Office files.

37 Robert Price, interview with author, GSFC, Greenbelt, Maryland, 16 January 1998; Dorothy Zukor, interview, 19 November 1997; W. Henry Lambright, "Administrative Entrepreneurship and Space Technology: The Ups and Downs of 'Mission to Planet

Earth,'" *Public Administration Review*, Vol. 54, No. 2, March/April 1994, 97-104; Antonio J. Busalacchi, interview, 28 February 1998; "Understanding Our Changing Planet: NASA's Mission to Planet Earth," 1997 Fact Book, from MTPE program office files; "GSFC MPTE Lead Center," viewgraph, June 1997, from Joseph H. Rothenberg files.

38 Discovery 5 Space Mission astronaut, as quoted in *Atlas of the World* (Maplewood, N.J.: Hammond Incorporated, 1993), back cover.

CHAPTER 6

1   "The National Aeronautics and Space Act, As Amended," 13 October 1962, Sec. 102(a), as reproduced in Robert L. Rosholt, *An Administrative History of NASA 1958-1963*, (Washington, D.C.: National Aeronautics and Space Administration, 1966), 305.

2   The Jet Propulsion Laboratory in Pasadena, California is dedicated to scientific research, as well, but it is operated and staffed by CalTech under contract to NASA, not by NASA directly.

Bibliographic Essay

The single most important group of sources for this book consists of over 70 individual interviews with scientists, engineers, administrative personnel, and managers who worked at or with Goddard over the past 40 years, along with documents they provided from their files.

Additional information on the organizational structure of Goddard and the history of its launches was obtained from Goddard's technical library, with the help of Jane Riddle and Chao Yang. Further project information was obtained from individual project offices, Goddard's "web" pages on the internet, and from fact sheets and informational material provided by Goddard's Public Affairs Office. A critical resource for specific details on individual spacecraft was the *NASA Space Missions Since 1958* (Alfred Rosenthal, ed., Washington, D.C., National Aeronautics and Space Administration, 1991).

Information on the evolution of Goddard and the work the Center performed was also provided by numerous other books. These sources included: Alfred Rosenthal, *Venture Into Space* (Washington, D.C.: National Aeronautics and Space Administration, NASA SP-4301, 1968); Robert Rosholt, *An Administrative History of NASA, 1958-1963* (Washington, D.C.: National Aeronautics and Space Administration, 1966); Homer G. Newell, *Beyond the Atmosphere* (Washington, D.C.: National Aeronautics and Space Administration, 1980); William R. Corliss, *NASA Sounding Rockets, 1958-1968* (Washington, D.C.: National Aeronautics and Space Administration, NASA SP-4401, 1971); John E. Naugle, *First Among Equals* (Washington, D.C.: National Aeronautics and Space Administration, 1991); Alfred Bester, *The Life and Death of a Satellite* (Boston, MA: Little, Brown and Company, 1966); Harold D. Wallace Jr., *Wallops Station* (Washington, D.C.: National Aeronautics and Space Administration, NASA SP-4311, 1997); Wallace H. Tucker, *The Star Splitters*, (Washington, D.C.: National Aeronautics and Space Administration, NASA SP-466, 1984); Claire L. Parkinson, *Earth From Above* (Sausalito, CA: University Science Books); and John C. Mather and John Boslough, *The Very First Light* (New York: Basic Books, 1996).

Additional Goddard-produced monographs and historical notes, such as Kathleen M. Mogan and Frank P. Mintz, *Keeping Track: A History of the GSFC Tracking and Data Acquisition Networks: 1957-1991*, and William R. Corliss, "The Evolution of the Satellite Tracking and Data Acquisition Network (STADAN)" (Goddard Historical Note Number 3, January 1967), provided valuable information on the evolution of Goddard's tracking and data networks.

Other articles and research reports helped trace the evolution of various long-term programs at Goddard and the factors that influenced their development. These include such publications as W. Henry Lambright, "Administrative Entrepreneurship and Space Technology: The Ups and Downs of 'Mission to Planet Earth'," *Public Administration Review*, Vol. 54, No. 2, March/April 1994; and Donald T. Lauer, et al., "The Landsat Program: Its Origins, Evolution, and Impacts," *Photogrammetric Engineering and Remote Sensing*, Vol. 53, No. 7, July 1997.

A final group of sources for information on recent scientific research included the American Astronomical Society, as well as articles in current journals and newspapers, including the *Los Angeles Times*, *Science*, *Natural Science*, and *Science News*.

Appendix A:
Glossary of Acronyms

ACE	Advanced Composition Explorer	DMR	Differential Microwave Radiometer
ADEOS	Advanced Earth Observing System (Japanese satellite)	DOD	Department of Defense
		DSN	Deep Space Network
AET	Applied Engineering and Technology (directorate)	EOS	Earth Observing System
AO	Announcement of Flight Opportunity	EOSDIS	Earth Observing System Data and Information System
APT	Automatic Picture Transmission	EPA	Environmental Protection Agency
ARPA	Advanced Research Projects Agency	ERBE	Earth Radiation Budget Experiment
ATS	Applications Technology Satellite	ERBS	Earth Radiation Budget Satellite
AXAF	Advanced X-Ray Astrophysics Facility	EROS	Earth Resources Observation System (data center)
CERES	Clouds and the Earth's Radiant Energy System (instrument)	ERTS	Earth Resources Technology Satellite
		ESA	European Space Agency
CFC	Chlorofluorocarbons	ESSA	Environmental Science Services Administration
CGRO	Compton Gamma Ray Observatory	EUVE	Extreme UltraViolet Explorer
CME	Coronal Mass Ejection	EVA	Extra-Vehicular Activity
COBE	Cosmic Background Explorer	FAST	Fast Auroral Snapshot Explorer
COSTAR	Corrective Optics Space Telescope Axial Replacement	FIRAS	Far Infrared Absolute Spectrophotometer
CZCS	Coastal Zone Color Scanner	GAS	Get Away Special
DAAC	Distributed Active Archive Centers	GISS	Goddard Institute for Space Studies
DARPA	Defense Advanced Research Projects Agency	GOES	Geostationary Operational Environmental Satellite
DIRBE	Diffuse Infrared Background Experiment	GPS	Global Positioning System

GSFC	Goddard Space Flight Center	NASCOM	NASA Communications Network
HALOE	Halogen Occultation Experiment	NICMOS	Near-Infrared Camera and Multi-Object Spectrometer
HEAO	High Energy Astronomy Observatory	NGST	Next Generation Space Telescope
HEASARC	High Energy Astrophysics Science Archival Research Center	NOAA	National Oceanic and Atmospheric Administration
HST	Hubble Space Telescope	NRL	Naval Research Laboratory
ICBM	Intercontinental Ballistic Missile	NSF	National Science Foundation
ICE	International Cometary Explorer	NSSDC	National Space Science Data Center
IGY	International Geophysical Year	OAO	Orbiting Astronomical Observatory
IMP	Interplanetary Monitoring Probe/Platform	OGO	Orbiting Geophysical Observatory
ISAS	(Japanese) Institute of Space and Astronautical Science	OSO	Orbiting Solar Observatory
ISEE	International Sun-Earth Explorer	ROSAT	Roentgen Satellite
		RXTE	Rossi X-Ray Timing Explorer
ISTP	International Solar Terrestrial Physics (program)	SAGE/AEM	Stratospheric Aerosol and Gas Experiment Applications Explorer Mission
ITOS	Improved TIROS Operational Satellite	SAS	Small Astronomy Satellite
IUE	International Ultraviolet Explorer	SAMPEX	Solar, Anomalous and Magnetospheric Particle Explorer
LAGEOS	Laser GEOdynamics Satellite	SBUV	Solar Backscatter UltraViolet (instrument)
MAP	Microwave Anisotropy Probe	SeaWiFS	Sea-viewing Wide Field-of-view Sensor
MMS	Multi-mission Modular Spacecraft	SIRTF	Space Infrared Telescope Facility
MSFN	Mercury/Manned Space Flight Network	SMEX	Small Explorer
MTPE	Mission to Planet Earth	SMM	Solar Maximum Mission
NACA	National Advisory Committee for Aeronautics	SMS	Synchronous Meteorological Satellite
NAS	National Academy of Sciences	SOHO	Solar and Heliospheric Observatory
NASA	National Aeronautics and Space Administration	SSBUV	Shuttle Solar Backscatter UltraViolet (instrument)

SST	Supersonic Transport
STAAC	Systems, Technology and Advanced Concepts (directorate)
STADAN	Satellite Tracking And Data Acquisition Network
STDN	Spaceflight Tracking and Data Network
STGT	Second TDRSS Ground Terminal
STIS	Space Telescope Imaging Spectrograph
STSI	Space Telescope Science Institute
SWAS	Submillimeter Wave Astronomy Satellite
TDRSS	Tracking and Data Relay Satellite System
TIROS	Television Infrared Observation Satellite
TOMS	Total Ozone Mapping Spectrometer
TRACE	Transition Region and Coronal Explorer
TRMM	Tropical Rainfall Measuring Mission
UARS	Upper Atmosphere Research Satellite
UNEP	United Nations Environmental Program
WFF	Wallops Island Flight Facility
WSGT	White Sands Ground Terminal

APPENDIX B:

Goddard Launches

DATE	MISSION	LAUNCH VEHICLE	REMARKS
17 February 1959	Vanguard II	Vanguard SLV–4	20–inch sphere. First Earth photo from satellite
13 April 1959	Vanguard	Vanguard SLV–6	Did not achieve orbit
22 June 1959	Vanguard	Vanguard SLV–6	Did not achieve orbit
16 July 1959	Explorer (S–1)	Juno II	Did not achieve orbit
7 August 1959	Explorer 6	Thor–Able III	Particles and Meteorology
18 September 1959	Vanguard III	Vanguard SLV–7	Magnetic fields, radiation belts, micrometeorites
13 October 1959	Explorer 7	Juno II	Energetic particles, magnetic storms, micrometeorites
23 March 1960	Explorer (S–46)	Juno II	Did not achieve orbit
1 April 1960	TIROS I	Thor–Able II	First successful weather-study satellite
13 May 1960	Echo A–10	Thor–Delta	Did not achieve orbit
12 August 1960	Echo I	Thor–Delta	First passive communications satellite (100–ft sphere)
3 November 1960	Explorer 8	Juno II	Ionosphere research
23 November 1960	TIROS II	Thor–Delta	Weather satellite
4 December 1960	Explorer (S–56)	Scout	Did not achieve orbit
16 February 1961	Explorer 9	Scout	Atmospheric density research
24 February 1961	Explorer (S–45)	Juno II	Did not achieve orbit
25 March 1961	Explorer 10	Thor–Delta	Solar wind and flare research
27 April 1961	Explorer 11	Juno II	Cosmic gamma rays
24 May 1961	Explorer (S–45a)	Juno II	Did not achieve orbit
30 June 1961	Explorer (S–55)	Scout	Did not achieve orbit
12 July 1961	TIROS III	Thor–Delta	Weather satellite, discovered Hurricane Esther
16 August 1961	Explorer 12	Thor–Delta	Solar winds, magnetosphere
25 August 1961	Explorer 13	Scout	Micrometeorites (3rd stage failed to ignite)
19 October 1961	Probe A (P–21)	Scout	Electron density research
15 January 1962	Echo (AVT–1)	Thor	Suborbital test. 135–ft sphere ruptured.
8 February 1962	TIROS IV	Thor–Delta	Weather satellite
7 March 1962	OSO–1	Thor–Delta	Solar phenomena
26 April 1962	Ariel I	Thor–Delta	First international satellite
19 June 1962	TIROS V	Thor–Delta	Weather satellite

DATE	MISSION	LAUNCH VEHICLE	REMARKS
10 July 1962	Telstar I	Thor–Delta	First privately built communications satellite
18 July 1962	Echo (AVT–2)	Thor–Delta	Passive communication satellite
18 September 1962	TIROS VI	Thor–Delta	Weather satellite
29 September 1962	Alouette I	Thor–Agena	Designed and built by Canada
2 October 1962	Explorer 14	Thor–Delta	Solar wind and radiation
27 October 1962	Explorer 15	Thor–Delta	Study effects of high-altitude nuclear blast
13 December 1962	Relay I	Thor–Delta	Communications satellite
16 December 1962	Explorer 16	Scout	Micrometeoroid research
14 February 1963	Syncom I	Thor–Delta	Contact lost 20 seconds into orbit
3 April 1963	Explorer 17	Thor–Delta	Atmospheric research
7 May 1963	Telstar II	Thor–Delta	Communications satellite
19 June 1963	TIROS VII	Thor–Delta	Weather satellite
26 July 1963	Syncom II	Thor–Delta	Geosynchronous communications test satellite
27 November 1963	Explorer 18/IMP 1	Thor–Delta	First in IMP series
19 December 1963	Explorer 19	Scout	Atmospheric density research
21 December 1963	TIROS VIII	Delta	Weather, test of automatic picture transmission
21 January 1964	Relay II	Delta	Communications satellite
25 January 1964	Echo II	Thor–Agena	135–ft. inflatable sphere–communications satellite
19 March 1964	Beacon Explorer A	Delta	Did not achieve orbit
27 March 1964	Ariel 2	Scout	Cooperative with U.K.
19 August 1964	Syncom III	Delta	Geosynchronous communications satellite
25 August 1964	Explorer 20	Scout	Ionosphere topside sounder
28 August 1964	Nimbus I	Thor–Agena	Weather research satellite
4 September 1964	OGO I	Atlas–Agena	20 instruments; geophysical research
4 October 1964	Explorer 21/IMP 2	Delta	Magnetic field, radiation, solar wind research
10 October 1964	Explorer 22	Scout	Beacon explorer; ionosphere
6 November 1964	Explorer 23	Scout	Meteoroid research
21 November 1964	Explorer 24/Explorer 25	Scout	First dual payload; upper atmospheric research
15 December 1964	San Marco 1	Scout	Cooperative with Italy; air density, ionosphere
21 December 1964	Explorer 26	Delta	Energetic Particles Explorer
22 January 1965	TIROS IX	Delta	First "cartwheel" configuration weather satellite
3 February 1965	OSO B–2	Delta	Solar phenomena; UV, X-ray, gamma ray
6 April 1965	Intelsat 1	Delta	First operational satellite for Comsat Corp.
29 April 1965	Explorer 27	Scout	Beacon Explorer; Earth's magnetic field
29 May 1965	Explorer 28/IMP 3	Delta	Third in IMP series
1 July 1965	TIROS X	Delta	First U.S. Weather Bureau–funded TIROS

DATE	MISSION	LAUNCH VEHICLE	REMARKS
25 August 1965	OSO-C	Delta	Did not achieve orbit
14 October 1965	OGO II	Thor–Agena	Near-Earth space phenomena
6 November 1965	Explorer 29	Delta	GEOS–A; geodetic research
18 November 1965	Explorer 30	Scout	Solar UV and X-rays
29 November 1965	Explorer 31/Alouette II	Thor–Agena	Cooperative with Canada; ionospheric research
3 February 1966	ESSA I	Delta	Sun-synchronous orbit; weather
28 February 1966	ESSA II	Delta 1	Paired with ESSA I, initial global weather system
8 April 1966	OAO I	Atlas–Agena	Astronomy observatory; battery malfunctioned
14 May 1966	Nimbus II	Thor–Agena	Weather research satellite
25 May 1966	Explorer 32	Delta	Atmosphere Explorer
7 June 1966	OGO III	Atlas–Agena	Geophysical and solar phenomena
23 June 1966	Pageos I	Thor–Agena	Geodetic research
1 July 1966	Explorer 33/IMP 4	Delta	IMP–Earth's magnetosphere and magnetic tail
2 October 1966	ESSA III	Delta	Operational weather satellite
7 December 1966	ATS I	Atlas–Agena	Applications technology satellite
26 January 1967	ESSA IV	Delta	Operational weather satellite
8 March 1967	OSO III	Delta	Solar phenomena
6 April 1967	ATS II	Atlas–Agena	Tested gravity gradient control system
20 April 1967	ESSA V	Delta	Operational weather satellite
26 April 1967	San Marco II	Scout	Cooperative with Italy; from sea–based platform
5 May 1967	Ariel 3	Scout	UK-built atmospheric and ionospheric research
24 May 1967	Explorer 34/IMP 5	Delta	Fifth IMP; Sun–Earth relationships
19 July 1967	Explorer 35/IMP 6	Delta	IMP; lunar orbit
28 July 1967	OGO IV	Thor–Agena	Sun–Earth relationships
18 October 1967	OSO IV	Delta	Solar phenomena; 1st extreme UV pictures of Sun
5 November 1967	ATS III	Atlas–Agena	Applications Technology Satellite
10 November 1967	ESSA VI	Delta	Operational weather satellite
11 January 1968	Explorer 36	Delta	GEOS; geodetic research
4 March 1968	OGO V	Atlas–Agena	Radiation belt, bow shock research
5 March 1968	Explorer 37	Scout	Solar Explorer–UV and X-ray emissions
18 May 1968	Nimbus B	Thor–Agena	Did not achieve orbit
4 July 1968	Explorer 38	Delta	Radio Astronomy Explorer
8 August 1968	Explorer 39/Explorer 40	Scout	Dual payload; upper atmosphere research
10 August 1968	ATS IV	Atlas–Centaur	Centaur 2nd burn failed; remained in parking orbit
16 August 1968	ESSA VII	Delta	Operational weather satellite
7 December 1968	OAO II	Atlas–Centaur	Astronomy observatory

DATE	MISSION	LAUNCH VEHICLE	REMARKS
15 December 1968	ESSA VIII	Delta	Operational weather satellite
22 January 1969	OSO V	Delta	Solar phenomena–X-rays, gamma rays and radio
30 January 1969	ISIS–A	Delta	Cooperative with Canada; ionosphere
26 February 1969	ESSA IX	Delta	9th and last in TOS series
14 April 1969	Nimbus III	Thor–Agena	Research weather satellite
5 June 1969	OGO VI	Thor–Agena	Last in the OGO series
21 June 1969	Explorer 41/IMP 7	Delta	7th in IMP series
9 August 1969	OSO VI	Delta	Solar phenomena; X-ray, gamma ray and radio emissions
12 August 1969	ATS V	Atlas–Centaur	Applications Technology Satellite
23 January 1970	ITOS A	Delta	2nd generation meteorological satellite
8 April 1970	Nimbus IV	Thor–Agena	Stabilized, Earth-oriented research weather satellite
30 November 1970	OAO B	Atlas–Centaur	Did not achieve orbit
11 December 1970	ITOS A	Delta	Operational weather satellite
12 December 1970	Explorer 42	Scout	Small Astronomy Satellite; 1st X-ray satellite
13 March 1971	Explorer 43/IMP 8	Delta	2nd generation IMP; solar-lunar relationships
31 March 1971	ISIS B	Delta	Cooperative with Canada; ionosphere research
24 April 1971	San Marco C	Scout	Atmospheric research, with Italy
8 July 1971	Explorer 44	Scout	Solar radiation; X-ray and UV emissions
29 September 1971	OSO H	Delta	Solar phenomena and effect on Earth
21 October 1971	ITOS B	Delta	Operational Weather Satellite; 2nd stage failed
15 November 1971	Explorer 45	Scout	Magnetosphere research
11 December 1971	Ariel 4	Scout	Ionosphere research
23 July 1972	ERTS–A	Delta	Earth Resources Technology Satellite
13 August 1972	Explorer 46	Scout	Meteoroid technology satellite
21 August 1972	OAO 3	Atlas–Centaur	"Copernicus" Astronomy observatory
22 September 1972	Explorer 47/IMP 9	Delta	Interplanetary Monitoring Platform
15 October 1972	ITOS D	Delta	Operational weather satellite
15 November 1972	Explorer 48	Scout	Small Astronomy Satellite; gamma ray research
11 December 1972	Nimbus V	Delta	Research weather satellite
16 December 1972	AEROS–A	Scout	Upper Atmosphere & Ionosphere research
10 June 1973	Explorer 49	Delta	Radio Astronomy Explorer
16 June 1973	ITOS E	Delta	Did not achieve orbit
25 October 1973	Explorer 50/IMP 10	Delta	Last Interplanetary Monitoring Platform
6 November 1973	ITOS F	Delta	Operational weather satellite
16 December 1973	Explorer 51	Delta	Atmosphere Explorer
18 February 1974	San Marco C–2	Scout	Atmospheric research with Italy

DATE	MISSION	LAUNCH VEHICLE	REMARKS
17 May 1974	SMS–A	Delta	Geostationary weather research satellite
30 May 1974	ATS F	Titan II	Applications Technology Satellite
3 June 1974	Explorer 52	Scout	"Hawkeye" spacecraft; solar wind
6 July 1974	AEROS–B	Scout	Upper Atmosphere & Ionosphere research
15 October 1974	Ariel 5	Scout	Cosmic X-ray research
15 November 1974	ITOS–G	Delta	Operational weather satellite
10 December 1974	Helios A	Titan III	Cooperative with W. Germany; solar research
22 January 1975	Landsat 2	Delta	2nd Earth Resources Technology Satellite
6 February 1975	SMS–B	Delta	Geostationary weather satellite
9 April 1975	GEOS C	Delta	Geodetic research
7 May 1975	Explorer 53	Scout	Small Astronomy Satellite; X-ray astronomy
12 June 1975	Nimbus VI	Delta	Research weather satellite
21 June 1975	OSO I	Delta	Solar phenomena
6 October 1975	Explorer 54	Delta	Atmosphere Explorer
16 October 1975	SMS–C/GOES–A	Delta	First operational geostationary weather satellite
20 November 1975	Explorer 55	Delta	Atmosphere Explorer
15 January 1976	Helios B	Titan III	Solar research; cooperative with Germany
4 May 1976	LAGEOS	Delta	Geodetic laser ranging research
29 July 1976	ITOS H	Delta	Operational weather satellite
20 April 1977	GEOS	Delta	Malfunction placed in unusable orbit
16 June 1977	GOES B	Delta	Operational geostationary weather satellite
12 August 1977	HEAO A	Atlas–Centaur	High Energy Astronomy Observatory
22 October 1977	ISEE A/B	Delta	Dual payload; Internat'l Sun/Earth Explorer
26 January 1978	IUE	Delta	International Ultraviolet Explorer; cooperative with U.K.
5 March 1978	Landsat 3	Delta	Third Earth Resources remote sensing satellite
26 April 1978	AEM–A/Explorer 58	Scout	Heat Capacity Mapping Mission (HCMM)
16 June 1978	GOES–C	Delta	Operational geostationary weather satellite
26 June 1978	Seasat–A	Atlas	Lost contact after 106 days
12 August 1978	ISEE–C	Delta	Renamed ICE in 1985 for cometary research
13 October 1978	TIROS–N	Atlas	3rd generation polar orbiting weather satellite (research)
24 October 1978	Nimbus VII	Delta	Research environmental/weather satellite
13 November 1978	HEAO–B	Atlas–Centaur	2nd High Energy Astronomical Satellite–X-rays
18 February 1979	SAGE/AEM–2	Scout	Stratospheric Aerosol & Gas Experiment Applications Explorer
27 June 1979	NOAA–6	Atlas	Operational weather satellite
20 September 1979	HEAO 3	Atlas–Centaur	High–energy astronomy/gamma ray research

DATE	MISSION	LAUNCH VEHICLE	REMARKS
30 October 1979	Magsat	Scout	Measure near-Earth magnetic fields
14 February 1980	SMM	Delta	Solar Maximum Mission
29 May 1980	NOAA–7	Atlas	Weather satellite–launch vehicle malfunctioned
9 September 1980	GOES D	Delta	Operational geostationary weather satellite
22 May 1981	GOES E	Delta	Operational geostationary weather satellite
23 June 1981	NOAA–C	Atlas	Operational weather satellite
3 August 1981	Dynamic Explorer A&B	Delta	Dual payload; Earth's magnetic field research
6 October 1981	SME	Delta	Solar Mesosphere Explorer; atmospheric research
22 March 1982	OSS–1	Shuttle Columbia/STS–3	Plasma & Solar physics, Shuttle capabilities
27 June 1982	GAS	Shuttle Columbia/STS–4	Carried first Get Away Special (GAS) experiment
16 July 1982	Landsat 4	Delta	Earth resources remote sensing satellite
28 March 1983	NOAA–8	Atlas	Operational weather satellite
4 April 1983	TDRS –A	Shuttle Challenger/STS–6	Deployed first Tracking and Data Relay Satellite
28 April 1983	GOES F	Delta	Operational geostationary weather satellite
1 March 1984	Landsat 5	Delta	Earth resources remote sensing satellite
6 April 1984	SMM Repair	Shuttle Challenger/STS–41C	Shuttle crew retrieved & repaired SMM satellite
16 August 1984	AMPTE	Delta	Three magnetospheric particle tracer explorers
5 October 1984	ERBS	Shuttle Challenger/STS–41G	Earth Radiation Budget Satellite
12 December 1984	NOAA–9	Atlas	Operational weather satellite
17 June 1985	Spartan 1	Shuttle Discovery/STS–51G	Deployed and retrieved Spartan 1
28 January 1986	TDRS–B	Shuttle Challenger/STS–51L	Did not achieve orbit
5 May 1986	GOES–G	Delta	Did not achieve orbit
17 September 1986	NOAA–10	Atlas	Operational weather satellite; included ERBE
26 February 1987	GOES–H	Delta 1	Operational geostationary weather satellite
25 March 1987	San Marco D/L	Scout	Solar–meteorological activity relationship
24 September 1987	NOAA–11	Atlas	Operational weather satellite
29 September 1988	TDRS–C	Shuttle Discovery/STS–26	2nd Tracking and Data Relay Satellite
13 March 1989	TDRS–D	Shuttle Discovery/STS–29	3rd Tracking and Data Relay Satellite
18 November 1989	COBE	Delta 2	Cosmic Background Explorer
24 April 1990	HST	Shuttle Discovery/STS–31	Hubble Space Telescope deployed
1 June 1990	ROSAT	Delta 2	Roentgen Satellite–X-ray telescope with Germany, U.K.
2 December 1990	BBXRT	Shuttle Columbia/STS–35	X-ray telescope
5 April 1990	CGRO	Shuttle Atlantis/STS–37	Compton Gamma Ray Observatory
14 May 1990	NOAA–12	Atlas	3rd generation operational weather satellite
2 August 1991	TDRS–E	Shuttle Atlantis/STS–43	Tracking and Data Relay Satellite
12 September 1991	UARS	Shuttle Discovery/STS–48	Upper Atmosphere Research Satellite

DATE	MISSION	LAUNCH VEHICLE	REMARKS
7 June 1992	EUVE	Delta 2	Extreme Ultraviolet Explorer
3 July 1992	SAMPEX	Scout	First in Small Explorer series; cosmic ray research
24 July 1992	GEOTAIL	Delta 2	Joint NASA/Japan; geomagnetic tail research
22 October 1992	LAGEOS	Shuttle Columbia/STS–52	Geodetic research
13 January 1993	TDRS–F	Shuttle Endeavor/STS–54	Tracking and Data Relay Satellite
20 February 1993	Astro–D	M–3 SII (Japanese)	ASCA–X-ray astronomy
8 April 1993	Spartan 201	Shuttle Discovery/STS–56	Solar corona research
2 December 1993	HST 1st Servicing mission	Shuttle Endeavor/STS–61	Repair/servicing of Hubble Space Telescope
9 April 1994	GOES–I (GOES 8)	Atlas–Centaur	Next generation operational geostationary weather satellite
9 September 1994	Spartan 1	Shuttle Discovery/STS64	Solar wind and corona research
1 November 1994	WIND	Delta 2	Solar wind research
30 December 1994	NOAA–14	Atlas E	Operational weather satellite
23 May 1995	GOES–J	Atlas II	Operational geostationary weather satellite
13 July 1995	TDRS–G	Shuttle Discovery/STS–70	Tracking and Data Relay Satellite
2 December 1995	SOHO	Atlas II	Joint ESA/NASA; Solar Heliospheric Observatory
30 December 1995	RXTE	Delta 2	Rossi X-ray Timing Explorer
24 February 1996	Polar	Delta 2	Polar orbiting satellite; magnetospheric phenomena
4 June 1996	Cluster	Ariane–5	Did not achieve orbit
2 July 1996	TOMS–EP	Pegasus XL	Total Ozone Mapping Spectrometer Earth Probe
17 August 1996	ADEOS	H–2 (Japanese)	Japanese mission; satellite failed after 90 days
21 August 1996	FAST	Pegasus XL	Fast Auroral Snapshot Explorer
4 November 1996	SAC–B/HETE	Pegasus XL	Did not separate from rocket
11 February 1997	HST 2nd Servicing Mission	Shuttle Discovery/STS–82	Hubble Space Telescope 2nd Servicing mission
25 April 1997	GOES–K	Atlas II	Operational geostationary weather satellite
25 August 1997	ACE	Delta 2	Advanced Composition Explorer
27 November 1997	TRMM	H–2 (Japanese)	Tropical Rainfall Measuring Mission
26 February 1998	SNOE	Pegasus XL	Student Nitric Oxide Explorer
1 April 1998	TRACE	Pegasus XL	Transition Region and Coronal Explorer
13 May 1998	NOAA–K	Titan IV	Operational Weather Satellite

Dr. Harry J. Goett

Dr. John C. Clark

Dr. Robert S. Cooper

A. Thomas Young

Dr. Noel W. Hinners

Dr. John W. Townsend, Jr.

Dr. John M. Klineberg

Joseph H. Rothenberg

Alphonso V. Diaz

APPENDIX C:

Directors of the Goddard Space Flight Center 1959-1998

1959–1965	Dr. Harry J. Goett
1965–1976	Dr. John C. Clark
1976–1979	Dr. Robert S. Cooper
1979–1982	A. Thomas Young
1982–1987	Dr. Noel W. Hinners
1987–1990	Dr. John W. Townsend, Jr.
1990–1995	Dr. John M. Klineberg
1995–1998	Joseph H. Rothenberg
1998–	Alphonso V. Diaz

Acknowledgements

A book of this size and scope is never the result of a single person's effort. Creating a history of a space center takes almost as many people as building a spacecraft itself.

First and foremost, I am indebted to the tremendous number of talented, bright and accomplished people who took the time to share their memories, notes, and knowledge with me, sometimes patiently going over topics numerous times until I understood the science behind the spacecraft and the technology behind the accomplishments. In the end, the history of any organization is the history of its people, and I could not have told that story without the help of the people who had lived it first-hand, in the trenches. If I ever wondered how the United States managed to accomplish so much in a field as difficult as space exploration, the drive and enthusiasm I found among the people at Goddard has given me my answer.

I am also extremely grateful to the staff of the public affairs office, who welcomed me into their midst, found me a place to work even when there wasn't one, helped me track down people and places to interview them, and always had a spare smile for me when I walked in the door. Michelle Jackson, Kisha Wright, Nakia Reams, Jan Ruff, Mark Hess, and Diann Harwood helped make the daunting challenge of this project manageable.

My thanks to Jane Riddle, Chang Yao and Jim Sahli, as well, who helped me find launch histories and other research documents to supplement the oral histories I got from the people I interviewed. Special thanks to Terri Randall whose careful attention to detail in editing and proofreading the book was invaluable. Louise Alstork also deserves thanks for undertaking the task of creating the book's index.

In addition, I am indebted to the numerous people, including George Pieper, John Naugle, Roger Launius, Dick Stock, Bill O'Leary, Bill Bandeen, Steve Maran, Orlando Figueroa, Vince Salomonson, Tony Busalacchi, Mark Schoeberl, John Mather, Yoji Kondo, Rick Obenschain, Darrel Williams, Tom Huber, Al Diaz and Jan Ruff who volunteered to read drafts of the manuscript, offering technical accuracy checks and many helpful suggestions.

The beautiful photos that illustrate this book were also a product of numerous people's efforts. My thanks to Bill O'Leary, Keith Koehler, Yoji Kondo, Ann Jenkins, Barbara Summey, Padi Boyd, Mike Carlowicz, Jim Eckles, Pat Rader, Mark deBord and especially Carol Ladd for helping to find the images that grace these pages. I also need to thank Carol Ladd and Mona Kiely for turning mere words into a beautiful work of art with their wonderful flair for graphic design and layout.

The production of this book involved many other people, as well. There are many I didn't meet or talk to, but their efforts are evident on every page, and I am grateful to each and every one of them. I also owe a special thanks to Jan Ruff, who was as much of a coach, cheerleader and trouble-shooter as she was a contract supervisor. Her guidance, support, perspective and wonderful ability to still laugh at it all were all truly invaluable gifts.

In the end, however, my greatest debt is to the thousands of people who have worked for Goddard and its contractors over the years. Without their efforts and sacrifices—the late nights, early mornings, lost weekends, lost sleep—and their willingness to endure whatever frustration, setbacks, and problems stood between them and success—there would have been no story to tell. I offer all of you not only my thanks, but my greatest admiration and respect.

Lane Wallace
Los Angeles, California
January 5, 1999

Index

The NASA History Series

REFERENCE WORKS, NASA SP-4000:

Grimwood, James M. *Project Mercury: A Chronology.* (NASA SP-4001, 1963).

Grimwood, James M., and Hacker, Barton C., with Vorzimmer, Peter J. *Project Gemini Technology and Operations: A Chronology.* (NASA SP-4002, 1969).

Link, Mae Mills. *Space Medicine in Project Mercury.* (NASA SP-4003, 1965).

Astronautics and Aeronautics, 1963: Chronology of Science, Technology, and Policy. (NASA SP-4004, 1964).

Astronautics and Aeronautics, 1964: Chronology of Science, Technology, and Policy. (NASA SP-4005, 1965).

Astronautics and Aeronautics, 1965: Chronology of Science, Technology, and Policy. (NASA SP-4006, 1966).

Astronautics and Aeronautics, 1966: Chronology of Science, Technology, and Policy. (NASA SP-4007, 1967).

Astronautics and Aeronautics, 1967: Chronology of Science, Technology, and Policy. (NASA SP-4008, 1968).

Ertel, Ivan D., and Morse, Mary Louise. *The Apollo Spacecraft: A Chronology, Volume I, Through November 7, 1962.* (NASA SP-4009, 1969).

Morse, Mary Louise, and Bays, Jean Kernahan. *The Apollo Spacecraft: A Chronology, Volume II, November 8, 1962-September 30, 1964.* (NASA SP-4009, 1973).

Brooks, Courtney G., and Ertel, Ivan D. *The Apollo Spacecraft: A Chronology, Volume III, October 1, 1964-January 20, 1966.* (NASA SP-4009, 1973).

Ertel, Ivan D., and Newkirk, Roland W., with Brooks, Courtney G. *The Apollo Spacecraft: A Chronology, Volume IV, January 21, 1966-July 13, 1974.* (NASA SP-4009, 1978).

Astronautics and Aeronautics, 1968: Chronology of Science, Technology, and Policy. (NASA SP-4010, 1969).

Newkirk, Roland W., and Ertel, Ivan D., with Brooks, Courtney G. *Skylab: A Chronology.* (NASA SP-4011, 1977).

Van Nimmen, Jane, and Bruno, Leonard C., with Rosholt, Robert L. *NASA Historical Data Book, Volume I: NASA Resources, 1958-1968.* (NASA SP-4012, 1976, rep. ed. 1988).

Ezell, Linda Neuman. *NASA Historical Data Book, Volume II: Programs and Projects, 1958-1968.* (NASA SP-4012, 1988).

Ezell, Linda Neuman. *NASA Historical Data Book, Volume III: Programs and Projects, 1969-1978.* (NASA SP-4012, 1988).

Gawdiak, Ihor Y., with Fedor, Helen. Compilers. *NASA Historical Data Book, Volume IV: NASA Resources, 1969-1978.* (NASA SP-4012, 1994).

Astronautics and Aeronautics, 1969: Chronology of Science, Technology, and Policy. (NASA SP-4014, 1970).

Astronautics and Aeronautics, 1970: Chronology of Science, Technology, and Policy. (NASA SP-4015, 1972).

Astronautics and Aeronautics, 1971: Chronology of Science, Technology, and Policy. (NASA SP-4016, 1972).

Astronautics and Aeronautics, 1972: Chronology of Science, Technology, and Policy. (NASA SP-4017, 1974).

Astronautics and Aeronautics, 1973: Chronology of Science, Technology, and Policy. (NASA SP-4018, 1975).

Astronautics and Aeronautics, 1974: Chronology of Science, Technology, and Policy. (NASA SP-4019, 1977).

Astronautics and Aeronautics, 1975: Chronology of Science, Technology, and Policy. (NASA SP-4020, 1979).

Astronautics and Aeronautics, 1976: Chronology of Science, Technology, and Policy. (NASA SP-4021, 1984).

Astronautics and Aeronautics, 1977: Chronology of Science, Technology, and Policy. (NASA SP-4022, 1986).

Astronautics and Aeronautics, 1978: Chronology of Science, Technology, and Policy. (NASA SP-4023, 1986).

Astronautics and Aeronautics, 1979-1984: Chronology of Science, Technology, and Policy. (NASA SP-4024, 1988).

Astronautics and Aeronautics, 1985: Chronology of Science, Technology, and Policy. (NASA SP-4025, 1990).

Noordung, Hermann. *The Problem of Space Travel: The Rocket Motor.* Stuhlinger, Ernst, and Hunley, J.D., with Garland, Jennifer. Editor. (NASA SP-4026, 1995).

Astronautics and Aeronautics, 1986-1990: A Chronology. (NASA SP-4027, 1997).

MANAGEMENT HISTORIES, NASA SP-4100:

Rosholt, Robert L. *An Administrative History of NASA, 1958-1963.* (NASA SP-4101, 1966).

Levine, Arnold S. *Managing NASA in the Apollo Era.* (NASA SP-4102, 1982).

Roland, Alex. *Model Research: The National Advisory Committee for Aeronautics, 1915-1958.* (NASA SP-4103, 1985).

Fries, Sylvia D. *NASA Engineers and the Age of Apollo.* (NASA SP-4104, 1992).

Glennan, T. Keith. *The Birth of NASA: The Diary of T. Keith Glennan.* Hunley, J.D. Editor. (NASA SP-4105, 1993).

Seamans, Robert C., Jr. *Aiming at Targets: The Autobiography of Robert C. Seamans, Jr.* (NASA SP-4106, 1996)

PROJECT HISTORIES, NASA SP-4200:

Swenson, Loyd S., Jr., Grimwood, James M., and Alexander, Charles C. *This New Ocean: A History of Project Mercury.* (NASA SP-4201, 1966).

Green, Constance McL., and Lomask, Milton. *Vanguard: A History.* (NASA SP-4202, 1970; rep. ed. Smithsonian Institution Press, 1971).

Hacker, Barton C., and Grimwood, James M. *On Shoulders of Titans: A History of Project Gemini.* (NASA SP-4203, 1977).

Benson, Charles D. and Faherty, William Barnaby. *Moonport: A History of Apollo Launch Facilities and Operations.* (NASA SP-4204, 1978).

Brooks, Courtney G., Grimwood, James M., and Swenson, Loyd S., Jr. *Chariots for Apollo: A History of Manned Lunar Spacecraft.* (NASA SP-4205, 1979).

Bilstein, Roger E. *Stages to Saturn: A Technological History of the Apollo/Saturn Launch Vehicles.* (NASA SP-4206, 1980).

SP-4207 not published.

Compton, W. David, and Benson, Charles D. *Living and Working in Space: A History of Skylab.* (NASA SP-4208, 1983).

Ezell, Edward Clinton, and Ezell, Linda Neuman. *The Partnership: A History of the Apollo- Soyuz Test Project.* (NASA SP-4209, 1978).

Hall, R. Cargill. *Lunar Impact: A History of Project Ranger.* (NASA SP-4210, 1977).

Newell, Homer E. *Beyond the Atmosphere: Early Years of Space Science.* (NASA SP-4211, 1980).

Ezell, Edward Clinton, and Ezell, Linda Neuman. *On Mars: Exploration of the Red Planet, 1958-1978.* (NASA SP-4212, 1984).

Pitts, John A. *The Human Factor: Biomedicine in the Manned Space Program to 1980.* (NASA SP-4213, 1985).

Compton, W. David. *Where No Man Has Gone Before: A History of Apollo Lunar Exploration Missions.* (NASA SP-4214, 1989).

Naugle, John E. *First Among Equals: The Selection of NASA Space Science Experiments.* (NASA SP-4215, 1991).

Wallace, Lane E. *Airborne Trailblazer: Two Decades with NASA Langley's Boeing 737 Flying Laboratory.* (NASA SP-4216, 1994).

Butrica, Andrew J. Editor. *Beyond the Ionosphere: Fifty Years of Satellite Communication* (NASA SP-4217, 1997).

Butrica, Andrews J. *To See the Unseen: A History of Planetary Radar Astronomy.* (NASA SP-4218, 1996).

Mack, Pamela E. Editor. *From Engineering Science to Big Science: The NACA and NASA Collier Trophy Research Project Winners.* (NASA SP-4219, 1998).

Reed, R. Dale. With Lister, Darlene. *Wingless Flight: The Lifting Body Story.* (NASA SP-4220, 1997).

CENTER HISTORIES, NASA SP-4300:

Rosenthal, Alfred. *Venture into Space: Early Years of Goddard Space Flight Center.* (NASA SP-4301, 1985).

Hartman, Edwin, P. *Adventures in Research: A History of Ames Research Center, 1940-1965.* (NASA SP-4302, 1970).

Hallion, Richard P. *On the Frontier: Flight Research at Dryden, 1946-1981.* (NASA SP-4303, 1984).

Muenger, Elizabeth A. *Searching the Horizon: A History of Ames Research Center, 1940-1976.* (NASA SP-4304, 1985).

Hansen, James R. *Engineer in Charge: A History of the Langley Aeronautical Laboratory, 1917-1958.* (NASA SP-4305, 1987).

Dawson, Virginia P. *Engines and Innovation: Lewis Laboratory and American Propulsion Technology.* (NASA SP-4306, 1991).

Dethloff, Henry C. *"Suddenly Tomorrow Came...": A History of the Johnson Space Center.* (NASA SP-4307, 1993).

Hansen, James R. *Spaceflight Revolution: NASA Langley Research Center from Sputnik to Apollo.* (NASA SP-4308, 1995).

Wallace, Lane E. *Flights of Discovery: 50 Years at the NASA Dryden Flight Research Center.* (NASA SP-4309, 1996).

Herring, Mack R. *Way Station to Space: A History of the John C. Stennis Space Center.* (NASA SP-4310, 1997).

Wallace, Harold D., Jr. *Wallops Station and the Creation of the American Space Program.* (NASA SP-4311, 1997).

GENERAL HISTORIES, NASA SP-4400:

Corliss, William R. *NASA Sounding Rockets, 1958-1968: A Historical Summary.* (NASA SP-4401, 1971).

Wells, Helen T., Whiteley, Susan H., and Karegeannes, Carrie. *Origins of NASA Names.* (NASA SP-4402, 1976).

Anderson, Frank W., Jr. *Orders of Magnitude: A History of NACA and NASA, 1915-1980.* (NASA SP-4403, 1981).

Sloop, John L. *Liquid Hydrogen as a Propulsion Fuel, 1945-1959.* (NASA SP-4404, 1978).

Roland, Alex. *A Spacefaring People: Perspectives on Early Spaceflight.* (NASA SP-4405, 1985).

Bilstein, Roger E. *Orders of Magnitude: A History of the NACA and NASA, 1915-1990.* (NASA SP-4406, 1989).

Logsdon, John M. Editor. With Lear, Linda J., Warren-Findley, Jannelle, Williamson, Ray A., and Day, Dwayne A. *Exploring the Unknown: Selected Documents in the History of the U.S. Civil Space Program, Volume I, Organizing for Exploration.* (NASA SP-4407, 1995).

Logsdon, John M. Editor. With Day, Dwayne A., and Launius, Roger D. *Exploring the Unknown: Selected Documents in the History of the U.S. Civil Space Program, Volume II, Relations with Other Organizations.* (NASA SP-4407, 1996).

Logsdon, John M. Editor. With Launius, Roger D., Onkst, David H., and Garber, Stephen E. *Exploring the Unknown: Selected Documents in the History of the U.S. Civil Space Program, Volume III, Using Space.* (NASA SP-4407, 1998).

About the Author

*L*ane E. Wallace is a professional writer who lives in Los Angeles, California. She is the author of three other books: *Flights of Discovery: 50 Years at the NASA Dryden Flight Research Center*; *Airborne Trailblazer*, a history of the Langley Research Center's 737 testbed aircraft, which won the 1994 Washington Edpress Silver Award for Excellence in Print, and a commemorative history of the Defense Technical Information Center. She is also one of the authors of *From Engneering Science to Big Science*, an anthology published in 1998 about the NACA and NASA Collier Trophy award-winning projects.

In addition to her books, Ms. Wallace has written and co-produced a 3-part video documentary series entitled *Test Flights: Flights of Discovery*, exploring the human drama and adventure of flight research. She has also published over 200 articles on a wide variety of aviation and aerospace topics ranging from biplanes and air racing to new developments in NASA research and military aircraft technology. Her writing has appeared in a number of national and international magazines, including *AOPA Pilot* and *Flight International*, and she is a regular columnist for *Flying* magazine. Her work has also earned her an honorary membership in the United States Air Force Society of Wild Weasels, as well as a citation for "Outstanding Contributions to Preserve General Aviation" by the Torrance, California Airport Association.

Ms. Wallace graduated with honors from Brown University in 1983, with a degree in Semiotics. She is a private pilot and has owned a 1946 Cessna 120 as well as her current plane, a 1977 Grumman Cheetah. In addition to her own airplane projects, she has also worked as a volunteer for the Planes of Fame Air Museum in Chino, California and both the "Tsunami" and "Pond Racer" Unlimited air racing crews.

Book design and production by
Mona L. Kiely

Type is set in Classic Garamond (Sabon) and Bauer Bodoni Bold Condensed.

On the following page:
A SeaWiFS satellite image of the Earth's biosphere.
Notable features include the coral reefs off the
coasts of Florida and Australia and the plankton
bloom in the Bering Sea, all of which appear as
turquoise-colored waters.